GCSE DESIGN AND TECHNOLOGY

Food Technology

Celia Barker

Sue Kimmings

Charmian Phillips

CAUSEWAY PRESS

Charlie, Celia and Sue could not have done this without Nigel, Gordon and Steve - with our thanks and love.
Special thanks to Lisa for her continual encouragement and ideas.

Cover and page design	Caroline Waring-Collins
Cover photograph	Telegraph Colour Library
Original graphics	Elaine Sumner
Original photographs	Ian McAnulty, Lisa Fabry, Celia Barker
Cartoon	Sarah Guthrie
Educational consultant	Sheila Stewart
Reader	Mary Walton
Editor	Lisa Fabry

Acknowledgements

The publishers and authors would like to thank the following for their help in the production of this book: Advanced Hygienic Walls, Ceilings and Floors, Birds Eye, Bonnet (Cidelcem Industries), Bradford Education, Bradshaw Microwave, Bramley's Coffee House, British Bakeries, Cadbury, Cauldron Foods, Centre for Alternative Technology, Cinders Barbecues, Co-operative Wholesale Society, Coughlans Patisserie, Croydon Environmental Health, Dansco-Tolona, Dawn Food Products Inc., Electrolux-Zanussi, Elro, Ethical Consumer, Doris Fabry, Falcon Catering Equipment, Film Cuisine, Food Commission, Green Meadow Foods, Sarah Guthrie, Kate Haralambos, Heathcotes Brasserie, H J Heinz, Heygates Mill, Tracey Higgins, HMSO, Rory Johnson, Debbie Kenyon, Lockhart, McVitie's, Market Research Society, Marlow Foods, McCain Foods, Milk Marque, National Dairy Council, National Heart Forum, Oxford Refrigeration, Parkwood House Day Nursery, Potato Marketing Board, Tom Rigby, Safeway, S.J.H. Row & Sons Ltd., St. Ivel, Tate & Lyle, Tesco, United Biscuits, Vegetarian Society, Caitlin Walton Doyle, Caroline Waring-Collins and Alyssa, Hugh Weeks, retired Master Baker for Renshaws.

Picture credits:

Advanced Hygienic Walls, Ceilings and Floors p. 140; Birds Eye p. 102; Bonnet p. 88 (b); Bradford Education p. 48 (br), p. 65 (tr), p.71 (r), p. 86 (t), p. 88 (t), p. 141; Bradshaw Microwave p. 87 (b); Cadbury p. 113 (m, r), p. 123 (m), p. 127 (tr); Caterer and Hotelkeeper p. 49; Cauldron Foods p. 103 (l); Cinders Barbecues p. 90 (tr); Classic p. 91 (r); Co-op p. 7; Coughlans Patisserie p. 119; Dansco-Tolona p. 11; Dawn Food Products Inc. p.118 (tr); Elro p. 94; Falcon Catering Equipment p. 87 (t); Film Cuisine p. 120; Green Meadow Foods p. 84; Heathcotes Brasserie p. 95 (mt, mb, mr); Image Bank p 92; Kenwood p. 79 (tl); Lockhart p. 45 (bl), p. 75, p. 79 (tr), p. 80 (m), p. 83, (t, m), p. 86 (b), p. 91 (l); McCain Foods p. 65 (tr); Milk Marque p. 53; Parkwood House p. 61 (t); Robot coupe p. 80 (br); Spectrum p. 36 (bl, t); p. 59 (tr); S.J.H. Row & Sons Ltd. p. 79 (tr); St. Ivel p. 17; Tesco p. 60; Zanussi p. 89.
All other photographs Photodisc Inc. © 1995.

Crown copyright is reproduced with the permission of the Controller of HMSO.

Photographs provided by Bradford Education were taken from 'Take a Bite into...', a cross-curricular resource pack looking at the beginning of school meals, food issues and food production today. Pack available from: Kalpana Mistry, Client Support Team, Bradford Education, Flockton House, Flockton Rd, Bradford, BD4 7RY.
SMAP computer program (pp. 38 and 39) available from: SMAP, PO Box 7, London, W5 2GQ.

Every effort has been made to locate the copyright owners of material used in this book. Any errors and omissions brought to our attention are regretted and will be credited in subsequent printings.

Causeway Press Limited
P O Box 13, Ormskirk, Lancashire, L39 5HP
© Celia Barker, Sue Kimmings and Charmian Phillips, 1996
1st impression 1996
Reprinted 1997, 1999, 2007

British Library Cataloguing in Publication Data
A catalogue record for this book is available from the British Library

ISBN 1-873929-62-5

Origination and layout by John Collins and Elaine Sumner (Waring Collins Partnership), Ormskirk, Lancashire
Printed and bound by Scotprint

Contents

Meat

When menu planning, the meal is often designed around the meat chosen for the main dish. Different animals are eaten as food in different parts of the world. Table 1 shows the types of meat eaten in Britain.

Nutritional content of meat

Meat is composed of three types of HBV (high biological value) protein (see Unit 6).

- COLLAGEN, a soluble protein, makes up the sheaths surrounding the muscle bundles.
- ELASTIN is a protein element of blood vessel walls and ligaments, most easily seen as a thick yellow strip that runs along the

Bovine spongiform encephalopathy (BSE) or 'mad cow disease' is a disease affecting the nervous system of cattle. First identified in 1986, the number of cases of BSE has risen dramatically in recent years. Sales of British beef have been badly affected as many people refuse to eat beef because of the risk of a link between BSE in cows and Creutzfeldt-Jakob Disease (CJD), the fatal human equivalent.

Table 1 Types of meat

MAIN SOURCES OF MEAT
- cattle (beef)
- sheep (lamb, mutton)
- pigs (pork, bacon)

NEW MEATS
- ostrich
- deer (venison)

POULTRY
- chicken ⎤
- turkey ⎦ low fat white meats
- duck ⎤
- goose ⎦ high fat darker meats

GAME
Animals and birds which are hunted, e.g.
- pheasant
- quail
- rabbit

back and neck of animals.
- MYOGLOBIN carries the oxygen in the muscles. The older the animal the more myoglobin is present and the stronger the colour of the meat. Myoglobin is naturally purple red, but when exposed to air becomes bright red. If the cut meat is exposed to the air for a long time, the surface becomes darker and less appealing.

Buying, preparing and storing meat

You can buy meat ready prepared or prepare it at home. Depending on the size of the animal and the recipe used meat will be prepared in different ways:
- whole: chicken, duck, goose, turkey, game birds, suckling pigs
- jointed: beef, lamb, pork, bacon
- portioned: chops, steaks, burgers, jointed poultry and game
- minced: beef, lamb, turkey, pork
- cubed: beef, kidney
- sliced: bacon and cooked meats

- processed: sausages, meat pies, meat rolls, pâtés.

Animal products are perfect breeding grounds for bacteria (see Unit 9). It is therefore vital to practise good hygiene when preparing and storing meat.

- Prepare raw meat and poultry on boards and using knives kept solely for that purpose (if this is not possible, all equipment should be cleaned with great care after use).
- Always keep meat away from other foods during preparation.
- Always wash hands after handling meat and before touching other foods.
- Keep meat refrigerated or frozen.
- Defrost frozen meat thoroughly in a refrigerator or microwave, before cooking.
- Store raw meat at the bottom of the refrigerator and away from cooked meats to avoid cross-contamination.
- Cook meat thoroughly.
- Keep hot foods hot.

● Refrigerate leftovers as soon as possible or discard.

Cooking meat

Cooking decreases the nutritional value of meat as the heat destroys some vitamins and water soluble protein. A combination of heat (temperatures of 80°C-100°C) and water converts collagen to water soluble gelatine. This increases the tenderness of meat and makes it more digestible. Table 2 shows the main methods used to cook meat and Table 3 explains the physical changes which take place when meat is cooked.

Fish

Nutritional content of fish

Fish is composed of HBV (high biological value) protein (see Unit 6). The protein in fish contains a higher percentage of water than meat, so weight for weight there is less protein in fish than meat. White fish contains almost no fat. It is a low energy value and easily digested food, making it a useful part of a slimmer's or invalid's diet. Oily fish is a rich source of vitamins A and D and also contains essential fatty acids. There is growing evidence that these acids work against the effects of saturated fats and protect against heart disease (see Unit 6). Oily fish is not as easily digested as white fish and is not recommended for invalids. Calcium and phosphorous are found in the softened bones of tinned sardines, salmon and whitebait. Iron is found in molluscs, cockles, mussels and winkles. Vitamin C is found in oysters. Fish is similar to lean meat in structure and composition. Collagen is the connective tissue which holds the short muscle fibres together.

Table 2 Methods of cooking meat

Dry Heat	Moist Heat	Combination methods
Roast Whole birds and tender cuts of meat.	**On the hob** Stewing and boiling are used for tougher cuts of meat, which need long slow cooking.	**Combi-oven** Uses steam as well as conventional heating. When roasting large joints and turkeys, the dual action of heat and moisture helps to prevent weight loss and the meat from drying out.
Grill, fry & barbecue Portion sized tender meats.		
Stir fry Tiny pieces of meat and poultry cooked for 1-2 minutes.	**Pressure cooker** Rapid method of cooking tougher cuts of meat.	
Sauté Tossing meat in a hot pan so that the outside is browned quickly.		**Combination microwave** Microwave energy alone will not produce the desired crisp or browned surface on the meat. Using a combined microwave with gas or electric element enables the meat to be cooked rapidly and with the conventional 'roast' finish.
Simulated charcoal grill Used commercially. Takes up to 30 minutes to heat up. Used for steaks, chops and small tender pieces of meat.	**In the oven** Braising and casseroling are used for tougher cuts of meat which need long slow cooking.	
Brander Used commercially. Solid quite heavy grilling surface used with an overhead grill.		
Bake Meats covered with either pastry or egg and bread crumb and cooked without fat or oil. (The contents of many pies have been roasted, boiled or steamed prior to cooking.)		

Table 3 Changes when meat is cooked

Meat changes from red to brown at temperatures above 65°C. Heat changes the pigment in myoglobln.

The MAILLARD or browning reaction between sugars and amino acids or proteins also produces brown pigments.

Savoury substances are released producing characteristic smells.

Coagulation of proteins produces a firmer texture. Over cooking using a dry heat will produce hard and dry meat.

As collagen contracts, juices are squeezed out of the meat, containing soluble protein, mineral salts and vitamins. In moist methods of cooking these juices become part of the sauce or gravy. In dry cooking a savoury coating is left on the outside.

Loss of juices causes meat to shrink and lose weight - an important consideration when meal planning for economy and portion control.

activities

1. Give TWO reasons why meat turns brown when cooked.

2. A staff canteen serving 125 meals a day wants to offer one chicken and one lamb dish. Suggest recipes, methods of preparation and methods of cooking.

3. Many people eat less red meat than they used to. Design a questionnaire to find out the meat eating habits of people in your school.
   a) What are the three most popular meats eaten?
   b) What are the three most popular ways of cooking meat?
   c) If people are cutting down or do not eat meat:
      i) Why?
      ii) What do they eat instead?

There is no elastin in fish. Between the bones the muscles are divided into flakes.

Buying, preparing and storing fish

When buying fish, check that the skin is shiny and the eyes clear. The flesh should be firm and springy and the underside of the gills should be bright red. The fish should have a mild fresh scent of the sea. Fish has a short storage life. Enzymes found in fish remain active at low temperatures, and if kept too long a memorable smell develops. Table 5 shows the key points for storing fish.

Depending on the size of the fish, and the recipe being used, fish will be cooked in different ways:

- whole (e.g. herring, mackerel, parrot fish)
- filleted (e.g. plaice, sole, haddock)
- steaks (e.g. cod, salmon, halibut)
- cutlets (e.g. halibut)
- dressed (e.g. crab, lobster).

Cooking fish

Because of its delicate structure, fish is often coated in some way before cooking. The three basic coverings are:

- seasoned flour
- breadcrumbs
- batter.

These coverings protect the fish and give it a good colour, texture and flavour as well as

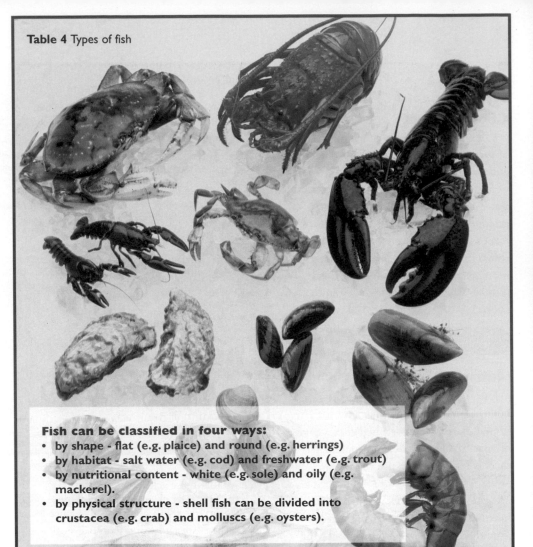

Table 4 Types of fish

Fish can be classified in four ways:
- **by shape** - flat (e.g. plaice) and round (e.g. herrings)
- **by habitat** - salt water (e.g. cod) and freshwater (e.g. trout)
- **by nutritional content** - white (e.g. sole) and oily (e.g. mackerel).
- **by physical structure** - shell fish can be divided into crustacea (e.g. crab) and molluscs (e.g. oysters).

making the surface brown and crisp. Fish flesh is always tender. Most fish is cooked in portions. Cooking time is therefore short as heat penetration is rapid. Cooked fillets and

Table 5 Storage of fish

COMMERCIAL
- **Store fish separately to prevent transfer of smells and flavours - ideally in a separate refrigerator.**
- **Store fresh fish in a box containing ice at a temperature of 1-2°C. The temperature must be maintained at just above freezing point.**
- **Frozen fish must be stored in a deep freeze cabinet or compartment at -18°C.**
- **Smoked fish should be stored in a refrigerator.**
- **Ready to eat cooked fish such as smoked mackerel should be stored on shelves above raw fish to avoid cross-contamination (see Unit 9).**
- **Prepared fish should be stored separately from unprepared fish.**
- **Different varieties of fish should be kept apart to ensure that there is no confusion when removing portions for preparation.**

DOMESTIC
- **Store fresh fish wrapped loosely and away from other foods.**
- **Always check to find out if the fish has been frozen, before freezing at home - fish must be very fresh if it is to be frozen domestically.**

activities

1. Why is white fish a useful food for a person trying to lose weight?

2. Using the information in Tables 5 and 6, how should a restaurant store the following fish and fish dishes:
   a) fresh trout
   b) fresh mackerel
   c) prepared cod mornay
   d) prepared prawn cocktail?

Table 6 Storage times for fish

Fish	Refrigerator	Freezer
white	1-2 days	3 months
oily	1-2 days	up to 2 months
smoked	4-7 days	up to 3 months
shell	1-2 days	2 months
cooked	1-2 days	2 months

Table 7 Methods of cooking fish

DRY COOKING METHODS	WET METHODS	Boiling

DRY COOKING METHODS

Fried
Shallow fried: fish is cooked on a moderate heat with little or no fat.
Stir fried: small pieces or strips of fish are cooked very quickly.
Deep fried: fish is submerged in fat or oil to cook, lifted out and drained before serving. White fish is the most suitable for frying. Oily fish is not generally fried.

Grilled
Whole fish, steaks and fillets, fish cakes and fish fingers may be grilled. Oily fish are particularly suitable, requiring only a light brushing of oil before cooking.

Baked
Fish may be brushed with oil or butter and then baked.

WET METHODS

Poaching
Fish is cooked in a stock over a gentle heat, usually on the hob, but can also be cooked in the oven.

Shallow poaching: small cuts or fillets are partially covered with liquid and cooked in a shallow, covered pan.

Deep poaching: generally used for whole fish such as salmon. The fish is immersed in a long covered pan known as a fish kettle and cooked very gently to prevent breakage. Deep poached fish are generally left in the cooking liquid as it cools. This should be completed as quickly as possible to prevent the risk of contamination.

Steaming
Suitable for small whole fish or for pieces. Oily fish does not steam well.

Boiling
Fish soups and stews are boiled, the best known is bouillabaisse. The flesh cooks very rapidly when boiled.

COMBINATION METHODS

Combi-oven
A combination of heat and steam in the oven, creates a higher temperature than a conventional steamer and shortens the cooking time. The advantage of using this method is that the fish remains very moist.

slices are ready when a creamy white substance appears from between the flakes. Collagen is converted to gelatine when cooked. Fish protein COAGULATES when cooked. This begins at a temperature of 60°C. When baking, moderate temperatures are required. A good indication that fish is cooked is when the flesh 'flakes' easily. It is easy to overcook fish, making the flesh tough and hard. Table 7 shows the main methods of cooking fish.

Eggs

Eggs are a versatile and valuable food, which can be cooked whole or used as a key ingredient in a wide variety of dishes. The most popular eggs are hens' eggs, although the following eggs can also be eaten:

- duck
- goose
- turkey
- guinea fowl
- quail
- gull.

Around 28,000,000 hens' eggs are consumed each day in Britain and approximately 95% of these are home

produced. Figure 1 shows the structure of an egg.

Nutritional content of eggs

Eggs contain most nutrients except carbohydrate and vitamin C. However they are often eaten with foods which compensate for this deficiency e.g. scrambled eggs on toast. They are low in calories: two eggs contain about 180 calories. The white is composed largely of the protein OVALBUMIN and water, with small amounts of riboflavin (vitamin B2) and the mineral sulphur. This protein causes the egg white to foam which is an important characteristic in baking. The yolk contains two important proteins, VITALIN and LIVETIN. Fat is present in a very fine emulsion, making the yolk easy to digest. A substance called lecithin (a mixture of fat and phosphorous) allows the yolk to stabilise emulsions (for example in the preparation of mayonnaise). Traces of cholesterol are present in the yolk fat. Many other minerals are present in the yolk, including iron, magnesium, sodium, potassium, sulphur, and chlorine. The extent to which the iron from eggs is absorbed by the body depends on the amount of vitamin C in a meal. The fat soluble vitamins A, D, E, K and the water soluble B group are found in the yolk.

Buying and storing eggs

The porous nature of the shell makes eggs high risk products, which must be handled and stored correctly to avoid contamination.

- Store eggs in their boxes or packing trays, with the blunt end upwards.
- Keep them in the fridge (between 0-5°C) but for best results remove them half an hour before use.
- Store away from strong-smelling foods as the porous shell will absorb odours.
- Store away from raw meat and fish to prevent cross-contamination (see Unit 9).

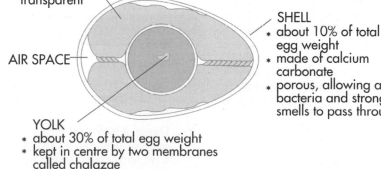

Figure 1 The structure of an egg

WHITE
* about 60% of total egg weight
* two layers, the white surrounding yolk is thick and viscous, the white nearer the shell is thinner and more transparent

AIR SPACE

SHELL
* about 10% of total egg weight
* made of calcium carbonate
* porous, allowing air, bacteria and strong smells to pass through

YOLK
* about 30% of total egg weight
* kept in centre by two membranes called chalazae

Figure 2 Uses of eggs in cookery

alone: boiled, fried, poached, scrambled, coddled, omelettes
thicken: sauces, soups, custards **bind**: fish cakes, burgers, nut roasts **coat**: batter, egg and breadcrumbs
garnish: chopped, sliced **glaze**: scones, pastry **clarify**: consommé soup **emulsify**: mayonnaise
aerate: cakes, meringues, mousses **enrich**: sauces **create a foam**: meringues, Swiss rolls, soufflés

● Do not wash eggs as this could remove the natural protective coating.
● Practise stock rotation.
● Cracked eggs should not be used.
● Use eggs within 21 days of laying. Many eggs now have a best before date stamped on each shell. However, eggs can be kept for up to nine months under cold storage conditions (with the temperature a little above freezing point, and the humidity and carbon dioxide controlled).

There are several methods for testing the freshness of an egg

● The shell should feel rough.
● When floated in salt water a fresh egg will sink to the bottom and a stale egg will float. This is because the air space expands as an egg ages due to evaporation of the white through the porous shell.
● If broken onto a plate a fresh egg has three distinct levels. A high domed yolk surrounded by a raised thick white sitting in a thin watery white. As the egg ages the yolk and whites flatten, thin and spread. A fresh egg has a clearly defined circular shape while an older egg loses this definition and becomes irregular in shape.
● An extremely stale egg will give off an unpleasant sulphurous smell.

Preparing and cooking eggs

Because of the risk of salmonella poisoning the government recommends that we do not eat raw eggs or dishes that contain raw eggs (e.g. mousses or home-made mayonnaise). In addition, young children, pregnant women, ill or frail elderly people should only eat eggs if the yolk has been cooked until it is solid. Figure 2 shows the uses of eggs in cookery. When eggs are heated the proteins coagulate: the white at 60°C, the yolk at 68°C and the whole egg at about 64°C. The heated egg protein thickens mixtures (e.g. egg custard). It also holds other ingredients together (e.g. Spanish omelette, egg and breadcrumb coating). As the temperature increases the protein hardens and shrinks. Excessive heat makes egg white tough and leathery, and egg yolk crumbly. When making egg custards, too much heat will make the mixture curdle.

When egg white is beaten partial coagulation of the proteins occurs - a process called DENATURATION. Air bubbles are surrounded by a thin film of coagulated protein forming a foam. The addition of sugar makes this foam stable. If the mixture is over beaten it breaks down - the protein shrinks and liquid is pushed out from the foam.

When whole eggs are cooked a black discolouration may form around the yolk. This is iron sulphide (formed by a combination of hydrogen sulphide in the egg white and iron in the egg yolk). Immediate cooling can prevent this discolouration.

Key Terms

Collagen - **protein found in meat and fish.**
Elastin - **protein found in meat.**
Myoglobin - **protein found in meat.**
Maillard reaction - **when foods are heated this reaction between amino acids and sugars results in browning.**
Coagulate - **to change a liquid such as egg white into a soft semi-solid or solid mass.**
Ovalbumin - **protein found in egg white.**
Vitalin - **protein found in egg yolk.**
Livetin - **protein found in egg yolk.**
Denaturation - **process where proteins in egg white partially coagulate when beaten.**

activities

1. What happens when eggs are heated?
2. Figure 2 gives some examples of the ways that eggs can be used in cookery. State THREE dishes containing eggs and suggest what function the egg performs in each dish.
3. Design a leaflet on buying and storing eggs, including advice on safe preparation of eggs for different groups of people. The design should incorporate text in different sizes and original artwork.

Whenever you travel down a motorway or along a country lane, you are likely to see lots of cattle or sheep, but you probably won't see many hens. So where do all the eggs in the shops come from?

INTENSIVE SYSTEMS

Most eggs come from hens that live in battery cages. This intensive system allows eggs to be produced cheaply and efficiently. But many people are concerned about the conditions in which battery hens are kept (see Table 1). Intensively Produced eggs are normally packed and delivered to the shops within two to three days of laying, which means they can accurately be described as fresh. However, many producers add meaningless words such as 'Country' Fresh or 'Farm' Fresh. Co-op fresh eggs are clearly described as 'Intensively Produced'.

COLONY SYSTEMS

There are two other main commercial egg producing systems, which are less intensive. Hens live in colonies, either in barns (Barn or Perchery eggs) or with access to open air runs (Free Range eggs). Eggs produced in this way cost more, as the systems are not so 'efficient'. The majority of Free Range and Barn eggs come from large scale commercial producers, operating to minimum standards set by UK and EU regulations.

Source: adapted from Co-op information leaflet

The Co-op sells Intensively Produced, Barn and Free Range eggs. Each pack is clearly labelled so that the consumer can make an informed decision about which eggs to buy. The price varies according to the type of egg. In July 1996, six medium eggs cost 72p (Intensively Produced), 83p (Barn) and 89p (Free Range).

Table 1 - EU egg maketing regulations

Battery (Intensively Produced) - up to 6 hens per cage; 450cm^2 space per bird; constant supply of food and water.

Barn/Perchery - up to 25 hens per m^2 of floor space, perches in vertical tiers.

Free Range - maximum of 1 hen per 10m^2 of ground; continuous day-time access to outside space covered with vegetation; houses must contain perches and scratching areas covered with litter (e.g. sand or straw).

Activities

1. What are the three main systems of egg production?
2. Why do you think intensive systems are more 'efficient' than colony systems?
3. Suggest factors that might influence a customer's decision about which eggs to buy.
4. The Co-op believes that customers have a 'right to know' about the food products they are buying. What effect do you think their decision to label eggs as 'Intensively Produced' will have on the buying habits of consumers?
5. Eggs can be date stamped giving the use by date on either the egg shell, the box or both. What are the advantages of date stamping on the shell?

Milk

Milk is produced by female mammals for feeding their young. Most milk produced in this country comes from cows although the milk from goats and ewes can also be used. The flavour of milk varies depending on the breed of cow and the degree of processing after the milk has left the farm.

Figure 1 shows the types of milk available.

Buying and storing milk

Milk has to be treated with the greatest care and under strictly controlled hygienic conditions in order to reach the consumer uncontaminated. The health of the dairy herd is an important factor as well as the conditions under which the animals are milked and the milk is processed. Milk is a perishable product, but can be kept for 4-5 days in refrigerated conditions.

- Check use by dates on cartons.
- Containers such as milk jugs and cooking utensils should always be scrupulously clean to prevent contamination.
- Old and new milk should not be mixed.
- Use milk on a rotational basis.

Using milk in cookery

Milk can be used in:
- cold drinks - milk shakes, milk cocktails, on its own
- hot drinks - hot chocolate, cocoa, cappuccino, coffee, tea
- breakfast cereals
- hot and cold desserts
- bread and cakes
- as a liquid for cooking fish and vegetables

Table 1 Nutritional content per pint (568ml) of milk

	WHOLE	SEMI-SKIMMED	SKIMMED
energy (kcal)	1610	1145	824
protein	18.7g	19.4g	19.4g
fat	22.8g	9.4g	0.6g
carbohydrate (lactose)	26.9g	28.2g	28.2g
calcium	673mg	693mg	706mg
iron	0.29mg	0.29mg	0.29mg
vitamins: A	334µg	135µg	6µg
B1	0.23mg	0.23mg	0.24mg
B2	1mg	1.1mg	1.1mg
B3	6mg	6mg	6mg
B12	2.3µg	2.3µg	2.4µg
C	6mg	6mg	6mg
D	0.18µg	0.06µg	0

- sauces and soups.

When milk is heated the proteins lactalbumin and lactoglobulin coagulate to form a skin on the surface. This occurs when milk boils which is at 86°C. In batters, scones and cakes where milk is used the water

activities

Look at Figure 1. Which milk would be most suitable for the people below? Consider the type of milk, the quantity and the packaging.

1. A family including a 3 year old who live near the shops and have easy access to milk.

2. A couple who are going camping for two weeks in France.

3. An old person living alone and with limited mobility.

4. A teenager who wants to lose weight.

is turned to steam and acts as a raising agent. Curdling occurs when the protein coagulates and separates from the liquid part of the milk. This results in a lumpy appearance. Curdling will occur if milk or cream is added to a mixture which is too hot or too acidic. To prevent this, dilute some of the milk or cream with the hot liquid, before adding it to the bulk of the mixture. To sour milk artificially (for use in soda bread, for example) add an acid such as lemon juice to warmed milk. This will change the lactose to lactic acid resulting in curdling.

Milk Products

Cream was traditionally made by leaving milk to stand in a cool dairy. The lighter cream would rise to the top of the bowl and could be skimmed off for use as cream or for making butter. Now the milk is heated and spun in a mechanical separator which takes the heavier milk to the side and the lighter cream remains in the centre. The cream and milk are then siphoned off through two separate outlet pipes. By adjusting the outlet valves, the fat content of the cream can be controlled to produce a variety of creams which can be used in different ways.

Yogurt is made from homogenised milk. The lactose in the milk is changed into lactic acid by the addition of a culture made up from streptococcus thermophilus and lactobacillus bulgaricus bacteria (see

Figure 1 Types of milk

Pasteurised whole milk. Milk is heated to 72°C for 15 seconds and rapidly cooled. This makes it safer for consumption by destroying PATHOGENIC BACTERIA and other organisms. Bottled with a silver foil cap.

Channel Islands milk, is pasteurised whole milk from Jersey and Guernsey cows. It has a higher fat content, about 5%, giving a creamier taste. Bottled with a gold foil cap.

Semi-skimmed milk is pasteurised and part of the cream is removed. Bottled with a red and silver foil cap.

Skimmed milk is pasteurised and the cream is removed. It is a useful low calorie alternative to whole milk. Bottled with a blue foil cap.

Homogenised milk has the same nutritional value as whole milk. Homogenisation breaks up the fat globules and distributes them evenly through the milk. Bottled with a red foil cap.

UHT (Ultra Heat Treatment) milk is heated to not less than 132°C for at least 1 second. All micro-organisms are destroyed. The milk is packaged and will remain fresh without refrigeration for up to 6 months. Once opened it should be treated as fresh milk, i.e. refrigerated and used quickly.

Sterilised milk. Homogenised milk is bottled and sealed, then heat treated to 115-130°C for 10-30 minutes. All micro-organisms are destroyed. The milk will keep for 2-3 weeks without refrigeration.

Evaporated milk has half the water content removed. Milk is evaporated, homogenised, sealed into cans and sterilised at 115-120°C for 10 minutes.

Condensed milk is evaporated milk which has been preserved using a high proportion of sugar instead of by sterilising.

Dried milk is produced by homogenising and heat treating whole or skimmed milk, then evaporating the water to produce a powder. Vitamins C, B1 and B12 are lost in the drying process and dried skimmed milk does not contain the fat soluble vitamins A and D. Some dried milks are fortified with vitamins A and D.

Infant formula milks are intended to replace breast milk for babies under 1 year old. They are based on modified cows' milk, and do not contain the same ingredients as breast milk, which is better for babies as it is free, safe and provides natural immunity against infection.

Unit 9). During fermentation, the yogurt thickens and at this stage flavourings and artificial sweeteners may be added.

Butter is made by churning the cream

activities

1. Suggest reasons why people choose to a) have milk delivered to their door; b) buy fresh milk from a shop.

2. Compare the advantages and disadvantages of the various forms of milk packaging. You should consider cost, convenience and environmental impact (see Unit 25 for more information on packaging).

The British doorstep delivery service of milk is valued by many people. However, it is increasingly under threat from supermarkets and corner shops who are often able to undercut the price of a pint of milk. Milk is delivered to thousands of households daily, packaged in glass bottles. The bottles are the property of the dairy and must be returned for re-use. Although glass bottles cost more to produce than non-returnable containers, they remain the most economical way of packaging milk, because they are re-used about twenty times.

Table 2 Dairy products

CREAM	**Types**	Single, double, whipping, soured, clotted, sterilised, half, UHT, extra thick, crème fraîche, aerosol, frozen.
	Nutritional Content	Cream has a high fat content, the level depends on the type of cream. There is a legal minimum amount of fat permitted in each type of cream. This ranges from 12% for half cream up to 55% for clotted cream. Calcium level also depends on the type of cream, e.g. single cream has 91mg per 100g while double cream has only 50mg per 100g.
	Storage	Pasteurised creams - up to 14 days refrigerated. UHT cream - up to six months unopened. Sterilised cream - up to two years unopened. Aerosol creams - up to three months. Any cream, once opened, should be refrigerated and kept covered as it will pick up strong flavours.
	Use	Coffee, milk shakes, sweet and savoury dishes, sauces, poured onto desserts, whipped and used for piping onto desserts and cakes.
YOGURT	**Types**	Very low fat, low fat, whole milk, creamy, Greek style, bio. The different yogurts are made by using skimmed or full cream milk, adding extra cultures or adding cream to the finished product.
	Nutritional Content	Both natural and flavoured yogurts contain good levels of protein and calcium. Flavoured yogurts, usually sweetened with sugar, are higher in carbohydrates and calories. Some yogurts are low in fat. Greek style yogurts contain a much higher proportion of fat than others.
	Storage	If refrigerated, most yogurts will keep for up to a fortnight. Yogurt does not freeze well.
	Uses	Alone or with cereals for breakfast, as a snack or dessert, instead of cream with a dessert, sweet and savoury dishes, soups, salads and salad dressings, dips, frozen dessert - a healthier alternative to ice cream
BUTTER	**Types**	Salted, unsalted, continental (slightly ripened), clarified, ghee, concentrated
	Nutritional Content	An average butter will contain 82% fat, 15% water, 2% salt and vitamins A and D. This will vary depending on the time of year and where the cows are fed (in winter when cows are kept inside the vitamin content will drop).
	Storage	Keep in a cool place (if refrigerated it becomes very hard and difficult to spread). Use on a strict rotational basis.
	Uses	Spread for bread, toast, etc., cakes and pastries, butter icing, shallow frying, basting foods prior to grilling, roux base for sauces and soups, maître d'hôtel butter for grilled dishes, garlic bread etc., glazing freshly cooked vegetables.
CHEESE	**Types**	Hard (e.g. Cheddar), semi-hard (e.g. Lancashire), soft, (e.g. cottage), ripened soft (e.g. Brie), blue (e.g. Roquefort).
	Nutritional Content	Much of the protein, fat, vitamin A and calcium in milk remain in cheese, Cheddar cheese consists roughly of one third fat, one third protein, and one third water. These proportions are similar in most cheeses. In general hard cheeses contain more nutrients per 100g than soft cheeses.
	Storage	Keep away from other foods to prevent spoilage by smell. Store on cool, dry, well ventilated shelves. Whole cheeses should be turned if they are kept for any length of time. Natural rind can be exposed to the air, so that it can breathe, but if the cheese is cut, the surface should be covered to prevent drying. If stored in a refrigerator, remove one hour before use to come up to room temperature.
	Uses	Sandwiches, salads, cheese pastry, scones, bread, sauces for fish or vegetables, savoury dishes, cheese board.

from milk. The movement allows the fat globules to clump together to form butter. The excess liquid separates and is drained off as buttermilk. In Britain sweet cream butter is produced and salt is added to enhance flavour and to lengthen shelf life. The continental method of making butter involves ripening the pasteurised cream and using a lactobacillus culture before churning to give the slightly acidic flavour. This also enhances keeping qualities thus requiring little additional salt. Clarified butter is produced by gently heating butter until it has melted, and draining off the separated milk solids. Clarified butter can be

activities

Yogurt is a relatively new food in Britain. Thirty years ago it was difficult to buy yogurt. Now there are hundreds of different types in the supermarket.

1. Brainstorm a list of different types of yogurt.
2. Yogurts may be aimed at 'niche' markets, such as slimmers or children. Can you suggest any other groups targeted by yogurt manufacturers?
3. Make a table including the yogurts you have listed and identifying the market at which they are aimed.

used at much higher temperatures without burning. Ghee is a clarified butter used in Indian cookery. Concentrated butter is produced by removing most of the water and milk solids and is useful for cooking and baking.

Buttermilk used to be a liquid by-product of butter making, but now it is usually skimmed milk, treated with a culture to produce a sharp taste and thickened consistency. Smetana is another cultured milk product.

Cheese is made in every part of the world, from cows', goats' or ewes' milk. There are thousands of different types of cheese in the world. For instance, in France, it is claimed that there is a different type of cheese for every day of the year. Every country has its own speciality in cheeses. To produce $^1/_2$ kilo (1lb) cheese 5 litres (9 pints) milk is required. The fermenting agent needed to start cheese is rennet, a chemical substance found in the stomach of a calf or lamb. Vegetarian cheese can be made using a non-animal rennet. The rennet causes the milk to curdle and the whey is poured off. The curds are cut up, salt is added and the cheese is then pressed according to the type being produced. A soft cheese will not be pressed as much as a harder cheese.

Key Terms

Pathogenic bacteria - harmful bacteria which can cause food poisoning

activities

Dansco is a company based in Skelmersdale producing mozzarella cheese for the catering industry. This is an extract from their brochure:

WHY MOZZARELLA?

Mozzarella is the perfect choice for pizza for a number of very good reasons.

* Pleasant mild flavour - The secret of a great pizza is that the basic ingredients of crust and cheese should allow the other flavours, like tomato sauce and toppings, to come through.
* Melt and stretch - Mozzarella has a good melt and displays stretch and elasticity which keeps all the toppings in place, whilst retaining a tender chewy texture.
* High moisture, low fat - Pizza is cooked in very, very hot ovens. The high moisture content prevents burning of the cheese and the low fat content prevents pools of grease occurring which would happen with other higher fat cheeses such as Cheddar.
* Ideal for shredding - Unlike other cheeses, mozzarella doesn't clump when shredded which makes it flow freely for easy use and good portion control.

1. Identify the qualities of mozzarella that make it a good choice for pizza.
2. How could a company save time and money by using mozzarella instead of a hard cheese?
3. Suggest other dishes for which mozzarella might be
   a) a good choice.
   b) unsuitable.

unit 3 Vegetable foods

Cereals

Cereals are cultivated grasses grown for their seeds which are known as grains. Cereals may be eaten as they are (e.g. rice) or processed into cereal products (e.g. pasta, noodles and breakfast cereals).

Processing cereals

Milling is the earliest form of food processing. Its object is to grind the grain in order to separate the ENDOSPERM (see Figure 2) from the rest of the grain, reducing it to fine particles which are used in the production of flour, semolina, pasta and breakfast cereals. During milling (non-starch polysaccharide, also known as fibre - see Unit 6), protein and some B vitamins are lost, therefore fortification is necessary by the flour manufacturers. Flour improvers are also added to enhance baking performance. The degree of milling varies to produce different flours (see Table 1).

Cooking cereals

When starch is subjected to dry heat, for example when bread is grilled to make toast, the starch is converted to sugar and then to

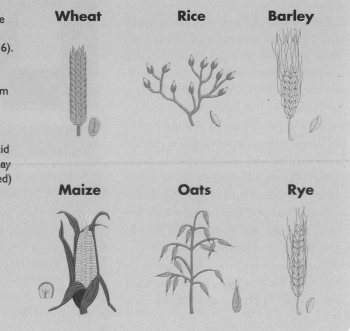

Figure 1 Cereals

Cereals have a high nutritive value compared to their production costs (see Unit 6). They provide the following nutrients:

- carbohydrate in the form of starch proteins (GLIADIN and GLUTENIN)
- iron (although phytic acid which is also present may stop iron being absorbed)
- calcium
- vitamins B1 and B3
- NSP
- fat (unsaturated)
- water

Wheat   Rice   Barley

Maize   Oats   Rye

caramel. This is known as DEXTRINISATION and gives bread and any other baked product its characteristic golden brown colour. When starch is moistened and heated it thickens in a process called GELATINISATION. Starch is insoluble in cold water but heat causes liquid to penetrate the starch granule and make it swell. The swollen grains create a substance known as a gel. Over-cooked rice shows the effect of gelatinisation - the starch turns into a gel

which causes the rice grains to stick together. The degree of gelatinisation is affected by three factors.

- Proportion and type of starch. Large granules such as those in arrowroot produce a clear transparent gel.
- Temperature of the liquid. Lumps form if dry starch is mixed with a hot liquid. This is because the surface of the granule immediately gelatinises forming a coating which prevents liquid from entering the

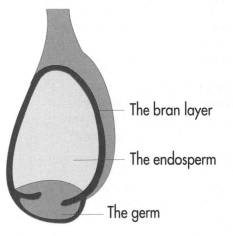

Figure 2 Cross-section of a grain of wheat

The bran layer

The endosperm

The germ

Table 1 Types of flour milled from wheat

Wholemeal - contains 100% of the grain
Wheatmeal - contains 85% of the grain, some of the bran is removed
White - contains 72% whole grain, with the germ, bran fat and minerals removed
Wheatgerm - white flour with 10% finely ground germ added
Strong - milled from spring wheat and has a high gluten content, suitable for bread making
Soft - milled from winter wheat and contains only a small amount of gluten, used for cakes
Self raising can be wholemeal or white and includes a raising agent

Table 2 Bread

When water is added to wheat the proteins combine to form a protein called GLUTEN. Gluten is particularly important in bread-making because of its ability to stretch and hold pockets of gas produced by the yeast during rising and baking. Adding salt strengthens the gluten and kneading develops the protein and increases the elasticity of the dough. Once the gluten has been developed and stretched the heat of the oven coagulates the protein. This forms the framework or typical spongy texture of freshly baked bread which can be referred to as a solid foam. See the case study on p. 69 for more information on bread-making.

Table 3 Types of pulse

There are three main types of pulse:

PEAS
chick peas, marrow fat peas, green and yellow split peas.

BEANS
aduki, black eyed, black, borlotti, broad, butter, cannellini, Dutch brown, flageolet, haricot, mung, pinto, red kidney, soissons, soya, etc. (There are over 200 types of bean known and grown across the world.)

LENTILS
Egyptian lentil (orange), brown lentils from Canada, continental lentils (green).

granule. Failure to stir the mixture also creates lumps as gelatinised granules settle at the base of the pan instead of remaining in suspension throughout the liquid.

- Effect of other ingredients. Acids decrease the thickening power of the starch. Sugar softens the gel making it more runny especially if used in large amounts. It is better to add sugar to an already thickened liquid.

Storing cereals

Cereals should be stored in a cool, dry place to avoid mould. Cereals are prone to infestation from weevils so they should be kept sealed in airtight containers and not stored for long periods of time. Wholegrain cereals have a shorter shelf life due to their fat content.

Pulses

Pulses are the dried seeds of plants which form pods. They are also known as legumes. Pulses are a good source of protein, carbohydrates and NSP but have virtually no fat (except soya beans, which contain some fat). Pulses form an important part of a vegetarian diet. Table 3 lists some of the main types of pulse.

Nutritional content of pulses

Pulses are rich in vegetable protein. Soya beans contain protein which is of high biological value (see Unit 6 and the case study on p.103). Pulses are also rich in B vitamins and NSP.

Buying and storing pulses

Pulses are usually bought dried or ready-cooked in tins. Both forms have a long shelf life.

- Packets should be in good condition and not torn.
- Tins should not be rusty or blown.
- Drain tinned beans before use.
- Store dried pulses in a cool dry place away from direct sunlight.
- Once a packet of dried pulses is open, store the remainder in an air tight jar.
- Dried pulses are best eaten as fresh as possible. The older they are, the longer they take to cook.

Cooking pulses

Pulses can be used in a wide range of dishes:

- baked beans
- bean salad
- soups and sauces
- rissoles and burgers
- loaves and bakes
- casseroles and curries
- stir fry recipes.

Most pulses can also be sprouted. Freshly sprouted beans have very high levels of protein, vitamins and minerals.

Most pulses require a long soaking before cooking and a long cooking time to make them tender. Cooking time can be reduced by using a pressure cooker, or you can use tinned beans but these are more expensive. Kidney beans contain a toxin which causes food poisoning. They must be boiled rapidly for at least 15 minutes at the beginning of cooking time to make them safe to eat. Tinned kidney beans have already undergone this process.

activities

METHOD FOR MAKING ROUX
Melt butter. Add flour, cook for a minute or two. Add the milk off the heat, a little at a time, stirring after each addition, until all the milk has been added. Return to a gentle heat and, stirring all the time, bring back to the boil to thicken the sauce. Simmer, stirring all the time, for 2 minutes.
ALTERNATIVE METHOD. Put ingredients in a saucepan and whisk to incorporate flour. Stir until thick.

1. Figure 1 shows the different types of cereal.
   a) Which of these cereals (or products made from them) have you eaten?
   b) Which is the most commonly eaten cereal in Britain? List TEN food products containing this cereal.

2. The method for making a roux sauce is described above.
   a) Describe what happens to flour when it is cooked.
   b) Suggest TWO things that could go wrong when making this sauce. How could you overcome these problems?

Nuts and seeds

Nuts are the seeds from a plant or a tree. Nuts are sold whole, shelled, sliced, flaked, chopped, ground and as pastes, butters or milk. Nuts most frequently seen in the shops are: almonds, brazils, chestnuts, coconut, hazels, macadamias, pecans, cashews, pistachios and walnuts. Strictly speaking, the peanut is not a nut. It is a bean, a member of the pulse family. However, peanuts are usually classed with other nuts. Seeds (e.g. sunflower, pumpkin and sesame) have a similar nutritional value to nuts.

Nutritional content of nuts and seeds

Nuts and seeds are a good source of protein, especially almonds, cashews, and pistachios. Nuts (except chestnuts) are high in unsaturated fat. Nuts and seeds are high in B vitamins and minerals.

Buying and storing nuts

Nuts in their shells are much cheaper than shelled nuts and keep for longer if stored in a dry well ventilated place. However, shelling the nuts can be a time-consuming job. Shelled nuts should be kept in airtight containers. Figure 3 shows some of the ways nuts and seeds can be used in cookery.

Figure 3 Using nuts and seeds in cookery

Ground or chopped in nut roasts (e.g. cashews, almonds, peanuts).

Ingredient in cakes, bread and biscuits (e.g. walnuts, hazelnuts, sunflower and sesame seeds).

Decoration for cakes and biscuits (e.g. walnut halves, nibbed almonds, almond paste).

Garnish for savouries (e.g. trout with flaked almonds).

Chestnut puree for gateaux or chopped for stuffings.

Roasted or salted as a snack (e.g. peanuts, cashews, pumpkin seeds).

Grated coconut or coconut milk in curries.

Tahini (sesame seed paste) in hummus.

Grated coconut or coconut milk in curries.

Peanut butter in sandwiches, or as ingredient in biscuits or savouries

Chopped nuts or whole seeds mixed into pastry dough or crumble topping.

Vegetables

Vegetables and fruit should be an important part of our diet. There is evidence that the risk of cancer and heart disease can be decreased by eating a good variety of fruit and vegetables regularly. As well as playing an important role in keeping us healthy, vegetables add colour and a variety of flavours and textures to each meal.

Although they contain up to 95% water, vegetables are an important source of NSP due to the cellulose in the cell walls. They also supply minerals, vitamins, carbohydrates and protein. Table 4 shows the types of vegetable and their nutritional content.

Buying and storing vegetables

To ensure good quality, low cost and nutritional value, buy local vegetables in season. Look for:
- clean vegetables
- no soil except for new potatoes or organically grown vegetables
- good colour, shape and appearance
- undamaged, unblemished and disease free
- green vegetables which are bright, crisp and unwilted.

To help customers make informed purchases, the European Union has created the following quality grades:
- Extra class - produce of top quality
- Class 1 - good quality
- Class 2 - reasonable quality
- Class 3 - low marketable quality

After purchase:
- handle vegetables gently to prevent bruising (damaged vegetables lose vitamin C)
- do not leave vegetables in plastic bags - pierce or remove to prevent condensation forming
- do not leave vegetables tightly packed
- check before storage and remove any blemished items
- store in a cool dry place with a good circulation of air

activities

1. What types of pulse are used in this recipe?
2. Which ingredients in this recipe supply: a) protein; b) NSP?
3. You want to have Spicy Bean Patties for tea at 6pm on Monday. Plan a work schedule, including all the things you need to do in advance.

SPICY BEAN PATTIES
100g butter or haricot beans, soaked overnight
100g green lentils
500ml vegetable stock
50g mixed nuts, ground
1 tbsp olive oil
1 onion, chopped
1 carrot, grated
1 green pepper, chopped
1 tsp ground coriander
1 tsp ground cumin
salt and pepper

TO COAT:
1 egg, beaten
100g porridge oats

METHOD:
Drain beans and rinse lentils. Place both in pan with stock and bring to boil. Simmer until tender (about 40 minutes). Drain and puree. Fry onion in oil until soft. Add carrot, pepper and nuts and fry for a further 5-6 minutes. Add seasoning, mix into bean and lentil puree and cool. Then shape into patties, dip in egg and coat with the oats. Shallow fry for 6-8 minutes, turning once.

Table 4 Types of vegetable and nutritional content

TYPE	NUTRITIONAL CONTENT	EXAMPLES
ROOTS	carbohydrate as starch and sugar carrots contain vitamin A (carotene)	beetroot, carrots, celeriac, horseradish, mooli, parsnips, radishes, salsify, swede, turnip.
TUBERS	carbohydrate as starch iron vitamins B and C	Jerusalem artichokes, potatoes, sweet potatoes, yams.
BULBS	carbohydrate as sugar cycloallin, an oil in onions may help dissolve blood clots	garlic, leeks, onions, shallots, spring onions.
LEAFY VEGETABLES	low energy value dark green leaves – vitamin A (carotene), folic acid, calcium, iron	chicory, Chinese leaves, lambs' lettuce, mustard and cress, radiccio, rocket, sorrel, spinach, Swiss chard, watercress.
BRASSICAS	low energy value broccoli and cauliflower – vitamin C, potassium broccoli – calcium	broccoli, brussels sprouts, cabbage, cauliflower.
PODS AND SEEDS	protein carbohydrate vitamins B and C whole beans (e.g.runner) – vitamin A and NSP	broad beans, butter or lima beans, runner beans, mange tout, okra, peas, sweetcorn.
FRUITING	carbohydrates as starch and sugar vitamin C avocados – high energy value (due to high fat content), but contain protein, vitamins A and B, folic acid, potassium	aubergine, avocado, courgette, cucumber, marrow, peppers, pumpkin, squash, tomatoes.
STEMS AND SHOOTS	NSP iron vitamins A and B calcium	asparagus, bean sprouts, cardoon, celery, globe artichokes, kohlrabi, sea kale.
MUSHROOM AND FUNGI	some protein and minerals trace vitamins useful flavour, colour and texture	ceps, chanterelles or girolles, morels, oyster mushrooms, field mushrooms, cultivated mushrooms.

- use root vegetables within 5-6 days
- buy green vegetables daily, or keep a maximum of 2 to 3 days
- store frozen vegetables at the correct temperature, use in strict rotation and before the 'best before' date
- keep salad in drawer of the refrigerator.

In a commercial environment:
- ideally have a refrigerator only for vegetables
- keep salad in containers and store in a cool room
- store root vegetables in bins or racks
- keep green vegetables in well ventilated racks.

Preparing vegetables

Vegetables should be washed, prepared and washed again as close to service time as possible. A separate vegetable sink is ideal, but if a multipurpose sink is used, particular care should be taken cleaning between uses to prevent cross-contamination. Commercial establishments may have machines which peel potatoes in bulk, or vegetables may be bought in 'ready prepared'. Table 5 shows some of the points to remember when preparing vegetables.

Cooking vegetables

Some vegetables cannot be eaten raw because their texture is too tough. Cooking reduces the bulk, alters the texture and flavour, and in some cases changes the colour. Cooking vegetables, however, reduces their nutritional value. Vitamins B and C are both water soluble and heat sensitive. Green vegetables can lose 50-70% of nutrients and potatoes can lose 20-40% of nutrients. In order to minimise this loss, vegetables should be cooked as quickly as possible, using the minimum amount of water and served immediately. The cooking water can be used to make gravy, soup or stock. Serve immediately - vitamin loss is greatest during cooking and if the vegetables are kept warm.

When heat is applied to vegetables, the starch glutinises and the cellulose softens. If vegetables are over-cooked they will become soft and mushy. Older, larger vegetables containing lignin will remain tough and stringy.

Given enough time, potatoes will turn brown or black, even if in water. This is caused by tannin compounds and enzymes coming into contact with the air. The same ENZYMIC BROWNING occurs with white fruits such as pears and bananas. A little vinegar or lemon will prevent this. The chlorophyll on green vegetables alters on application of heat. Acids released change the vegetables to an olive colour. This can be reduced by correct cooking which will also minimise the loss of vitamin C. In restaurants presentation may outweigh nutritional content and the chlorophyll in vegetables can be stabilised by using bicarbonate of soda. However, this destroys the vitamin C. Orange and yellow vegetables are not affected by heat. In an alkaline water, red vegetables turn a blue or purple colour. To retain the red use a little vinegar or lemon juice. Table 6 shows the different methods of cooking vegetables.

Table 5 Preparing vegetables

* Do not soak vegetables in water.
* Peel only if absolutely necessary using a parer or very sharp knife (most nutritional content is found near the skin).
* Trim out blemishes and outer leaves.
* Look out for hidden dirt and livestock, especially in loose leaf varieties, e.g. leeks, lettuce.
* Treat delicate vegetables gently to avoid bruising.

Table 6 Methods of cooking vegetables

Baking - potatoes, sweet potato, onions
Boiling - potatoes, carrots, corn on the cob
Casseroling - carrots, potatoes
Frying/Sauté - courgettes, peppers, aubergines, mushrooms, onions
Microwave - most vegetables - particularly good for retaining nutrients
Roasting - parsnips, potatoes, peppers, pumpkin
Steaming - leeks, broccoli, cauliflower, asparagus

The best method is not to cook at all. Raw vegetables have the best nutritional content. Many vegetables make excellent salad ingredients.

Fruits

Fruits are a source of natural sweetness, vitamins and NSP. Some fruits are available all the year, others may have a short season.

However, improved transport and storage mean that many fruits are available all year round.

Types of fruit

Stone fruits: e.g. apricot, cherry, damson,

activities

Potatoes are a staple food in Britain. In the quantities eaten, they provide a large proportion of the vitamin C needed in the diet. They also contain protein, energy in the form of starch, NSP, iron, calcium and vitamins B and E.

1. Vitamin C helps the body to absorb iron, so it is important to conserve this vitamin in vegetables where iron is also present. Suggest THREE ways of conserving vitamin C in potatoes and other vegetables.
2. Healthy eating guidelines suggest that we eat more vegetables (including potatoes) but reduce our fat intake. Suggest TWO low fat recipes using potatoes.

Table 7 Using fruit
Stone fruits: eaten fresh, stewed, jam, pie, flan. Apricots, damsons and peaches can also be used in meat dishes.

Hard fruits: apples and pears can be either dessert or cooking variety - both may be used in pastry dishes, dessert varieties eaten fresh, apples as a sauce or garnish for pork, duck and nut roasts.

Soft fruits: eaten fresh, jam, summer pudding, sauces or coulis.

Citrus fruits: eaten fresh, used as flavouring (both zest and juice), marmalades, garnish for both savoury and sweet dishes.

Tropical fruits: eaten fresh, bananas as garnish for both fish and poultry, pineapple served with gammon.

Dried fruit: eaten alone as a snack, cakes, biscuits and puddings, stewed.

nectarine, peach, plum.

Hard fruits: apple, pear.

Soft fruits and berries: bilberry, blackberry, blackcurrant, raspberry, redcurrant, strawberry, grape.

Citrus fruits: clementine, grapefruit, kumquat, lemon, lime, mandarin, orange, tangerine, ugli.

Tropical fruits: banana, date, fig, guava, kiwi fruit, lychee, mango, passion fruit, papaya, pineapple.

Dried fruits: dates, raisins, figs, etc.

Nutritional content of fruit

Water and carbohydrate are the main components in fresh fruit. Sucrose, glucose and fructose are found in ripe fruit, and are easily absorbed by the body. Fruit is a useful aid when slimming, because of its low energy value and high NSP content. There are negligible amounts of fat and protein in fruit, but it is a major source of vitamin C, especially as so much is eaten raw. The amount of vitamin C in fruit differs widely. Table 7 suggests some ways of using fruit.

Buying and storing fruit

● Keep stone fruits in single layers so that any which are damaged can be removed.
● Ensure hard fruits are not bruised on purchase. Store in a cool area.
● Keep soft fruits in their punnets in a cool area. Deterioration is rapid.
● Bananas should not be allowed to get too cold - their skins turn black.

Gliadin - protein found in wheat.
Glutenin - protein found in wheat.
Gluten - protein formed when wheat is cooked.
Endosperm - the starchy part of a cereal grain.
Dextrinisation - a process where dry heat turns starch to sugar, giving bread and other baked products a brown colour.
Gelatinisation - a process where heat causes liquid to penetrate starch and make it swell.
Enzymic browning - browning of fruits and vegetables caused by tannin compounds and enzymes coming into contact with the air.

activities

1. List reasons why parents might choose St. Ivel Pure Fruit for their children.
2. Pure Fruit comes in a pack of four different flavours. Why might this variety be important?
3. It is recommended that babies and young children avoid sugar and salt. Does St. Ivel Pure Fruit fulfil this need?
4. A 10 month old baby girl needs 865 kilocalories a day. What proportion of her daily requirement is met by a 90g pot of Pure Fruit?

Parents want to give their children a varied and wholesome diet. Foods that are tasty as well as convenient are important. St. Ivel Baby and Toddler Pure Fruit is a delicious blend of natural fruit purée and apple juice. Fruit purée is one of the first foods recommended for babies being introduced to solids. There are no added preservatives, colour or salt. Pure Fruit is gluten free and suitable for vegetarians. Available in four 90g pots.

NUTRITION INFORMATION

100g provides	
Energy	49 kcal
Protein	0.5g
Carbohydrate	11.2g
of which sugars	11.2g
Fat	0.2g
of which saturates	trace
Fibre	1.4g
Sodium	trace

Source: adapted from St. Ivel product information

4 Fats and oils

Where do fats come from?

Fats may be of animal, fish or vegetable origin. Animal fats may come from the flesh of animals (e.g. suet, lard) or they may be manufactured from an animal source (e.g. butter). Fish such as herring, mackerel, salmon and trout are rich sources of oil. Oils can also be extracted from various seeds, flowers and beans and may even be found in wheat, barley, oats and some fruits and vegetables in the form of polyunsaturated fatty acids.

Composition of fat

Fats and oils are composed of large molecules built up from long chains of glycerol and a wide variety of fatty acids. The fatty acids vary in chemical composition; some are saturated others are unsaturated (see Unit 6). Animal fat will tend to be solid at room temperature and have a high melting point. Vegetable fat will be soft or liquid at room temperature and has a lower melting point. There are over 40 different fatty acids so there are a large number of possible combinations. This results in a great variety of different fats and oils on the supermarket shelves.

Types of fat

There are two main types of fat.

- Pure fats which occur naturally (e.g. lard, olive oil).
- Emulsified fats which contain a percentage of water. This water may occur naturally

A salad dressing made of oil and vinegar. Fats and oils do not mix with water. When a fat or oil is forced to mix with water (e.g. if the salad dressing is shaken) it is known as an emulsion. This emulsion is not stable (if left the dressing would soon separate into oil and vinegar again).

However, a third ingredient can be added to stabilise the emulsion (e.g. in mayonnaise it is egg yolk). Emulsions are found in many processed products like margarine and salad dressings. The proportions of oil and water are significant. If there is more water than oil it is known as an oil in water emulsion (e.g. milk, low fat spreads). If there is more oil than water it is known a water in oil emulsion (e.g. butter, margarine).

(e.g. butter) or it may be added to fat during processing (e.g. low fat spread).

Animal fats

To extract the fat from an animal the carcass is heated. The liquid fat is collected, cooled and re-formed into hard blocks of fat. Suet comes from beef cattle and lard comes from pigs. Fat can be extracted from milk to form cream and cream can be churned to form butter (see Unit 2).

Fish oils

These are sometimes used in the manufacture of margarine. Vitamin rich oils are also obtained from cod and halibut liver.

Margarine

This was invented over one hundred years ago as a butter substitute. By law margarine

must not contain more than 16% water. It must be fortified with vitamins A and D. Colourings are strictly controlled and it must not contain additives. Margarines are made from a variety of fats and oils from animal and vegetable sources.

Low fat spreads

These contain more than 16% water. They are oil in water emulsions and contain a much lower percentage of fat than butter or margarine. They are vitamin fortified but cannot be used for baking or frying.

White fats

These do not contain any water and are made of varying brands of vegetable oils, fish oils and lard. They can be used as a lard substitute for pastry making and frying. Some products have air whipped into them so that they rub in and cream more easily. White fats have a very bland flavour.

Vegetable oils

Many plants produce seeds which contain oil. Processing involves squeezing the oil from the hard tough seeds. The oil is then refined to:
- remove any fatty acids which would cause the oil to go rancid
- improve the taste and smell
- lighten the colour.

Refined oils are used extensively in the food industry either in their liquid form or after they have been hydrogenated (see Unit 6) to create a solid fat. Liquid oils may be pure such as olive oil or blends of mixed vegetable oils.

Storing fat

Fat should be stored in sealed containers in a refrigerator or freezer. It is important to exclude air to prevent the fat from absorbing strong flavours. Oils may be stored in a cool, dry cupboard.

Cooking with fat

We use fat as an ingredient in many dishes and as a cooking medium for frying food. Table 1 shows some of the uses of fats and oils. Fats vary in cost and flavour and they behave differently on heating. It is important to choose the right fat for the cooking task. Figure 1 shows what happens when a fat is heated. Fats and oils melt and reach smoke and flash points at different temperatures. Fats with more water, salt and emulsifiers in them (e.g. butter) will reach each point at lower temperatures than pure fats (e.g. lard). Rapid deterioration of the fat takes place if:

● it is over-heated
● it is over-used
● too much food is fried at one time
● the stored fat is exposed to air or light
● sediment is left in the fat during storage.

Signs that the fat is deteriorating are: foaming; smoking at lower temperatures; a dark colour; food greasy after cooking and an unpleasant smell. If these conditions occur the fat should be discarded.

Table 1 Uses of fats and oils

SPREADING
* Butter
* Margarine

FLAVOURING
* Melted butter on cooked vegetables
* Olive oil drizzled on a pizza

EMULSION
* Oils with interesting flavours for salad dressings

EXTEND SHELF LIFE OF FOODS
* Vegetable oil added to bread dough

SHORTENING
* Flour particles are coated with fat in pastry making or shortbread

AERATION
* Creamed butter or margarine helps to trap and hold air in cake making

SEALING
* Butter or lard creates a moisture repellent surface on pates

FRYING
* Oils can reach higher temperatures than solid fats without breaking down

Shallow frying

This is a rapid method of cooking. The outer coating of the food becomes crisp and the interior remains moist. The coating of oil in the pan stops the food sticking and burning and helps to conduct heat to the food's surface. However, there is a danger of cooking the outside before the centre if the temperature of the fat is too high.

Deep frying

This gives food a crunchy texture and a distinctive flavour. The food is submerged in preheated oil or fat. All frying causes some fat to be absorbed by food. If the correct temperature (165°C-190°C) is used the proportion should be quite small. When deep frying, the following points are important.

● Select the right food. Foods with a low water content are ideal. Foods such as potatoes should be patted dry before frying.
● Prepare food by cutting into small, even sized pieces.
● Use the right coating - batter, breadcrumbs, flour.
● Use the right oil - must heat without burning.
● Use correct timing and temperature.

FLASH POINT
Further heating will lead to the flash point and the fat will burst into flames - usually at 100°C above smoke point.

SMOKE POINT
Oils and some fats can be heated to very high temperatures before they start to smoke. Smoking shows that the chemical structure of the fat is beginning to break down. The fat will smell and a substance called acrolein which affects the eyes is produced. The fat will also go rancid.

MELTING POINT
When solid fats are heated they melt. This melting point varies for different fats.

Figure 1 Changes when fat is heated

activities

1. Bearing in mind the properties of different fats or oils, suggest a fat or oil which you think would be suitable for the following cooking tasks. Explain your choice.
   a) pastry for a sweet tart;
   b) dressing for a green salad;
   c) deep frying doughnuts;
   d) shallow frying white fish.

2. St. Ivel Mono is a spread high in monounsaturates and low in saturates, for all the family.
   a) Why might someone concerned about their health decide to eat Mono instead of butter?
   b) The ingredients list of St. Ivel Mono includes hydrogenated vegetable oil. Explain what this means (see Unit 6).
   c) Mono is described as 'a multi-purpose product'. Suggest FIVE recipes in which it could be used.

USAGE:
✔ Spreading
✔ Cooking/baking
✔ Shallow frying
✗ Deep frying

STORAGE:
Always store in a refrigerator. Suitable for freezing. Store in a deep freeze for up to 3 months and defrost in a refrigerator.

RAPESEED OIL; HYDROGENATED VEGETABLE OIL; WATER; SALT (1.3%); EMULSIFIERS - E471, SOYA LECITHIN; LACTIC ACID; FLAVOURING; VITAMINS A & D; COLOUR - BETA CAROTENE.

100g provides	Butter	St Ivel Mono
Energy	737 kcal	675 kcal
Protein	0.5g	nil
Carbohydrate	trace	nil
Fat	81.7g	75.0g
of which saturates	54g	11.5g
of which monounsaturates	14.3g	35.0g
of which polyunsaturates	2.6g	14.7g
Fibre	–	–
Sodium	0.9g	0.5g

Source: St. Ivel product information.

5 Sugar

Types of sugar

Granulated sugar is the most popular sugar, accounting for over 80% of sales. Caster sugar has smaller grains and is used for baking. Icing sugar is finely ground and blended with an anti-caking agent. It is used for decoration. Demerara sugar is raw cane sugar. It can be used to sweeten coffee or provide a distinctive crunchy topping for desserts. Light and dark brown sugars are white sugar with added molasses. They are used in baking to add extra colour and flavour. Preserving sugar is a white sugar with large crystals, suitable for making jam. Golden syrups and treacles are by-products of sugar processing and are used for baking. Figure 1 shows some of the uses of sugar. Molasses is another by-product. It is used by the food industry and as animal feed. Non-food uses, such as binding charcoal briquettes have also been developed.

Maize and wheat can also be converted into sweeteners such as maltodextrin, dextrose, fructose, glucose and corn syrup. These products are used by the food, brewing and pharmaceutical industries.

Nutritional content of sugar

Pure sugar is 99.9% sucrose, providing calories and no other nutritional benefit. Eating too much sugar can result in dental caries (see Unit 13). Molasses contains vitamins B, iron and other minerals. Brown sugar contains few nutrients. It is no 'healthier' than white sugar.

Cooking with sugar

Sugar behaves in different ways depending on how it is heated.

In baking, sugar slows down the process of starch GELATINISATION, by competing with the starch for the liquid in the mixture. This allows more time for raising agents to work. Sugar also reacts with proteins in the mixture causing a MAILLARD REACTION, resulting in browning. Further browning takes place as the surface sugar is heated above its melting point (about 175°C).

Sugar syrups are mixtures of sugar dissolved in water. The thickness of the syrup depends on the proportion of sugar to water - the more sugar, the thicker the syrup. When a syrup is heated and boiled it changes. As the temperature rises and more water boils away, the syrup becomes thicker and more concentrated. At each stage, the syrup is suitable for different uses, e.g. candied fruits, boiled sweets and spun sugar products. Caramel is formed during the final stages of cooking sugar.

During CARAMELISATION, the sugar turns brown. If the process continues, the product turns black and loses its sweet taste.

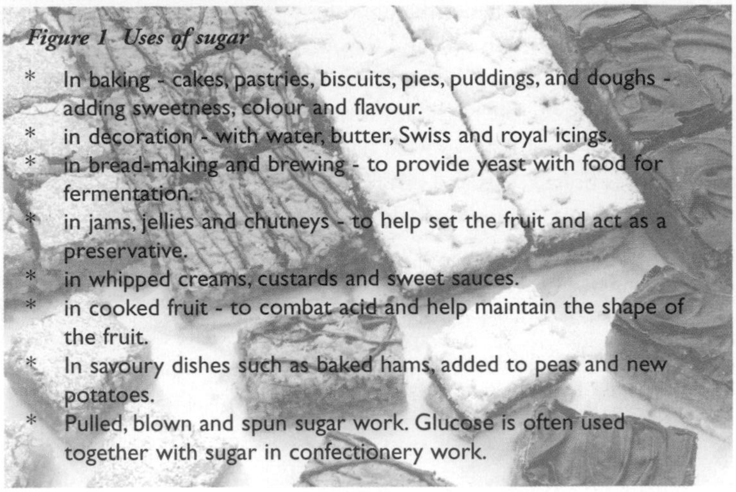

Figure 1 Uses of sugar

* In baking - cakes, pastries, biscuits, pies, puddings, and doughs - adding sweetness, colour and flavour.
* in decoration - with water, butter, Swiss and royal icings.
* in bread-making and brewing - to provide yeast with food for fermentation.
* in jams, jellies and chutneys - to help set the fruit and act as a preservative.
* in whipped creams, custards and sweet sauces.
* in cooked fruit - to combat acid and help maintain the shape of the fruit.
* In savoury dishes such as baked hams, added to peas and new potatoes.
* Pulled, blown and spun sugar work. Glucose is often used together with sugar in confectionery work.

Key Terms

Gelatinisation - a process where heat causes liquid to penetrate starch and make it swell
Maillard reaction - a process where heat causes a reaction between amino acids and sugars resulting in browning.
Caramelisation - a process where heat turns sugar into caramel.

activities

1. Table 1 suggests foods which demonstrate the properties of sugar. Suggest another example for each property.
2. In what ways is sugar useful to the baker?
3. What properties of sugar help in making preserves?

Table 1 Properties of sugar

PROPERTY	EXAMPLE
CONTRIBUTES TO:	
sweetness	confectionery
viscosity	chutney
volume	meringues
texture	creme brûlée
ENHANCES:	
flavour	tomatoes
appearance	preserves
INCREASES:	
moisture retention	gingerbread
boiling point	custards
ASSISTS:	
emulsification	ice cream
colour development	biscuits
fermentation	bread-making
DELAYS	
staling	cakes
discolouration	fresh fruit flan
lowers freezing point	ice cream
inhibits mould growth	jam

Source: adapted from Tate & Lyle Fact File on Sugar

CANE SUGAR PROCESSING AT TATE & LYLE

Sugar is processed from sugar cane or sugar beet. Sugar beet produces only white sugar. Sugar cane is processed to make white and brown sugars, syrups and treacles, molasses and useful by-products (see Figure 2). Sugar cane is grown in tropical or semi-tropical countries (e.g. Mauritius, India, Jamaica). The first stage of processing takes place in sugar mills located close to the growing areas, producing raw sugar. This is shipped to refineries in Britain, where the second stage of processing takes place (see Figure 1).

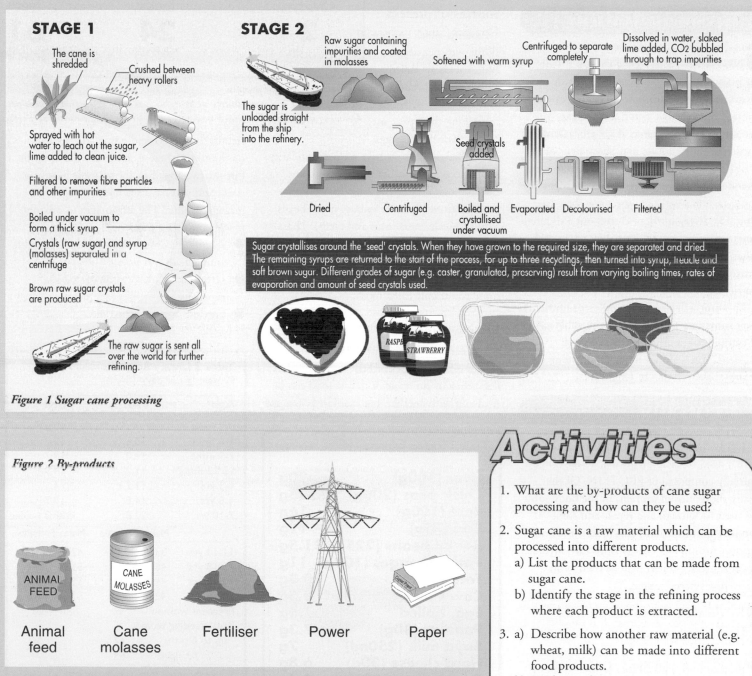

STAGE 1

The cane is shredded

Crushed between heavy rollers

Sprayed with hot water to leach out the sugar, lime added to clean juice.

Filtered to remove fibre particles and other impurities

Boiled under vacuum to form a thick syrup

Crystals (raw sugar) and syrup (molasses) separated in a centrifuge

Brown raw sugar crystals are produced

The raw sugar is sent all over the world for further refining.

Figure 1 Sugar cane processing

STAGE 2

The sugar is unloaded straight from the ship into the refinery.

Raw sugar containing impurities and coated in molasses

Softened with warm syrup

Centrifuged to separate completely

Dissolved in water, slaked lime added, CO_2 bubbled through to trap impurities

Seed crystals added

Dried   Centrifuged   Boiled and crystallised under vacuum   Evaporated   Decolourised   Filtered

Sugar crystallises around the 'seed' crystals. When they have grown to the required size, they are separated and dried. The remaining syrups are returned to the start of the process, for up to three recyclings, then turned into syrup, treacle and soft brown sugar. Different grades of sugar (e.g. caster, granulated, preserving) result from varying boiling times, rates of evaporation and amount of seed crystals used.

RASPBERRY   STRAWBERRY

Figure 2 By-products

ANIMAL FEED

CANE MOLASSES

Animal feed   Cane molasses   Fertiliser   Power   Paper

All the by-products of the first stage of sugar cane processing are used. Left over cane pulp, called 'bagasse', can be used as fuel for the mill. The ash from the fuel makes a good fertiliser for the cane fields. Surplus bagasse can be made into paper. Molasses is used by the food industry and as animal feed.

Activities

1. What are the by-products of cane sugar processing and how can they be used?

2. Sugar cane is a raw material which can be processed into different products.
   a) List the products that can be made from sugar cane.
   b) Identify the stage in the refining process where each product is extracted.

3. a) Describe how another raw material (e.g. wheat, milk) can be made into different food products.
   b) Produce a diagram, using original artwork and text, to show how this raw material is processed.

6 Nutrients

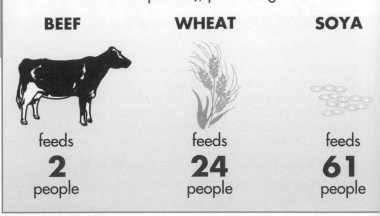

Ten hectares of land (the size of 5 football pitches), producing

BEEF	WHEAT	SOYA
feeds **2** people	feeds **24** people	feeds **61** people

Figure 1 The cost of protein
Although meat is a good source of protein, it is very expensive to produce. Growing vegetables is a much more cost effective way of producing protein.

Basic nutrition

Food is made up of different NUTRIENTS. We need these nutrients for body growth, repair, energy, warmth and protection from disease. If we do not eat enough nutrients we could lose weight, become ill or even starve. If we are lacking in particular nutrients we may show signs of a DEFICIENCY. If we eat too many nutrients or too much of the wrong sort of nutrient, we could put on weight and become obese (see Unit 13). Every nutrient carries out a different function and many of them depend on each other to work properly. It is therefore vital to eat an adequate amount of each of the nutrients.

This unit will look at the different nutrients, their functions, sources and the possible results of eating too much or too little of each nutrient. You will find more about eating a healthy balanced diet in Unit 12.

Proteins

The body is made up of millions of cells which need replacing regularly. These cells are partially composed of PROTEIN. Of the many thousands of proteins in the body some are used for growth and repair and some produce hormones and enzymes. If the body receives insufficient energy from carbohydrate or fat sources, protein may be used as an alternative energy source.

Why do we need to eat protein?

The human body needs 20 amino acids to construct the protein in its cells. However 8 of these amino acids (9 for children) cannot be made in the body and must be obtained from food. They used to be known as essential amino acids, but now we call them indispensable amino acids.

Sources of protein

Proteins which contain all the indispensable amino acids are called high biological value proteins (HBVs). Foods containing these proteins (meat, poultry, fish, eggs, milk, cheese and soya) have a closer similarity to amino acids found in the human body. Low biological value proteins (LBVs) are proteins from vegetable sources (peas, beans, lentils, cereals, pasta, nuts and seeds). These proteins contain only one or two indispensable amino acids per food. Table 1 shows how much protein is obtained from some commonly eaten foods.

Mixing proteins

You can mix HBVs with LBVs or eat several different types of LBV at one meal. A deficiency of amino acids in one food can be made up with another. For example pulses are rich in the amino acid lysine and poor in methionine, whereas cereals are the opposite. Put the two together, for example beans on toast, and you have a protein of high biological value. The advantages to mixing proteins within a meal are:

- ensures maximum intake of indispensable amino acids
- saves money - LBV proteins are less expensive
- provides a more varied diet.

Table 1 Sources of protein (single servings)

Liver (100g)	20g
Chick peas (200g)	16g
Beef (100g)	16g
Cod (75g)	12g
Baked beans (225g)	11.5g
Pork sausages (100g)	11g
Tofu (140g)	10.3g
Cow's milk (250ml)	8.5g
Egg, boiled	7.5g
Peanuts (30g)	7.3g
Soya milk (250ml)	7g
Hard cheese (30g)	6.8g
Brown rice (200g)	4.4g
Potatoes (200g)	2.8g
Yeast extract (7g)	2.8g

Table 2 Dietary Reference Values* for Protein (g per day)

Age	EAR		RNI	
0-3 mths	-		12.5	
4-6 mths	10.6		12.7	
7-9 mths	11.0		13.7	
10-12 mths	11.2		14.9	
1-3 yrs	11.7		14.5	
4-6 yrs	14.8		19.7	
7-10 yrs	22.8		28.3	
	Males	Females	Males	Females
11-14 yrs	33.8	33.1	42.1	41.2
15-18 yrs	46.1	37.1	55.2	45.4
19-49 yrs	44.4	36.0	55.5	45.0
50+ yrs	42.6	37.2	53.3	46.5
Pregnant women	42		51	
Breastfeeding women				
up to 6 mths	47		56	
6+ mths	44		53	

Source: adapted from Dietary Reference Values - A Guide, HMSO, 1991

* see Unit 7 for an explanation of Dietary Reference Values

Home sprouted beans or seeds contain valuable amounts of protein as well as most major vitamins and minerals.

Going without

A deficiency of protein is unlikely in the Western World. In fact, most people eat far more than they need. If excess protein is eaten, the body will use it for energy. If this energy is not needed, the body will store it as fat.

'New' proteins

Food scientists have been searching for alternative sources of protein to feed a growing world population. These are some of the sources that have been identified.

- Mycoprotein - a product made from a tiny plant similar to a mushroom and bound together with egg albumen.
- TVP (Textured Vegetable Protein) - a meat replacement product made from

soya beans.
- Sea vegetables such as nori, kombu and arame.
- Sprouting seeds (bean sprouts).
- Plankton, algae, leaves and micro-organisms are all being investigated as possible future sources of protein.

Carbohydrates

Foods high in carbohydrate are our main source of energy. There are three forms of carbohydrate in our diet: SUGAR, STARCH and NSP. Carbohydrates are usually plant products. Plants take energy from the sun

and, through a process of photosynthesis, convert it into carbohydrates.

A sweet tooth?

Sugar is known as a simple carbohydrate because it is composed of small sweet molecules. Sugar has many uses in cooking. It adds colour and flavour to foods (see Unit 5). Humans generally have a preference for sweet tasting foods.

Types of sugar

There are two main types of sugar: **monosaccharides** and **disaccharides**. These names refer to the cellular structure of sugars.

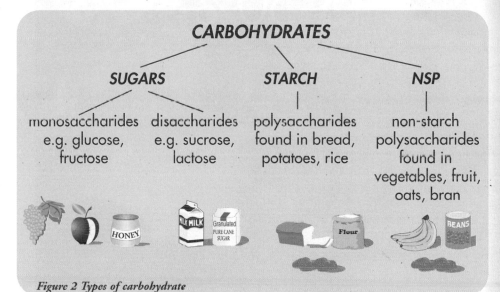

CARBOHYDRATES

SUGARS   **STARCH**   **NSP**

monosaccharides e.g. glucose, fructose

disaccharides e.g. sucrose, lactose

polysaccharides found in bread, potatoes, rice

non-starch polysaccharides found in vegetables, fruit, oats, bran

Figure 2 Types of carbohydrate

activities

Use the information given in Tables 1 and 2 to suggest a day's menu for each of the following people. Make sure that the protein intake meets the RNI level (see Unit 7 for an explanation of Dietary Reference Values).

Rory, (3) takes a packed lunch to his childminder.

Ken, (63) works as a building site supervisor.

Carmel, (31) is pregnant and a vegetarian

Figure 3 Carbohydrates in our diet. Carbohydrates should make up at least half of the human diet, ideally in these proportions:

complex carbohydrates 45-50%

simple carbohydrates 5-10%

Monosaccharides are the simplest units. **Glucose** and **fructose** are examples of monosaccharides. Disaccharides are made up of two monosaccharide units. **Maltose**, **lactose** and **sucrose** are examples of disaccharides.

Sugars are formed naturally in foods. Sometimes the food will taste sweet and sometimes it will not not. Sugar can be classified in this way.

Intrinsic sugar (in cell structure) - found in whole fruits and vegetables.

Extrinsic sugar (not in cell structure) - found in fruit juice, table sugar or the sugar added to home baked products and processed foods. These types of sugar may also be referred to as non-milk extrinsic sugars. It is recommended that we reduce the amount of non-milk extrinsic sugars in our diet.

Milk sugar (lactose) is an extrinsic sugar but it can be considered separately from other foods in the extrinsic group as it does not contribute to tooth decay in the same way.

Should we eat less sugar?

Although sugar is a good source of energy and contains less calories per gram than fat, it contains no other nutrients, such as vitamins or minerals. People sometimes refer to sugar as an 'empty calorie' food meaning that it provides energy but nothing else that is of use to the body. Tooth decay is directly linked to the consumption of non-milk extrinsic sugar. Eating too much sugar can contribute to an excessive intake of energy which could lead to obesity and diabetes. In Europe we consume 30-40kg of non-milk extrinsic sugars per person per year. We do not need sugar in our diet but many of us like the taste. Intrinsic and milk sugars are easier for our body to absorb and do little damage to teeth. We should reduce our intake of non-milk extrinsic sugars and replace them with fresh fruit, vegetables and starchy foods.

Complex carbohydrates

Complex carbohydrates have a more complicated molecular structure than sugars. They are known as **polysaccharides**.

STARCH is formed when hundreds of glucose molecules are strung together. The energy provided by starch is more long lasting than that provided by sugar. Starchy foods such as bread, rice, pasta and potatoes are good sources of energy and help to fill us up. They also provide valuable vitamins and minerals.

NSP (non-starch polysaccharide) is also known as fibre. It is found in the cell walls of plants which are made of long strings of glucose molecules but in a different formation from starch. Humans find NSP tough and indigestible but animals can handle it and digest it effectively. There are two types of NSP. The first will dissolve in water, for example pectin which is found in some acid tasting fruits and helps to set jam. The second is insoluble in water, for example bran. It speeds up the movement of food through the gut and prevents constipation.

Fats

FAT is a highly concentrated energy food, providing twice as many calories per gram as protein or carbohydrate. For information about the composition and properties of fat, see Unit 4.

Why do we need fat?

These are the reasons why we need fat:

- fat provides the body with a concentrated source of energy
- vitamins A, D, E and K are found in fatty foods
- vegetable oils contain substances called essential fatty acids which make hormones to control blood clotting, help prevent some skin conditions and aid growth.

Generally, we eat more fat than we need. Table 6 on p.26 gives some reasons why people like to eat fat.

Too much fat

It is the amount of fat we eat in this country that causes concern to doctors and nutritionists. Because of its high calorie content, eating too much fat can lead to obesity (see Unit 13). Eating saturated fat (see *Types of fat* below) is also linked to heart disease. Saturated fat makes our bodies produce a substance called CHOLESTEROL. This is natural fat made by the body in the liver. Normally it helps in the manufacture of hormones, bile and Vitamin D. Some cholesterol helps to protect the artery wall. But eating some kinds of fat can cause the body to produce too much

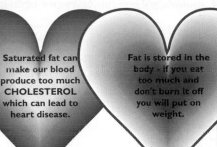

Saturated fat can make our blood produce too much **CHOLESTEROL** which can lead to heart disease.

Fat is stored in the body - if you eat too much and don't burn it off you will put on weight.

Table 3 Why should we eat less fat?

cholesterol. This over-production of cholesterol can clog up the arteries causing heart disease. Deaths from heart disease in Britain are among the highest in the world. Health experts recommend that we reduce our fat intake (see Unit 12).

Types of fat

There are different types of fat and some kinds are less harmful than others. Animal fats like meat, butter, lard and suet are called saturated fats. They are solid at room temperature. This type of fat can build up deposits in the arteries and can lead to heart disease. Palm and coconut oils also contain high proportions of saturates and should be eaten sparingly.

Polyunsaturated fats come from vegetable sources, like nuts, seeds and safflowers. Many soft spreads contain this type of fat.

Monounsaturated fats are found in all fatty foods but especially in olive oil and rape seed oil.

Fish liver oils and oily fish like tuna and

Table 4 Sources of fat

The following foods all contain fat:
Foods from a dairy source
Meat
Fish
Eggs
Spreads for bread
Vegetable and fish oils
Pastry, cakes and biscuits
Confectionery
Nuts
Avocado
Olives
Anything fried

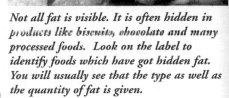

Not all fat is visible. It is often hidden in products like biscuits, chocolate and many processed foods. Look on the label to identify foods which have got hidden fat. You will usually see that the type as well as the quantity of fat is given.

activities

1. How do simple and complex carbohydrates differ?
2. What problems can be caused by having 'a sweet tooth'?
3. Many cultures rely heavily on one or two complex carbohydrates in their diet. For example, British people tend to eat a lot of bread and potatoes. These are called staple foods. Name the staple foods from TWO other cultures.
4. Which carbohydrates should we be cutting down on in our diet? Which should we be eating more of?
5. Why might some people be reluctant to increase the amount of complex carbohydrate in their diet?

6. On 1 February, 1996, the *Daily Mirror* compared breakfast cereals. The results are shown in Table 5.
   a) Prepare a bar chart showing the carbohydrate content of these cereals.
   b) Which cereal would you advise the following people to choose?
      i) Francesca is an active 6 year old
      ii) Jenny teaches aerobics and needs something to keep her going until lunchtime
      iii) Graham works in an office and is trying to lose a couple of kilos.

CEREAL BRAND	CALORIES per 100g	SUGARg per 100g	FIBREg per 100g
Quaker Sugar Puffs	387	49	3
Jordans Bran Hearts	384	20.2	12.5
Kellogg's Frosties	380	39	0.6
Kellogg's Coco Pops	380	39	1
Kellogg's Special K	370	15	2.5
Kellogg's Rice Krispies	370	10	0.7
Kellogg's Cornflakes	370	8	1
Nestlé Cheerios	369	22.4	6.2
Quaker Oats	368	1.1	7
Weetabix Alpen Original	365	28.1	7
Kellogg's Sustain	360	18	6
Nestlé Shredded Wheat	352	0.7	10
Weetabix	342	4.7	10.1
Kellogg's Common Sense	340	21	9
Kellogg's All Bran	270	18	24

Table 5 Breakfast cereals

Source: the Daily Mirror, 1 February, 1996

Table 6 Why is fat so appealing?

These are some of the reasons why fat is difficult to limit in the diet:
- Food containing fat usually tastes nice.
- The feel of fatty food in the mouth is comforting.
- Fatty foods make you feel full.
- Luxury foods are associated with fat e.g. cream, cheeses and meat.
- Fried foods are quick and easy to cook.

herring also contain unsaturated fats.

All unsaturated fats can help to lower blood cholesterol levels. Monounsaturated fats do a better job because they reduce excess cholesterol without damaging the amount we need to protect artery walls.

Trans fats are formed when food manufacturers pump hydrogen into oils in order to make them spreadable at room temperature. This changes the size of the fat molecules and the oil hardens. This process, called hydrogenation, causes unsaturated fats to become more like saturated fats. Research has suggested that high levels of trans fats can raise cholesterol levels in the body.

Low fat products

The low fat sector is a rapidly growing part of the food market, expanding 44% between 1988 and 1990. Manufacturers are aware that many people are beginning to search for the words 'low-fat' or 'reduced fat' on products. It is seen as a useful marketing tool.

activities

1. Give TWO reasons for reducing our intake of fat.
2. Do you think we should cut out fat altogether from our diets? Give reasons for your answer.
3. How could you modify the following recipes in order to reduce the intake of saturated fat in the diet? In each case, suggest a healthier alternative to the ingredient in italics.
   - shortcrust pastry made with *butter*;
   - chips fried in *lard*;
   - fresh fruit salad and *cream*.

Consumers must be aware that products labelled 'reduced fat' may still have a high percentage of fat within the product. It is essential to check the label to see just how much of the total food weight is fat. The claim 'fat free' is a good indication that a product has been processed without fat.

Vitamins and minerals

VITAMINS and MINERALS help to:
- promote health and prevent disease
- monitor the building and repair of body cells
- regulate the chemical reactions which release energy in the body.

The body needs very small amounts of vitamins and minerals (usually measured in milligrams (mg) or micrograms (μg)). However, the body cannot make its own supplies so we must make sure that we get enough in our diets. It is rare in developed countries for people to suffer a severe deficiency of vitamins or minerals, but some people may suffer mild deficiencies.

Am I getting enough?

Signs of a mild vitamin or mineral deficiency are:
- tiredness
- broken nails
- poor skin and hair condition
- dental problems.

Am I getting too much?

The body will react differently depending on the vitamin or mineral overdose. For instance an overdose of vitamin B could cause serious liver damage. Too much vitamin A in pregnancy can cause damage to the foetus.

Types of vitamin

The main vitamins are A, B, C, D, E & K. Vitamins are either **fat soluble** or **water soluble**. Water soluble vitamins may be found in some watery foods. Fat soluble vitamins may be found in fatty foods.

activities

WHICH FAT SHALL I CHOOSE?
All spreads for bread contain fat, but some are tastier, cheaper or healthier than others. List as many butters, margarines and low-fat spreads as you can. Design a table to help you compare the flavour, spreadability, cost, intended use, fat content and effects on health of these spreads. The facts on the right may help you. (Also see Units 4 and 12 for more information on fats.)

- If a spread contains a lot of saturated fat it will be hard like butter.
- If a spread contains a lot of polyunsaturated fat it will be softer and usually sold in a tub.
- Manufacturers often pump hydrogen into fats to make them easy to spread from the fridge. This is a process called hydrogenation. Hydrogenated fats can act like saturated fats in the body.
- All butters and margarines must by law contain 80% fat - the rest is mainly water. Any product with less than 80% fat must be called a spread.
- Low-fat spreads may still contain up to 75% fat.
- Low-fat spreads usually contain a high proportion of water. This makes them unsuitable for frying or baking.
- All margarines have the same energy value as butter.

VITAMIN A (retinol or carotene)
fat soluble

RNI: over 15 years - 700 µg (men), 600 µg (women)

GOOD SOURCES: retinol - liver, eggs, butter and fish oils
carotene - yellow and orange fruits and vegetables like tomatoes, mangoes, carrots and sweet potatoes, dark green vegetables like spinach, broccoli and watercress

CAUTION: destroyed by heat, air and when fats become rancid

FUNCTION:
● helps form cells of skin and internal linings
● aids bone growth
● aids night vision

DEFICIENCY:
● rough dry skin
● slowed growth in children
● night blindness
● internal linings can become dry and brittle

Vitamin A deficiency is a serious health problem world wide due to the poor diets eaten in developing countries. Chemical supplements are inexpensive.

VITAMIN B
water soluble

This complex group contains at least 13 vitamins. They tend to occur together and have similar functions. These are some of the most important: thiamin (B1), riboflavin (B2), niacin (B3) and folic acid. A balance of all B vitamins should be eaten.

RNI:
B1 (thiamin) - over 1 year - 0.4 mg per 1,000 calories eaten
B2 (riboflavin) - over 15 years - 1.3mg (men), 1.1mg (women)
B3 (niacin) - all ages 6.6mg per 1,000 calories eaten
folic acid - over 11 years 200 µg

GOOD SOURCES: The main sources of the B group vitamins are: cereals (especially wholegrain), wheatgerm, yeast and yeast extract, meat, fish, eggs, dairy products and pulses.
In addition, the following foods are also good sources of individual B vitamins:
B1 (thiamin) - brazil nuts, peanuts
B2 (riboflavin) - almonds, mushrooms, spinach, broccoli
B3 (niacin) - peanuts, dried peaches, dried apricots
folic acid - dark green vegetables (especially brussels sprouts), potatoes

CAUTION: water soluble, and some are affected by heat, cooking and storage

FUNCTION:
● helps the body to release energy from food
● essential for normal growth
● helps to make red blood cells

DEFICIENCY:
thiamin - loss of appetite, loss of muscle tone, mental confusion, beri-beri
riboflavin - wounds fail to heal, sore or cracked lips, slowed growth in children
niacin - dermatitis, diarrhoea, inflammation of mucus membranes, pellagra

activities

1. Why does the Department of Health recommend that women take folic acid BEFORE they become pregnant?
2. Folic acid is part of the B group of vitamins. What should you remember when preparing food containing folic acid in order to conserve as much of the vitamin as possible?
3. Using the information provided in Table 7, plan a day's menu for a pregnant woman, including foods rich in folic acid.

Table 7 Foods containing folic acid

High content: black eye beans, brussels sprouts, fortified breakfast cereal, fortified bread, yeast/meat extract, spinach, broccoli, oranges.

Medium content: soya beans, chick peas, potatoes, peas, okra, baked beans, bread, milk, yogurt, eggs, brown rice, bananas.

Two babies every day are born with neural tube defects like spina bifida. These are caused when the baby's neural tube, which becomes the spine, does not grow properly. This results in a disability of the spine. A baby is most at risk from this disease during the first 12 weeks of pregnancy. Doctors have discovered that folic acid can help to prevent neural tube defects and recommend that:
    Pregnant women and women who may become pregnant should eat a diet rich in folic acid.
    Pregnant women and women who may become pregnant should also take a tablet supplement of 400 µg (micrograms) folic acid per day. This should be taken until the 12th week of pregnancy.

Source: adapted from Department of Health leaflets.

VITAMIN C (ascorbic acid)
water soluble

RNI: over 15 years - 40mg

GOOD SOURCES: citrus fruits, strawberries, blackcurrants, green vegetables, tomatoes, potatoes, red and green peppers, parsley

CAUTION: water soluble and easily destroyed by cooking, air and heat

FUNCTION:
- helps absorb calcium and iron from food
- protects against infection
- protects against allergies

DEFICIENCY:
- slow healing of wounds
- poor skin
- low resistance to infection
- scurvy

VITAMIN D (calciferol)
fat soluble

RNI: age 4-64 years - no dietary needs as long as skin is exposed to sun (children, people who are rarely exposed to sunlight, the elderly, pregnant and breastfeeding women do need vitamin D in their diet).

GOOD SOURCES: oily fish, egg yolk, liver, fortified margarine

FUNCTION:
- helps absorb calcium
- works with calcium to build strong bones and teeth
- helps broken bones to heal

DEFICIENCY:
- weak or porous bones
- rickets

VITAMIN E
fat soluble

RNI: no RNI but safe intake set at more than 4mg (men) and 3mg (women)

GOOD SOURCES: vegetable oils, wheatgerm, cereals, nuts and seeds

FUNCTION:
- helps keep lungs and red cell membranes healthy
- may protect against some forms of cancer
- may protect against heart disease
- used as preservative in fats and oils

DEFICIENCY:
- rare in healthy adults

VITAMIN K
fat soluble

RNI: no RNI but intakes of 1μg per kg of body weight are safe and adequate

GOOD SOURCES: leafy green vegetables, sea vegetables, cereals, also made in the intestine

FUNCTION:
- helps blood to clot
- helps regulate amount of calcium in blood

DEFICIENCY:
- rare but can cause internal bleeding and anaemia

CALCIUM

RNI: over 19 years - 700mg

GOOD SOURCES: dairy products, bones in tinned fish, tofu, spinach, parsley, figs, almonds

FUNCTION:
- essential for healthy bones and teeth
- helps blood to clot

DEFICIENCY:
- softening of bones
- osteoporosis

IRON

RNI: over 19 years - 8.7mg (men), 14.8mg (women)

GOOD SOURCES: meat, fish, egg yolk, pulses, cereals, dried fruit, green vegetables

NB There are two types of iron: haem iron which is found in red meats with a 20% to 30% absorption rate, and non-haem iron found in green vegetables, cereals, pulses, fruits, eggs and dairy products. Non-haem iron is less easily absorbed unless the body has an urgent need to restock or with growing children and pregnant or menstruating women. Vitamin C assists the absorption of iron. Absorption of iron is decreased by the tannins in tea and some forms of fibre.

FUNCTION:
- keeps red blood cells healthy

DEFICIENCY:
- tiredness and irritability
- short attention span
- anaemia

SODIUM

RNI: over 15 years - 1600mg

GOOD SOURCES: meat, eggs, dairy products, cereals, pulses, main ingredient in salt which is added to many foods

FUNCTION:
- regulates fluid balance in body
- helps transmit electrical signals along nerves

DEFICIENCY:
- rare except when salt is lost through extreme perspiration, such as with heatstroke
- more common is excess intake which may lead to raised blood pressure

PHOSPHORUS

RNI: over 19 years - 540mg

GOOD SOURCES: meat, fish, dairy products, bananas, cereals, nuts and seeds

FUNCTION:
- strengthens bones and teeth

DEFICIENCY:
- rare

FLUORIDE

RNI: no RNI but upper limit of 0.05mg per kg body weight for children

GOOD SOURCES: tea, seafoods, fluoridated water

FUNCTION:
- increases retention of calcium in bones and teeth

DEFICIENCY:
- tooth decay more likely

IODINE

RNI: over 15 years 140µg

GOOD SOURCES: seafoods and sea vegetables, milk, meat, eggs

FUNCTION:
- makes the hormone thyroxine which helps control metabolism

DEFICIENCY:
- slow metabolism
- goitre

POTASSIUM

RNI: over 15 years - 3500mg

GOOD SOURCES: yeast extract, dried fruits, pulses, leafy vegetables, whole grains

FUNCTION:
- works with sodium controlling body fluids
- helps muscles contract
- helps to remove excess sodium from body

DEFICIENCY:
- rare, although can lead to high sodium levels

Key Terms

activities

1. Design a menu for one day in which vitamin A appears in every meal.
2. Give examples of two age groups who need vitamin D in their diet. Why do they need regular supplies of this vitamin?
3. What care should be taken when cooking foods which you know contain vitamin C? Is there a particular method of cooking which should be avoided?
4. Which mineral deficiency might be noticed by the dentist?
5. Sushma has been told that she is slightly anaemic. What is lacking in her diet? Suggest THREE meals she could eat to improve her intake of this vital nutrient.

Nutrient - a component found in food essential for growth, repair, energy, warmth and protection against disease.

Deficiency - a lack of or shortage.

Protein - a nutrient made of carbon, hydrogen, oxygen and nitrogen, containing amino acids; it is essential to eat protein for the growth and repair of the body.

Carbohydrate - a nutrient made of carbon, hydrogen and oxygen. There are three kinds of carbohydrate; sugar, starch and NSP.

Sugar - a class of water soluble carbohydrate. There are two types of sugar; monosaccharides and disaccharides.

Starch - another water soluble carbohydrate - a polysaccharide.

NSP (non-starch polysaccharide) - long, thick-walled cells that give strength and support to plant tissue; also known as fibre. NSP can be soluble or insoluble in water.

Fat - a nutrient made of carbon, hydrogen and oxygen. The group includes both fats and oils. Fats are solid at room temperature and oils are liquid. May be called lipids.

Cholesterol - a natural fat made by the body in the liver. Too much cholesterol can cause heart disease.

Vitamins - organic molecules essential for growth, maintenance and repair of the body.

Minerals - elements present in food in tiny quantities, usually in the form of salts. Many elements are essential for good health.

How mycoprotein is made

Mycoprotein is a fungus. The fungus is grown in a large fermentation tower. Oxygen, nitrogen, glucose, minerals and vitamins are added. It is then heat treated, filtered, drained and mixed with egg albumen, which is derived from battery eggs. Flavouring and colouring may also be added. The mycoprotein is textured to resemble meat, then shredded, chopped or sliced. Mycoprotein is a source of protein, fibre, biotin (a B group vitamin), iron and zinc, and is low in saturated fat.

Source: adapted from Vegetarian Society information sheet

Quorn products

Mycoprotein has been developed by Rank Hovis McDougall, and is marketed under the name of Quorn by Marlow Foods Ltd. This is an extract from an advertisement for Quorn:

Simply replace a meat meal for a Quorn meal and you'll find it an easy first step towards a healthier diet. Because gram for gram, Quorn contains a third less fat than cooked skinless chicken, as much protein as an egg and more fibre than a baked potato. It is also free of artificial additives and contains no cholesterol.

Quorn sausages

Activities

1. Give THREE reasons why someone might choose to eat mycoprotein instead of meat.

2. Design a flow chart showing the stages in the production of mycoprotein.

3. Is Quorn a suitable food item for vegetarians?

4. Quorn is available in the form of convenience meals such as sausages and burgers. It is also available in mince or chunks which you can use in your own recipes. Suggest two recipes where you could use Quorn instead of meat.

5. Quorn is one of a number of 'new' proteins. Why do we need new sources of protein?

Many food products are fortified with vitamins and minerals. This means that vitamins and minerals are added to the food. It is the law that margarine has added vitamins A and D, but usually fortification is voluntary. Heinz add B vitamins, iron sulphate and potassium iodide to their Spaghetti in tomato sauce. Compare the ingredients in this product with the recipe below for home made pasta with tomato sauce.

FREE FROM ARTIFICIAL
COLOUR, FLAVOUR & PRESERVATIVE

GUARANTEE
Price refunded, without affecting your statutory rights, if any Heinz variety fails to please. In correspondence please quote quality code on end.

Heinz
Made in England
H.J. HEINZ CO. LTD.
Hayes, Middx. UB4 8AL

e 400 g
Best before end - see can end

RECYCLABLE STEEL

HEINZ Spaghetti
IN TOMATO SAUCE
made from FRESH Pasta

Fortified with Vitamins & Iron

TO SERVE
Empty into a saucepan, stir gently while heating.

MICROWAVES (650W)
Empty contents into a microwave dish, cover and heat for approximately 4 minutes stirring occasionally. Empty out unused contents, cover, keep cool.

INGREDIENTS
Tomatoes, Spaghetti (made from Wheat) Sugar, Salt, Modified Cornflour, Citric Acid Herbs, Spices, Maltodextrin, Niacin Iron Sulphate, Riboflavin, Thiamin Vitamin B12, Potassium Iodide

Heinz original long cut pasta is freshly made using only the finest quality ingredients to create a wholesome, tasty food.

Our recipe has been vitamin enriched and we ensure that levels of added salt and sugar are kept to the minimum possible without impairing your enjoyment of the delicious tomatoey Heinz flavour.

This product is entirely free from artificial colour and preservatives.

NUTRITION INFORMATION

Typical Values	Amount per 100g	Amount per Serving (200g)
Energy	268kJ/63kcal	536kJ/126kcal
Protein	1.9g	3.8g
Carbohydrate (of which sugars)	13.4g (4.9g)	26.8g (9.9g)
Fat (of which saturates)	0.2g (Trace)	0.4g (Trace)
Fibre	0.6g	1.3g
Sodium	0.4g	0.9g
Iron	1.2mg (9% RDA)*	2.4mg (17% RDA)
Iodine	13µg (9% RDA)	25µg (17% RDA)
Thiamin	0.12mg (9% RDA)	0.24mg (17% RDA)
Riboflavin	0.14mg (9% RDA)	0.27mg (17% RDA)
Niacin	1.50mg (8% RDA)	3.00mg (17% RDA)
Vitamin B12	0.09µg (9% RDA)	0.17µg (17% RDA)

(RDA)* = Recommended Daily Amount

Activities

1. Use Dietary Reference Value tables or a computer programme to analyse the nutritional content of the home made pasta dish and the tinned alternative.

2. Give reasons why some commercially prepared foods are fortified.

3. Suggest ways of improving the NSP content in a meal of:
   a) home made pasta with tomato sauce
   b) Heinz spaghetti in tomato sauce.

4. Design a table to help you compare the ingredients in other tinned meal products. Indicate which ingredients form part of the basic recipe and which could have been added to fortify the products.

Steve's pasta with tomato sauce (serves 2)

Sauce
2 tbsps olive oil
1 onion, finely chopped
1 clove garlic, crushed
1 tsp dried mixed herbs
1 tin tomatoes
2 tbsps tomato puree
1 tsp honey
water
salt and pepper

To serve
150g spaghetti, cooked
freshly grated Parmesan cheese

Fry onion gently in oil until softened. Add garlic and herbs, cover, and continue to fry gently for about 10 minutes. Add tomatoes. Add tomato purée and honey and stir. Simmer gently for at least 30 mins, or until thick. Season to taste and serve with pasta and Parmesan cheese.

Am I getting enough?

How many KILOCALORIES does my 2 year old daughter need? Should I take a supplement of vitamin D? Is my father eating too much fat? In order to answer questions like these we need some idea of the amounts of nutrients (see Unit 6) that we should eat in order to stay healthy. The Department of Health has estimated the needs of different groups of people in the community. These standards used to be called Recommended Daily Intakes (RDI) or Amounts (RDA). Now they are called DIETARY REFERENCE VALUES (DRVs).

A new standard

In 1991 the Committee on Medical Aspects of Food Policy (COMA) published a report recommending the amount of energy, protein, fat, carbohydrate, vitamins and minerals needed by different people. Previous calculations were sometimes too high for some people and too low for others. They did not take into account the fact that people need

Hospitals have to provide food for many different groups of people. DRVs help the catering manager to ensure that meals provide the right nutrients for everyone.

Estimated Average Requirement (EAR) - the average need for a nutrient within a group of similar individuals. It is important to remember that this is an average - some people in the group will need more than this amount and some less.

Reference Nutrient Intake (RNI) - the amount of a nutrient which is thought to be enough for most people in a particular group, even those who require a high amount. The RNI supplies enough of a nutrient for at least 97% of the population. The quantity is actually higher than most people need so there is very little chance of deficiency.

Lower Reference Nutrient Intake (LRNI) - the quantity of a nutrient required by a few people with low needs (only about 3% of the population). Most people will need more than this level.

Safe intake - the amount of a nutrient judged to be enough for most people but not so large as to cause undesirable effects. This figure is given for nutrients where there is not enough information to estimate the amounts needed by different groups.

Figure 1 - Dietary Reference Values

and use up (metabolise) their nutrients at different rates. The new guidelines suggest a range of intakes for each group of people, recognising that different people have different needs (see Unit 8). Figure 1 explains the different Dietary Reference Values.

activities

1. What is the average requirement for vitamin C for people over 15?
2. A breastfeeding mother asks you how much vitamin C she should consume daily. What would you advise her?
3. You are planning a school lunch. How much vitamin C should you include to make sure that most people's needs are met?
4. A survey shows that a group of 8 year olds have an average intake of 22 mg of vitamin C a day. Do you think they need to increase the amount of vitamin C in their diet?

Table 1 Dietary Reference Values for vitamin C (mg per day)

Age	LRNI	EAR	RNI
0-12 mths	6	15	25
1-10 yrs	8	20	30
11-14 yrs	9	22	35
15+ yrs	10	25	40
Pregnant women	20	35	50
Breastfeeding women	40	55	70

Source: adapted from Dietary Reference Values - A Guide, HMSO, 1991.

What are DRVs for?

Different people need different amounts of nutrients. DRV tables show the requirements for various groups of people, such as babies, children, men and women of different ages, pregnant women and breastfeeding mothers. Dietary Reference Values can provide nutritional guidance in several ways.

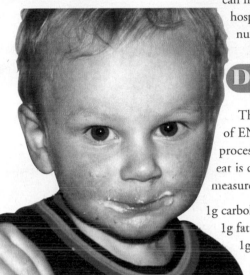

Assessing an individual's diet

If the intake of nutrients meets RNI it is unlikely that the individual will be deficient. If intake is below LRNI, deficiency could occur. The closer to the LRNI the more likely it is that they could be deficient.

Planning meals for groups

Making sure that meals meet the RNI level can help institutions such as schools and hospitals to ensure that adequate nutrients are provided for everyone.

DRVs and energy

The body requires a constant supply of ENERGY to maintain its internal processes even when resting. The food we eat is converted into energy and is measured in kilocalories (kcal).

1g carbohdrate = 4 kcal energy
1g fat = 9 kcal energy
1g protein = 4 kcal energy

Energy dense foods have a higher amount of energy per grain. Foods with a lower energy density have a lower amount of energy per grain.

We get most of our energy from carbohydrates and fat and some from any protein remaining after being used for body building and repair. If we eat too many kilocalories, the body stores the excess energy as fat. If we do not eat enough energy-giving foods compared to our energy requirement, we lose weight.

Different people require different amounts of energy. Our energy needs depend chiefly on two things:

● how much energy is expended - Physical Activity Levels (PAL)
● how much energy is used up by the body at rest - Basal Metabolic Rates (BMR).

The Dietary Reference Values for adults' energy requirements are worked out using these figures. Table 2 shows how much energy is needed by adults with a low physical activity level. People who expend more energy at work or at leisure could eat more kilocalories without putting on weight. The figures for the energy needs of children are based on lifestyle and the activity levels of different age groups.

activities

1. What do the figures in this table tell you about
   a) the changing energy needs of children from birth to 18
   b) the change in energy requirements between the ages of 18 and 75
   c) the difference between the energy needs of men and women?
2. Who needs more energy, a man aged 77 or a woman aged 17?
3. Tom is 2. How many kilocalories does he need every day? Apart from ensuring that he eats enough energy containing foods, state TWO other important things to remember when planning a day's menu for Tom.

Source: adapted from Dietary Reference Values - A Guide, HMSO, 1991

Table 2 shows the average energy requirements for different age groups. For example, the average 25 year old woman would need 1,940 kcal of energy from food a day. If she ate less than this, she would lose weight. If she ate more, she would put on weight.

Table 2 Estimated average requirement for total energy (kcal per day)

Age	Males	Females
	kcal/day	kcal/day
0-3 mths	545	515
4-6 mths	690	645
7-9 mths	825	765
10-12 mths	920	865
1-3 yrs	1,230	1,165
4-6 yrs	1,715	1,545
7-10 yrs	1,970	1,740
11-14 yrs	2,220	1,845
15-18 yrs	2,755	2,110
19-49 yrs	2,550	1,940
50-59 yrs	2,550	1,900
60-64 yrs	2,380	1,900
65-74 yrs	2,330	1,900
75+ yrs	2,100	1,810
Pregnant women		2,140
Breastfeeding women Last 3 mths only		
0-1 mth		2,390
1-2 mths		2,470
2-6 mths		2,510
6+ mths		2,490

Key Terms

Dietary Reference Values - scientifically calculated estimates of the amounts of nutrients needed by different groups of people.

RNI (Reference Nutrient Intake) - the amount of a nutrient that is enough for most people in a particular group.

LRNI (Lower Reference Nutrient Intake) - the amount of a nutrient that is enough for only a small number of people.

EAR (Estimated Average Requirement) - the average need for a nutrient.

Energy - needed by the body at rest (basal metabolic requirement) and to sustain all physical activities.

Energy density - a term used to describe the amount of energy in a particular weight of food.

Kilocalorie - 1,000 calories. A calorie is the amount of energy needed to raise the temperature of 1g water by one degree. People often shorten 'kilocalories' to 'calories'.

Choosing food

There are many factors which influence what people choose to eat and how they choose to prepare it. Whether you are planning meals for yourself or for others, it is important to be aware of these influences. Caterers, especially, need to be aware of the needs of different groups in society. A CROSS SECTION of the population would typically include:

- children
- teenagers
- pregnant women
- breastfeeding mothers
- vegetarians
- elderly people
- people from different cultural and economic backgrounds.

Each one of these groups has different dietary requirements which need to be considered when choosing and cooking meals.

Likes and dislikes

Children are given their first foods by their parents but soon develop individual likes and dislikes for particular tastes and textures. This is perhaps the most important factor affecting our choice of food. Most people eat because they enjoy the experience.

Eating 'on the hoof'

The time people have available for shopping, food preparation and eating influences food choice. Many people eat in a less formal way than they used to. The traditional three meals a day, eaten as a family, are being replaced by rushed

Colour, flavour, texture and attractive arrangement of food on the plate are all important influences on choice of food.

activities

1. Erika gets home from work late and has 30 minutes to prepare and eat a meal before she goes out. Suggest THREE quick and healthy meals from the ingredients she has available:

- **in the cupboard:** baked beans, yeast extract, mixed nuts, dried apricots, raisins and figs, tinned sardines, wholemeal bread
- **in the fridge:** mushrooms, eggs, milk, cheese, yogurt, tomatoes
- **in the freezer:** pizza, pitta breads, corn on the cob, chicken curry, stir-fried rice with vegetables
- fruit: apples, pears, bananas.

Fast food does not have to be unhealthy. Frozen or canned food, together with storecupboard basics can provide nutritious combinations. Microwave ovens (see Unit 17) mean that meals can be ready in minutes.

meals, fast foods and snacking. This can lead to a nutritionally unbalanced diet. More and more people, however, are becoming aware of the need to select and cook foods wisely to maintain and improve their health.

Culture, religion and morality

Dietary customs vary widely between people from different ETHNIC GROUPS. Some customs stem from religious rules. Other differences reflect the cooking practices of the country or region of origin. Table 1 shows some of these variations.

Many people are vegetarians. This may be because they object to the slaughter of animals or because they want to improve their diet by reducing the saturated fat content and placing more emphasis on cereals, grains, fruits and vegetables. Table 2 explains what foods different kinds of vegetarians eat.

Some people prefer not to buy produce from countries where they disagree with the political situation. The most famous BOYCOTT was of South African produce. Millions of people refused to buy goods from South Africa

during the time when it had an apartheid regime.

Special diets

Some people have food allergies or illnesses such as coeliac disease (see Unit 13) or DIABETES. Their diet has to be carefully monitored to ensure that the food they eat does not contribute to or worsen their condition. A DIETICIAN will offer advice when a person is first diagnosed as having a food related illness.

During pregnancy small increases are needed in the amount of protein and B group vitamins, but the most important thing to remember is to increase the folic acid content of the diet (see Unit 6). During breastfeeding the dietary requirements of women are at their highest. Increased quantities of all nutrients are required. Pregnant and breastfeeding women should reduce their intake of alcohol to well below the suggested limits, or preferably cut it out altogether.

The elderly generally require the same foods as an adult person who is relatively inactive. Special requirements may stem from physical problems such as deteriorating teeth causing difficulty

Table 1 Dietary customs of different cultural and religious groups within Britain

JEWISH COMMUNITY - no pork, no shellfish, meat must be kosher (ritually slaughtered under Jewish law), meat and dairy products must not be eaten at same meal, must be three hour gap between consumption of meat and dairy products, preparation of these foods must be controlled using separate equipment and/or kitchens.

ASIAN COMMUNITY
Main staples chapattis or rice.
Ghee, groundnut or mustard oil used for cooking.
Pulses a major source of protein.
Many regional and religious variations:

Muslims - no pork, meat must be Halal (ritually slaughtered by Halal butcher), no alcohol. Muslims from Gujarat or Pakistan eat little fish but do eat milk and yogurt. Muslims from Bangladesh eat a lot of fish and few dairy products.

Hindus - no beef, no alcohol. Most Hindus are vegetarians. Hindus from Gujarat eat some fish while those from the Indian Punjab tend not to eat fish.

Sikhs - no beef, no alcohol, some are vegetarian, others eat mainly chicken or mutton.

AFRO-CARIBBEAN COMMUNITY
Most Afro-Caribbeans in Britain are Christians, so diet is affected more by cultural practices than religious rules. Diet is often based on cereals like rice or maize and tubers like yams, sweet potatoes or plantains. Meat and fish are eaten and food is well flavoured with herbs and spices. A small minority of Afro-Caribbeans are Rastafarians.

Rastafarians - only natural foods, no processed or preserved foods, no meat, poultry, eggs or dairy products, no salt, no alcohol. Different Rastafarians follow the code with varying degrees of strictness.

Table 2 What is a vegetarian?
The Vegetarian Society defines a **vegetarian** as someone who eats no fish, flesh or fowl and avoids all by-products of slaughter (gelatine, animal fat, rennet, etc.).
Lacto-ovo-vegetarians eat both dairy products and eggs.
Lacto-vegetarians eat dairy products but not eggs.
Vegans avoid all animal products, i.e. fish, flesh, fowl, eggs and dairy products.
Source: The Vegetarian Society

activities

1. Suggest meals that you could prepare for the following people that would help to overcome the problems described:
    a) Francesca is 6. She does not like to drink milk and her mother is worried that she may not be getting enough protein and calcium.
    b) Sula is a lacto-vegetarian. Her father has told her that she may be deficient in B12 (a vitamin found in animal foods, including meat, milk and eggs).
    c) Charlie works in a warehouse. A typical lunch is a meat pie, chips and a Mars bar. He says he needs the energy to do the heavy work that is required of him.
    d) Arthur has arthritis and cannot walk very far. His

    limited mobility means that he sometimes gets constipated.
    e) Nell is 8 months pregnant. The growing foetus presses against her stomach and makes her uncomfortable after meals.

2. A meal consists of a main course of fish, three vegetables and a sauce, a dessert using fruit and pastry and a cold drink. Using your knowledge of the nutritional needs of different groups, suggest how these foods might be prepared for the following people:
    a) Sian is 14 and is trying to lose a few kilos.
    b) George is an active 71 year old.
    c) Jake is 3. His parents are having difficulty getting him to eat 'proper' meals.

with chewing, or arthritis causing problems with food preparation. It may be that a lack of mobility creates digestive problems which can be overcome with an increase of NSP (see Unit 12). Some elderly people may have poor diets because of financial or social problems. Buying food within a tight budget and transporting food from the shops may cause problems. The isolation of an elderly person living alone may result in dietary neglect. Scurvy (see Unit 6), OSTEOMALACIA and ANAEMIA are particular health risks for the elderly.

Energy requirements

Different groups of people have different energy requirements and should eat more or less kilocalories accordingly (see Unit 7).

The energy burned whilst carrying out work should be replaced equally by the energy value of foods eaten. This means that people doing hard manual work need more kilocalories than those who do not use their muscles so much.

Age also affects energy requirements. In general boys and men require slightly more kilocalories than girls and women and adults need more kilocalories than children. Figure 1 shows some of these differences.

A larger kilocalorie requirement should not be met by increasing the amount of 'empty

calories' (sugar) and fat in the diet. Complex carbohydrates such as rice, pasta, potatoes and bread are much more useful foods to increase as they have the added benefits of NSP, vitamins and minerals. A dietary requirement of teenage girls may be to provide increased levels of iron to compensate for iron loss during menstruation.

Figure 1 Dietary needs

Lewis, 2
Energy requirement: 1,230 kcal/day
Dietary needs: As well as protein required for growth, Lewis should eat plenty of starchy foods such as bread, pasta and potatoes. Sugar and salt should be limited. Lewis should not eat too much fibre as this could prevent the body absorbing vitamins and minerals. Full-fat dairy products should be given in preference to skimmed versions because Lewis needs the extra calories they provide.

Kate, 17
Energy requirement: 2,110 kcal/day
Dietary needs: Teenagers should follow the general guidelines for a healthy diet (see Table 1, Unit 12) - eat a wide variety of foods, aiming to increase those rich in starch and fibre and reduce those that are high in fat and sugar, maintain a healthy weight. Kate should also eat foods rich in iron (see Unit 6).

Doris, 71
Energy requirement: 1,900 kcal/day
Dietary needs: Doris should also follow the general guidelines for a healthy diet. However, as people become older, they tend to use up less energy, so they may eat less, making it difficult to obtain all the essential nutrients. Doris should make sure that the foods she chooses are concentrated sources of protein, vitamins and minerals. Eating oily fish can help to reduce the risk of heart disease and increasing the amount of fibre in the diet can help prevent constipation. Vitamins C and D may be lacking in the diet of an elderly person. Doris should eat fresh fruit and vegetables and try to spend some time outside in the summer (see Unit 6).

Availability and cost of food

A huge variety of foods is available all year round. Supermarkets offer a wide range of products from around the world. Developing technology in food preservation has extended the shelf life of food so that we can buy virtually anything at any time of year (see Unit 10).

Although all this food is available in stores it does not mean that people always have access to it. Many supermarkets are located on out of town sites that are difficult to get to without a car. Many families say that these stores can be too expensive - particularly if you are tempted to purchase more than you had originally planned. The amount of money that people have to spend on food is crucial to the type and quantity of food chosen. People on low incomes may find it difficult to eat a healthy diet. In Britain, households on lower incomes tend to buy less fruit

activities

1. Look at the menu extract on the right.
   a) How has the restaurant tried to cater for different groups of people?
   b) Comment on the choices available in terms of current healthy eating guidelines.
2. Using IT skills, plan and prepare menus for one of the following food outlets:
   a) a school cafeteria
   b) a vegetarian restaurant
   c) a motorway cafe often used by lorry drivers
   d) a tea shop.
   Try to include healthy and interesting dishes which are appropriate for the type of outlet. Remember to consider the needs of different groups of people.

Salad Platters
(Served with Bread, Salad & Dressings)
PLOUGHMAN'S - Lancashire or Cheddar Cheese with Pickle and Chutney £4.25
FARMERS - Baked Ham and Fruit Chutney £4.35
FISHERMAN'S - Tuna, Smoked Mackerel and Prawns, served with Salad and Lemon dressing £4.95
FRENCH PLATTER - A combination of Brie and our homemade Paté with Relish ... £4.55
GREEK SALAD - Feta Cheese, Olives and Salad in a light Vinaigrette, served with Garlic Bread £4.25
TUNA & BEAN SALAD - Tuna fish with Italian Bean Salad and served with Garlic Bread £4.25
LIFESTYLE PLATTER - A healthy Salad of Fruit, Nuts and Cottage Cheese £4.15

and vegetables than those on higher incomes. It is more likely that they will buy cheaper, processed foods which could be higher in sugar and fat. This means that they have a less well balanced diet and run higher risks of illness.

Key Terms

Cross section - a sample of people including a range of ages, social, economic and cultural backgrounds.
Ethnic group - the culture into which a person is born or brought up, e.g. Irish, English, Afro-Caribbean, Pakistani, Chinese, etc.
Boycott - avoid buying products as a protest against the policies of a country or company.
Diabetes - an illness where insulin production in the body is ineffective causing excess sugar in the blood
Dietician - an expert in nutrition who advises people on what foods to eat
Osteomalacia - a condition in which the bones of adults become soft, weak and painful due to an inadequate supply of vitamin D.
Anaemia - a deficiency caused by lack of iron in the diet.

activities

Figure 2 shows some examples of comments people on a low income have made about their diets.

1. How can not having enough money affect the diet?
2. Make a list of things that help low income parents to ensure their children eat well.
3. Look at the recommendations for a healthy diet in Table 1, Unit 12. What suggestions could you give a family on a low income to help them follow this type of diet?
4. Leanne and David have £45 a week to spend on food for themselves and their two children, Katy (6) and Darren (13). Write a shopping list and plan meals for the week. The children have free school lunches but all other meals and snacks must be provided.

Figure 2 The cost of food

Free school meals mean she gets meat, fruit and vegetables - all things I can't afford to buy very often

The most important thing is price. You might not think 1p or 2p off sounds like much but at the end of the day it adds up.

Usually we have burgers, fish fingers, sausages - things the kids will eat. I can't afford to try out new things that they might not eat.

Sometimes I go without. If there's only enough for the the kids, I say I'm not hungry. I just have a bit of toast or something.

All these programmes about healthy eating. They never think about how much you can afford to spend. I can't make half of those recipes.

I use frozen vegetables mainly. I never get fresh. That way, I only need to get out a bit at a time, and if the kids don't eat it, I haven't wasted much.

I buy apples and bananas once a week. I'd like to buy more healthy food if I had the money, but it's cheaper to eat unhealthily.

activities

Table 3 gives a list of dietary suggestions which apply to one or more of the groups pictured below. Get together with a partner and test each other to see how many you can guess correctly.

Table 3 Dietary suggestions

SUGGESTIONS	GROUP(S)
Should not have fat reduced milk as they need the kilocalories for energy.	1
Nuts are not suitable foods as they can cause choking.	1, 7
Should take care not to have too much fibre in the diet as it can prevent the absorption of other nutrients causing malnutrition.	1
Should aim to increase the fibre content of their meals to help digestion, prevent diseases of the digestive system and assist cholesterol production.	2,3,4,5,6,7,8
Need to ensure they have adequate protein by eating eggs, dairy products and/or a wide range of vegetables, seeds, nuts and pulses.	8
Should not have sugar and salt automatically added to their meals as it creates a habit which may last for life.	1
Should carefully monitor the amount of fat, sugar, salt and alcohol in their diet as they could be high risk groups for diet linked health problems.	1*,2,3,4,5,6,7,8,9
Should increase the amount of calcium, iron, protein, vitamins B1, B2 and C and folic acid in their diet as they are building the skin, bone and nervous system of the baby.	4
May lack vitamin B12 if they do not eat meat or dairy products. It can be supplied in the form of supplements if deficiency is likely.	8
Have a high energy requirement because their jobs involve physical labour. They will burn kilocalories rapidly so can have more carbohydrate and fat in their diet.	6
May have problems in coping with the bones in meat or fish or with the tough skins on some fruits. They may prefer some foods which are softer in texture.	1,7
May have to monitor very carefully the foods they eat. They may need doctor's advice or have to complete daily food charts.	9
Have the highest kilocalorie requirement of any group because the production of milk uses up a lot of energy.	5

*Children under 5 should not restrict the amount of full fat products in their diet as they need these foods for energy.

ASSESSING SCHOOL MEALS

School meals were started in 1906 to improve the health of children. Since then, lunch at school has been an important part of many children's diet, providing up to one third of their daily energy needs. For children from low income families in particular, school lunch is often the most important meal of the day (see Table 1).

School meals can still play an important part in improving the health of young people. The diet of many young people is high in the three Cs: crisps, chips and confectionery. This diet is high in fat and sugar, but low in fibre and many vitamins and minerals. As well as affecting growth and development, this kind of diet increases the risk of developing heart disease, cancer and bone deficiencies later in life. In 1994 a report by National Heart Forum showed that in one week the average teenager consumes:

- 4 packets crisps
- 6 cans fizzy drink
- 7 bars chocolate
- 3 bags chips
- 7 puddings

but only $1/7$ of the recommended intake of vegetables.

Healthy school lunches could help to improve the diet of young people, but since the abolition of nutritional standards for school meals in 1980, school meals have varied in quality. For example, many school meals contain up to 46% fat when the maximum recommended amount is 35%. The School Meals Assessment Pack (SMAP) has been developed to help check the nutritional quality of the food served in schools (see Table 2).

Natalie Brown used SMAP to assess the shool meals she ate over a week. Natalie kept a food diary of her school lunches in one week (see Table 3). She found out the exact ingredients and cooking methods used.

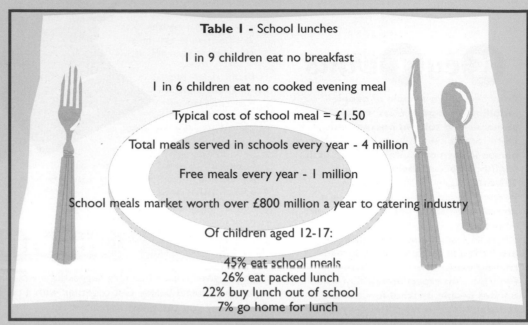

Table 1 - School lunches

1 in 9 children eat no breakfast

1 in 6 children eat no cooked evening meal

Typical cost of school meal = £1.50

Total meals served in schools every year - 4 million

Free meals every year - 1 million

School meals market worth over £800 million a year to catering industry

Of children aged 12-17:

45% eat school meals
26% eat packed lunch
22% buy lunch out of school
7% go home for lunch

Table 2 School Meals Assessment Pack

School Meals Assessment Pack

What is it?
A computer program developed by the National Heart Forum.

What can it do?
Assess the nutritional content of an average school meal or of an individual pupil's lunch selection, over a week or more.

Why?
To help to improve the diet of schoolchildren aged 11-16.

Who might want to assess the nutritional quality of school meals?
1) People who are concerned about school catering: caterers, head teachers, managers, school governors, school nurses, dieticians, parents.
2) Teachers and pupils: to learn about food and health; to develop their own school meals service.

Table 3 Natalie's food diary

MONDAY	*vegetable moussaka* *white rice* *jelly and tinned fruit* *cola drink*
TUESDAY	*hamburger in bun* *chips* *strawberry yogurt* *orange juice*
WEDNESDAY	*fish mornay* *peas* *carrots* *chocolate sponge* *and custard* *tea*
THURSDAY	*cheese sandwich* *crisps* *apple* *chocolate bar* *diet cola drink*
FRIDAY	*cheese and* *tomato pizza* *bowl of salad* *biscuit* *banana milkshake*

Natalie then entered the information from her food diary into the computer. Figure 1 shows how SMAP assessed an average meal from her menu. Because school lunch is only part of a child's intake of food for the day, SMAP bases its analysis on the RLA (recommended lunchtime amount) which is the proportion of nutrients that should be provided by this meal. The symbols show whether the meal meets healthy eating guidelines for each nutrient:

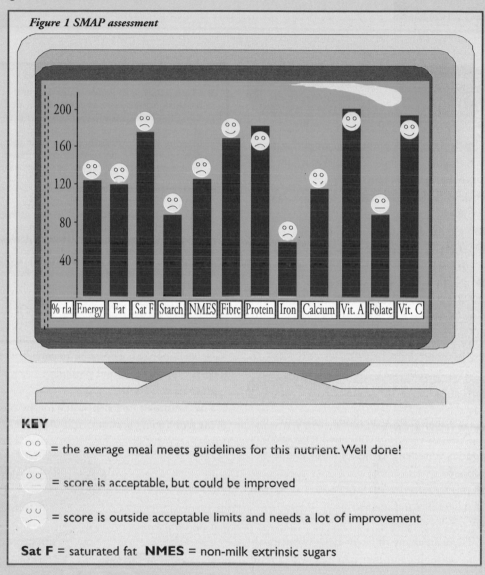

Figure 1 SMAP assessment

KEY

😊 = the average meal meets guidelines for this nutrient. Well done!

😐 = score is acceptable, but could be improved

☹ = score is outside acceptable limits and needs a lot of improvement

Sat F = saturated fat **NMES** = non-milk extrinsic sugars

Activities

1. Look at the SMAP assessment of Natalie's average meal. What does it tell you about the nutritional value of her weekly menu?
2. Suggest some changes Natalie could make in order to improve the assessment.
3. a) In 1979, nearly two-thirds of children had a school lunch. It is now less than half. Suggest possible reasons for this change.
   b) Conduct a survey to find out how many children in your school eat the following at lunchtime:
      a school meal; a packed lunch; a meal out of school; lunch at home.
   Compare your results with the national averages in Table 1.
4. Parents have made the following statements about their child's lunch. What nutritional advantages/disadvantages do you associate with each statement?
   • I like my child to have a hot meal at lunch time.
   • I prefer to make my daughter a packed lunch. That way I know what she is eating.
   • My son is old enough to decide what he wants to eat.
   • I can give my children all their favourite foods in a packed lunch.

Food hygiene

What is food hygiene?

Food is in danger of becoming infected at each stage of its production from the farm to the table. To produce food that is safe to eat, manufacturers must have:

- knowledge of food safety laws (see Unit 30)
- safe handling methods
- effective quality control systems (see Unit 29)
- food hygiene training for staff.

Once the consumer buys food, looking after it becomes their responsibility. All food handlers, in the workplace or in the home, should follow basic hygiene rules (see Table 1).

Food poisoning

Food poisoning is an illness caused by ingesting (eating) contaminated food or water. Food is considered to be contaminated if it contains:

- highly infective kinds of bacteria or viruses
- chemicals and metals
- poisonous plants.

There are many different types of bacterial food poisoning but they may be divided into three main types.

- Infectious - the bacteria are parasites. Their presence in the body causes illness.
- Toxic - the bacteria release a poisonous substance in the body. It is these toxins, not the bacteria, which cause harm to the body.
- Infectious and toxic - this is a combination of the two. The body is being harmed both by the bacteria and the substance they excrete.

The **incubation period** is the time from when the poisonous food is eaten to when the first symptoms occur. This period varies according to the amount of bacteria which

Table I Hygiene tips for food handlers

- Wash hands with warm water and anti-bacterial soap before touching food, after using the toilet, after handling raw meat, after touching refuse or pets and after blowing your nose or brushing your hair. Dry hands using disposable paper towels or a separate towel. Never use a tea towel.

- Always cover cuts and boils with waterproof dressings. In the catering industry plasters and dressings are usually blue and have a magnetic strip running through them so that they may be detected should they fall into the food.

- Make sure all utensils and work surfaces are clean.

- Use separate chopping boards for raw and cooked foods to prevent CROSS-CONTAMINATION.

- Ensure the fridge maintains a temperature between 1- 4°C.

- Always ensure that raw meat and poultry are stored below cooked foods in the fridge. Place raw meat and poultry in containers which will collect the drips.

- Eat food before its use by date.

- Cook food thoroughly so that the temperature at the centre reaches a minimum of 70°C for at least 2 minutes.

- Eat cooked food without delay, or cool it quickly and refrigerate within 1½ hours.

- Keep pets away from food preparation areas.

have been ingested. The more bacteria in the food the quicker the food poisoning symptoms will occur.

The symptoms vary depending on the type of food poisoning but often include abdominal pain, diarrhoea, vomiting, nausea and fever.

The **duration** of the illness is the complete length of time from when the symptoms first appear to when the last symptoms disappear.

Yogurt is usually made by introducing the bacteria Lactobacillus bulgaricus and Streptococcus thermophilus into milk. These ferment the milk and turn the lactose into lactic acid, giving the traditional sharp taste. More recently, the bacteria Bifido bacterium bifidum and Lactobacillus acidophilus have been used to make 'bio' yogurts, which are said to aid digestion and promote good health.

Bacteria may still remain in the intestinal tract even though there are no obvious symptoms and in this case a person is referred to as a convalescent carrier.

Anyone can suffer from food poisoning although certain high risk groups are more vulnerable than others:

- babies and infants (under two years)
- pregnant women and their unborn children
- elderly people
- people who are ill or convalescing
- the IMMUNOCOMPROMISED (people with an inability to fight infection).

How does food poisoning occur?

Bacteria are single-celled organisms found everywhere; in soil, water, air, on food and on people. Bacteria are extremely small and are measured in micrometres (μm) - 1 μm = 1/1000 mm. To see bacteria under the microscope you would need to magnify it 1000 times (a housefly magnified a 1000 times would be 9 metres long!)

There are thousands of different varieties of bacteria but only a very few cause food poisoning. These bacteria are called PATHOGENIC BACTERIA (see Table 2).

Some bacteria cause foods to go bad and are known as FOOD SPOILAGE BACTERIA. These bacteria do not usually cause food poisoning.

Some bacteria serve useful purposes e.g. in the fermentation of beer and wine, in the manufacture of cheese and yogurt and in the production of antibiotics.

Bacterial growth

Bacteria multiply or reproduce by BINARY FISSION. There are several factors which affect their growth.

Time

The time for each bacterium to divide is known as the **generation time**. For most bacteria this is about twenty minutes but some can reproduce in considerably less time. A common bacterium *Clostridium perfringens* has a generation time of ten

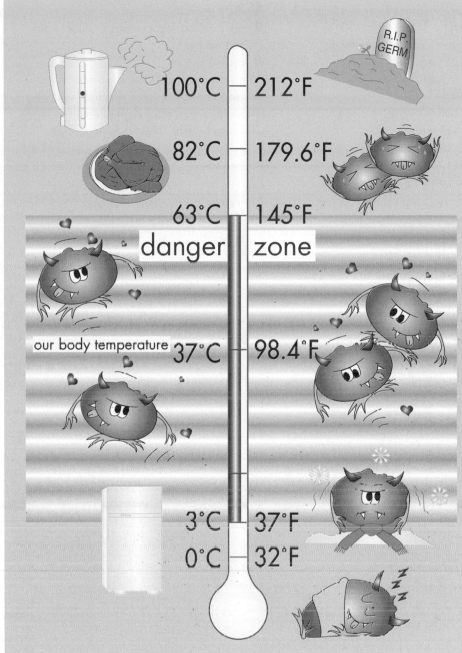

Figure 1 The germometer

100°C 212°F

82°C 179.6°F

63°C 145°F

danger zone

our body temperature 37°C 98.4°F

3°C 37°F

0°C 32°F

minutes or less. This means that 1,000 bacteria could become 1,000,000 in less than one and a half hours. Food poisoning could occur with this number of bacteria.

Temperature

Bacteria need warm conditions for growth. If it is too cold bacteria will lie dormant (inactive). If it is too hot many bacteria will be destroyed. Figure 1 shows the temperatures at which bacteria are active and inactive. The danger zone is the temperature range in which bacteria are mostly likely to multiply (3-63°C). Most pathogenic bacteria prefer a temperature close to that of the human body which is 37°C. It is very important when preparing food that is not kept in the danger zone for longer than necessary. The temperature of any kitchen will almost certainly be within the danger zone.

Food

Like all living cells, bacteria need food.

Most pathogenic bacteria will live and multiply in foods that are high in protein and moisture. Some foods are known as **high risk foods** because:

- bacteria grow easily on these foods
- they can be eaten without further cooking

Examples of high risk foods are:

- cooked meat
- cooked poultry
- shellfish and seafood
- gravies, sauces and stocks
- soups and stews
- dairy products
- egg products, e.g. raw eggs in mayonnaise and mousse
- cooked rice.

Low risk foods are those foods with a high salt, sugar or acid content which do not normally support the growth of food poisoning bacteria. This is why food preservation methods such as salting, jamming, pickling, or keeping foods in a syrup are successful.

Acidity

Acidity is measured using the pH scale which has 14 points: pH 7.0 is neutral, i.e. neither acid nor alkaline. Most pathogenic bacteria cannot grow in an acid environment of pH 4.5 or less.

Table 2 Food poisoning

Bacteria	General Information	Symptoms	Onset Time	Duration of illness	Found in	Control/prevention	Destruction	Target population
Salmonella .... A short, thin rod-shaped bacterium. .... Causes **infectious** food poisoning from eating large numbers of the bacteria.	The most common form of food poisoning in Britain, with between 20 and 50 fatal cases each year. Optimum conditions for growth are between 7°C and 45°C. Does not usually grow below 5°C. Found in the gut of most animals and birds with 80% of chickens infected.	Fever, headache, abdominal pains, diarrhoea and vomiting.	6-48 hrs usually 12-36hrs.	1-8 days.	Raw meat, poultry, eggs, milk and dairy products, fish, shrimps, sauces and salad dressing, cream filled desserts and toppings.	Wash hands before preparing food and after visiting the the toilet. Thaw frozen food thoroughly. Use different surfaces for preparing raw and cooked foods and store raw and high risk foods separately to avoid cross-contamination. Refrigerate all high risk foods.	Readily killed by heat. Cook thoroughly ensuring the temperature at the centre is high enough to kill bacteria. Does not form spores.	All age groups are susceptible but symptoms are most severe in the elderly, infants, immuno-compromised and the infirm.
Staphylococcus aureus .... A round-shaped bacterium. .... The bacteria creates toxins which cause **toxic** food poisoning.	Staphylococci exist in air, dust, sewage, water, milk equipment, surfaces and especially in humans and animals. It is present in the nose, throat and skin of over 50% of humans. It is particularly common in people who have contact with the sick or with hospital environments.	Vomiting, abdominal cramps, diarrhoea.	1-7hrs.	6-24hrs.	Meat and meat products; poultry and poultry products; salads such as egg, tuna, chicken and potato; baked products such as cream filled pastries; dairy products.	Foods that require considerable handling during preparation are frequently associated with this bacteria. High risk food should be refrigerated. High standards of personal hygiene are vital. Handle food as little as possible. Cover all cuts and boils.	Does not form spores and the bacteria can be killed by boiling for 1-2 minutes. The toxin produced by the bacteria is not killed at that temperature and needs 30 minutes boiling.	All people are believed susceptible to this type of food poisoning.
Clostridium perfringens .... A rod-shaped bacterium. .... **toxic** food poisoning is caused by the spores when multiplying.	Grows best between 15°C and 50°C. Does not grow below 5°C. Often found in human and animal intestines.	Abdominal pains and diarrhoea (vomiting is very rare).	8-22hrs usually 12-18hrs.	12-24hrs.	Meats, meat products and gravy.	Keep raw and cooked foods separate. Maintain high standards of hygiene. Ensure food is thoroughly cooked and rapidly cooled. Food must be refrigerated 1½ hours after cooking. Joints of meat should not be more than 2.5kg in weight.	Spores are not killed by normal cooking and can survive boiling, steaming or stewing for up to 4 hours. Spores do not multiply but if food is cooled too slowly or kept warm they will germinate and multiply.	All people are believed to be susceptible but it can be very serious for infants, the elderly, immuno-compromised and the infirm.

Bacteria	General Information	Symptoms	Onset Time	Duration of illness	Found in	Control/ prevention	Destruction	Target population
Clostridium botulinum .... A rod-shaped bacterium. .... This **toxic** bacteria is highly poisonous.	This type of food poisoning is very rare. In the majority of cases it is fatal if an antitoxin is not administered at the onset of the illness. The toxin is very poisonous. Eating only a tiny amount of infected food can result in death.	Difficulties in talking, breathing, swallowing, double vision, headaches, nausea, vomiting and paralysis of the cranial nerves.	2hrs-8 days usually 12-36hrs.	Death unless antidote given immediately after onset. Recovery may take months.	Foods not heated before eating or low acid foods may be involved. Often associated with under-sterilised food or vacuum packed foods. The toxin has been found in soil, fish, meat and vegetables.	Tight control over canning procedures, particularly low acid products. Care taken to to dispose of dented, damaged or blown tins. Control in production and handling of both raw and smoked fish. Care needed in cook-chill and sous-vide systems.	Extremely difficult to destroy; spores will survive ordinary cooking methods. Toxins, however, are not heat resistant and can be destroyed by boiling.	All people are susceptible. Incidences are low but mortality rates high. Infants and the elderly are more at risk.
Bacillus cereus .... A rod-shaped bacterium. .... This bacteria causes **toxic** food poisoning and it also forms spores.	There are two forms of this bacteria. The more common type occurs after eating food containing the toxin and leads to vomiting and nausea. The second type is rare in Britain and occurs when the the toxin is produced in the intestine.	Toxin in food - causes nausea, vomiting and occasionally abdominal cramps. Toxin in intestine - causes diarrhoea and abdominal cramps but seldom vomiting.	Eating toxin in food 1-7 hrs. Toxin produced in the intestine - 8-16hrs.	Toxin in food - recovery in less than 24hrs. Toxin produced in the intestine - recovery in 1-2 days.	Toxin found in rice, cereal products and starchy foods such as potatoes. The organism grows well in soil and can survive milling and processing of harvested grain. Toxin produced in the intestine is associated with meats, milk, vegetables and fish.	This form of food poisoning is often misdiagnosed because it is confused with staphylococcus aureus (toxin in food) or clostridium perfringens (toxin in intestine). Foods must be: • thoroughly cooked • rapidly cooled • stored at the correct temperature and re-warming should be avoided.	Very heat resistant and can withstand temperatures in excess of 126°C for more than 90 mins.	All people are believed to be susceptible.
Escherichia coli (E-coli) .... A kidney-shaped organism. .... Causes **infectious** and **toxic** food poisoning.	There are four types that cause gastroenteritis in humans. In adults symptoms have been known to recur for up to 3 weeks.	Diarrhoea, abdominal pain and nausea. In serious cases, kidney failure.	Usually 12-24hrs.	1-5 days.	Water contaminated with sewage. Outbreaks tend to occur in underdeveloped countries with poor standards of hygiene. Soft cheeses, minced beef, chicken.	Safe sewage disposal and use of chlorine in water is essential to avoid these infections. In suspect areas drink bottled water and avoid ice cubes in drinks. Also avoid high water content foods such as water melon.	Readily killed by by temperatures above 55°C.	Infants and travellers to underdeveloped countries.
Listeria monocytogenes .... Does not form spores. .... Causes **infectious** food poisoning.	Hardy bacteria which can survive freezing, drying and heat. Little is known about the contamination routes. It is suspected that up to 30% of known cases result in fatality.	Begins as flu-like illness including fever. Has been known to cause nausea, vomiting and diarrhoea. May cause abortion, stillbirth, meningitis and septicaemia.	Little data available but may range from a few days to a few weeks. 1-70 days.	Insufficient data available.	Pasteurised and raw milk, cheeses, particularly soft, ice cream, raw vegetables, raw meat, raw and cooked poultry, raw and smoked fish. Cook-chill foods may be implicated.	Good stock rotation in chill cabinets, minimal handling between cooking and chilling. The bacteria is salt tolerant and is still able to multiply at 0°C although growth is very slow. This has serious implications for the storage of chilled high risk foods.	Temperatures of up to 91°C are necessary to ensure destruction for solid foods.	Pregnant women and their unborn babies; immuno-compromised. Less frequently those with diabetes or asthma; the elderly.
Campylobacter jejuni .... Short spiral cells .... Causes **infectious** food poisoning.	The most frequent cause of diarrhoea in Britain. Often known as gastroenteritis. Can be transmitted by food handlers and the water from water storage tanks contaminated by birds or small animals.	Diarrhoea, flu-like symptoms, headache, fever and abdominal pain.	Usually 2-5 days after ingestion. May take up to 11 days to appear.	7-10 days, but can last up to 3 weeks. About 25% of cases relapse.	Meat, poultry, raw milk and untreated water supplies. Many healthy chickens carry Campylobacter bacteria in their intestinal tract.	Readily transmitted between humans and animals.	Readily killed, above 60°C.	All sections of the community are vulnerable.

Moisture

Living cells like bacteria require moisture to grow. The amount of moisture in any food is known as WATER ACTIVITY (A_w). The A_w of pure water is 1.00. Bacteria prefer an A_w of around 0.99. Most bacteria will not grow below 0.95 A_w. Table 3 shows the A_w value of some foods. Many foods contain enough moisture for growth, with the exception of dried foods. But even dried foods should not be considered totally safe particularly if they require reconstituting prior to use. Bacteria may be lying dormant and it is important that when the food is reconstituted it is kept under conditions which prevent bacteria multiplying.

Table 3 A_w values in foods

Food	A_w value
Pure water	1.00
Fresh meat	0.95-0.99
Fresh bread	0.94-0.97
Cured meat	0.87-0.95
Jam	0.75 -0.80
Saturated salt solution	0.75
Flour	0.67-0.87
Granulated sugar	0.19

Oxygen

Most bacteria require oxygen to grow - these are called **aerobic** bacteria. Some can grow without oxygen and are known as **anaerobic** bacteria.

Spores

When bacteria have the correct conditions to grow and multiply they are said to be in a **vegetative** state. In these conditions they can easily be destroyed by heat. If growth is not possible due to adverse conditions, some bacteria form spores. A spore forms inside the bacterial cell and consists of a hard outer coating or shell. The bacterial cell often disintegrates leaving the spore which lies dormant (inactive). When more favourable conditions return the wall of the spore splits open (germinates) and a new cell begins to grow and multiply. Spores can be very resistant to heat. High temperatures in excess of 100°C for long periods of time are often needed to destroy spores.

Toxins

Some bacteria produce poisons known as toxins. These poisons can act very quickly in the body and in the case of *Clostridium botulinum* can cause death.

Moulds

Moulds are thread-like filaments of fungi which can be black, white or coloured. They will grow on many foods including those which are moist or dry, acid or alkaline, or even in salt or sugar concentrations. The best temperatures for growth are between 20°C and 30°C. High humidity will quicken the growth of moulds. Moulds are often found in bakery products, particularly bread, and also on citrus fruits. Moulds do not usually cause food poisoning unless they produce **mycotoxins** which are poisonous substances. If mould is found on food it is usually considered unfit for human consumption. However, some cheeses are specifically produced to contain moulds such as Stilton and Danish Blue.

Yeasts

Yeasts are microscopic fungi which grow best in the presence of oxygen, although some can grow without oxygen. Yeasts can continue to grow in sugar and salt concentrations with an A_w (water activity) as low as 0.62. The optimum temperature for growth is around 25-30°C. Some yeasts have beneficial uses such as those used in the manufacture of bread, vinegar and beer. Yeasts can cause food spoilage in foods with high sugar concentrations like jam, honey and fruit juice.

Enzymes

Enzymes are chemicals produced by living cells. There are many different kinds of enzymes which cause a variety of reactions in food. Some enzymes are excreted by food spoilage bacteria. They spread over the food partially digesting it and causing it to rot. The enzyme **polyphenol oxidase** causes peeled apples and potatoes to brown. Many green vegetables are blanched before freezing to prevent the action of enzymes causing loss of colour and tainting.

Key Terms

Cross-contamination - the transference of bacteria between raw and cooked foods.
Immunocompromised - people with an inability to fight infection.
Pathogenic bacteria - harmful bacteria which can cause food poisoning.
Food spoilage bacteria - bacteria which cause food to go bad but do not usually cause food poisoning.
Binary fission - a process of dividing into two.
Water activity (A_w) - ('A' for activity; 'w' for water); the amount of moisture in any food which bacteria can use to multiply.

activities

Twice as many people think they've had food poisoning this year as last. The prime suspect is consumer malpractice. The Food and Drink Federation (FDF) said that, '6 out of 10 people are aware that food poisoning is most likely to be caused by not heating or cooking food properly' and, 'over half of us don't always follow manufacturers' preparation instructions and three-quarters don't always read them'. What the FDF did not mention was that *salmonella* is endemic in eggs, that 36% of British chickens are contaminated with *salmonella* and *campylobacter* is found in 41% of them. There was no reference to E coli 0157 which is often found in burgers, sausages and processed meats. The FDF also failed to mention the fact that we are now encouraged to store foods for longer and longer periods of time because supermarkets want us to shop once a week. No, just blame the consumer with the wonky fridge and the dirty chopping board.

Source: adapted from the Guardian, 15 July 1995

1. The number of reported cases of food poisoning is increasing. Suggest reasons why this is the case.
2. What precautions should the consumer take to avoid food poisoning?
3. Use Table 2 to help you answer these questions:
a) Which three bacteria are mentioned in the article?
b) Which foods could carry these bacteria?
c) How can these organisms be destroyed?

FOOD HYGIENE AT SAFEWAY

Safeway is committed to excellence in food hygiene. The 68,000 staff who work at Safeway all receive hygiene training and staff who work in the coffee shop, bakery or delicatessen receive further specialist training. There are two key factors in fresh food retailing: temperature and rotation of stock. Safeway's chill chain ensures that fresh and frozen products reach the customer in peak condition.

In the delicatessen, rotation of stock and keeping food at the correct temperature are still the key issues. Staff who work in the delicatessen also receive training in other important areas such as:
* *personal hygiene*
* *separating raw and cooked products to avoid cross-contamination*
* *serving food using one time gloves or serving tongs*
* *cutting hard, soft and blue cheeses on separate boards*
* *using the correct cleaning materials.*

Digital probe thermometers are used at several points in the chill chain to check the temperature of goods.

THE CHILL CHAIN

SUPPLIERS
All suppliers must be audited by an independent auditor to check their hygiene standards before Safeway will buy their products.

TRANSPORT BY CHILLED LORRY

SAFEWAY DISTRIBUTION CENTRE
On arrival the temperature of goods is checked. For chilled goods (cheeses, cold meats, ready meals, etc.) if the specified temperature for the load is exceeded, the load is rejected.

TRANSPORT BY CHILLED LORRY

SAFEWAY STORE
Goods are delivered to the store on a daily basis. On arrival, the temperature is checked. For chilled goods, if it is over 7.5°C, the load is rejected. Newer stores have a chilled unloading area and in older stores, the goods are loaded straight into fridges/freezers.

STORAGE REFRIGERATOR/FREEZER
When new products arrive they are transferred into fridges or freezers. All stock is rotated on the basis of 'first in, first out'.

REPLENISHMENT
Staff load up trolleys from the fridges or freezers and take the products to the chilled cabinets or freezers in the front of the store. One of the key points in the chill chain is the 20 minute rule - no products must be left out of chill for more than 20 minutes. When replenishing goods, staff must not take more stocks than they can safely stack into chilled cabinets or freezers within this time. As new goods are put on the shelves, the stock is rotated, so that items with a shorter 'use by' date are brought to the front.

CHILLED CABINETS/FREEZERS
The temperature in each cabinet is displayed above the compartment, enabling visual checks to be made. Each compartment is also linked to a central computer which displays all the temperatures. These are checked three times a day. If the temperature in any compartment rises above the required temperature, an alarm goes off on the computer and action is taken to remedy the situation. The temperature inside the cabinets is also checked regularly using a probe thermometer.

Activities

1. Why is effective stock rotation important in maintaining standards of food hygiene?
2. What is the 20 minute rule and why is it important?
3. What might happen if the temperature in one of the lorries delivering products to the store rose above 7.5 C?
4. How do Safeway staff monitor the temperature in the front of store chilled cabinets and freezers?
5. State FIVE points that you think should be included in the hygiene training for staff working in EITHER a) the bakery OR b) the coffee shop.

Food preservation

Home preserving

Nowadays, fresh produce is available all year round due to efficient production and transportation. Frozen, canned and vacuum-packed food is also easily available. Until relatively recently, however, people relied on local produce in SEASON and their own home preserved food.

Drying was a common method of PRESERVATION in Britain and the Mediterranean. In Britain, drying would be done with the use of the fire; in hotter countries the sun would do the work.

Salt would keep vegetables, fish and meats edible for a long period. Salt and smoke combined helped to create kippers and hams which have a pleasant flavour and aroma.

Vinegar was used to make pickles from fruits and vegetables. The use of **yeasts** and sugars with fruits and vegetables helped to create wines and beers worldwide.

The combination of **sugar** and fruit produces jams. Fruit may be boiled with water or a sugar syrup in special kilner jars to preserve the fruit.

Commercial preserving

In the food industry several methods of food preservation are used to prolong the SHELF LIFE of food. These methods preserve by:

● destroying or retarding the action of enzymes which cause food to become mouldy (see Unit 9)
● preventing the growth of micro-organisms (bacteria, viruses, mould and fungi) some of which produce harmful pathogens which can cause serious illness and even death (see Unit 9).

The main methods of destroying or retarding the action of enzymes or micro-organisms in food are:

● removing moisture
● heat treatment
● making food cold
● irradiation
● cook-chill
● sous-vide
● using chemicals (see Unit 11).

Removing moisture

Drying or dehydration is one of the oldest forms of food preservation. By removing water, enzymes and micro-organisms are unable to reproduce. Water is drawn out from the cells and this concentrates natural salts or sugars which preserves the food. Removing water from food also reduces the bulk and the weight of the product which in turn lowers transport and handling costs. Table 2 shows several ways of removing water.

In the past, home preserved food was essential for survival. Now people preserve food at home to save money, to make the most of a glut of seasonal fruit or vegetables or simply to enjoy the taste of delicious, home made produce.

activities

1. a) Explain why drying is a successful method of food preservation.
   b) Give THREE situations when dehydrated food could be useful.
2. Compare the soup products in Table 1 in terms of cost, attractiveness of packaging, sensory appeal of food, ease of use and preparation time. Carry out a survey to find out which product people would be most likely to buy.

Table 1 Soups

TYPE	PRICE	SHELF LIFE	PREPARATION TIME
DRIED	42p	1 year	10-15 minutes
CANNED	43p	1 year	4 minutes
GLASS JAR	89p	3 months	4 minutes
PLASTIC POUCH	99p	1 week	5-6 minutes

Heat treatment

Heat treatment destroys most of the enzymes and micro-organisms which cause food deterioration. One of the most important methods of preservation by heat treatment is canning. Nearly all foods can be canned. Food is cooked and sterilised in air tight containers. Canned food will last for many years provided the cans are not damaged. Once the can is opened or the seal broken in any way, bacteria can enter and reproduce. Avoid buying dented cans as the dents could cause a weakness in the metal where bacteria could enter. A blown can indicates the growth of bacteria from within the can.

Making food cold

Lowering the temperature at which foods are stored inhibits the growth of micro-organisms. The bacteria are not killed but they are prevented from multiplying.

Chilling

Chilled foods are promoted as quality foods and their growth within the food industry has been rapid over the last fifteen years. Chilled foods are perishable foods which are kept in prime condition for a limited amount of time by keeping them at a temperature of between -1°C and 8°C. This slows down enzyme action (which causes food deterioration) and reduces the growth of micro-organisms.

Some chilled products may only have a shelf life of one day so it is vital that deliveries are regular, turnover is rapid and stock control carefully managed.

Table 2 Commercial drying methods

1. **Spray drying** is used for liquids and products which may be damaged by excessive heating, such as milk or potato. A fine spray of liquid droplets meets a blast of warm air. The droplets rapidly dry and fall to the bottom of the chamber. This method produces a fine flour like product which is difficult to reconstitute.

2. **Fluidised bed drying** is a two-stage method and is used for foods such as coffee and potato. This is where granules rather than powder are formed. The first stage involves clumping of the dry particles into granules. The second stage involves drying the granules by blowing air through the product. The granules act like sponges which dissolve easily in water.

3. **Accelerated freeze drying** involves freezing food in a cabinet, pumping out the air and vapourising the ice so quickly that the ice turns to steam without turning into water. Food does not become less bulky but does become lighter. The advantages are that the colour, texture and most of the flavour of the product is retained, fewer vitamins are lost and products last longer than other dried products. Foods such as coffee, complete meals and fish benefit from this method of drying but it is a more costly process.

Due to research into the growth of listeria (see Unit 9) many chilled foods are now stored at below 4°C. Chilled foods are useful as they can be purchased, cooked and consumed without delay. Examples are ready prepared salads, fresh pasta, pies, sandwiches, pâtés

Freezing

The domestic freezer will store frozen food products at -18°C and a commercial freezer at between -18°C to -29°C. The speed at which food is frozen is critical. If food is frozen quickly small ice crystals will form reducing damage to the structure of the food. When food is frozen slowly large, uneven ice crystals are formed which break through the cells on thawing and affect the flavour, texture and nutritional value. Table 3 on p. 48 shows several ways of freezing foods. It is important to follow storage instructions on commercially prepared food which have either a 1, 2 or 3 star rating, indicating how long the food should be kept in a freezer:

*	= 1 week
**	= 1 month
***	
or ☆***	= until best before date.

activities

1. At what temperature should
   a) chilled food
   b) frozen food
   be stored in a supermarket?
2. Would you be likely to find the following products in:
   (a) the chilled cabinet;
   (b) the freezer;
   (c) both;
   in your supermarket?
   Pork sausages, vegetarian burgers, *coleslaw, corn on the cob, blackberry sorbet, pizza, tofu.*
3. Bestco supermarket have introduced a new line: chilled ready-to-eat sandwiches and salads. These products have a shelf life of only one day. How can Bestco make sure that they do not have to throw away food at the end of a day?

Table 3 Commercial freezing methods

1. **Blast freezing** - food is placed on trays and cold air is blown onto the product which can be of any shape or size.
2. **Plate freezing** - the oldest method where the product is in contact with plates which freeze the product rapidly to -18°C.
3. **Immersion freezing/spray freezing** - food passes through a tunnel on a conveyor belt during which it is sprayed with liquefied nitrogen or carbon dioxide producing a quick frozen product.
4. **Freeze flow** - a method where the food is quickly frozen without hardening it.

It was Clarence Birdseye, an American biologist, on an expedition to Labrador in 1918, who first recognised the commercial potential of frozen food. He ate fish that the Inuit people left in the open air to freeze. When thawed and eaten months later, the food still tasted fresh. When he returned to the USA, Clarence Birdseye set about developing a process that could freeze food as rapidly as the natural conditions in the Arctic. In the late 1920s he patented The Birdseye Plate Froster and in 1930 Birds Eye frozen food products began to be sold by shopkeepers.

Irradiation

IRRADIATION involves passing rays from a radioactive or electron beam source through the food. This reduces the number of bacteria, kills insects and pests and increases the shelf life of food by delaying enzyme activity. Table 4 shows some of the uses of irradiation.

Research is still needed to safeguard the public from:

- the irradiation of unfit food - food which has become infected with bacteria could be irradiated to reduce that level. There would then be no way of telling that the food was originally contaminated and it might still contain toxins and viruses.
- loss of nutrients - we know there is a loss of vitamin C but further investigation and monitoring is needed to find out if other nutrients are affected by irradiation.

There is no way of detecting that food has been irradiated, or how many times and with what dose. Food labelling regulations require all irradiated food to use the specific words 'irradiated' or 'treated with ionising radiation' on the label.

Cook-chill

COOK-CHILL is a catering system where food is prepared and cooked in bulk in a central kitchen, then rapidly chilled until it is required. It is suitable for most foods if the correct methods of preparation are used. Figure 1 shows the stages in cook-chill production.

The cook-chill process increases the storage life of food. Cook-chill products are stored at a temperature of 0-3°C. At this temperature bacterial growth and enzymic reactions are slowed down. To ensure safe food production it is important to:

- use only the best quality foods for the process
- ensure the correct temperatures are always maintained
- practise the highest standards of food hygiene throughout the process
- conform to the Food Safety Act 1990.

Table 4 Irradiating food

Many types of food can be irradiated. The dose depends on what result is required:

Low dose of radiation - **radurisation**:
- stops potatoes and onions from sprouting so they keep longer
- slows down the ripening of fruit so they can be transported longer distances
- kills pests in wheat, rice, spices and fruits.

Medium doses of radiation - **radicidation**:
- reduces micro-organisms such as yeasts, moulds and bacteria thus extending the life of foods and reducing the risk of food poisoning.

High doses of radiation - **radappertisation**:
- this amount completely sterilises by killing all bacteria and viruses. It would be used for meat products increasing the shelf life dramatically.

Cook-chill production. After cooking, the temperature of food is rapidly reduced in a blast chiller. Here, the temperature is being checked with a hand held testing device called a probe thermometer.

Sous-vide production

Cook-chill is used when food is needed in volume such as in hospitals, schools, factories, aircraft and trains. Food can be bought in bulk, and prepared in advance. Portions can be controlled reducing waste. When the food is to be served it can be:

● reheated in the central kitchen and served
● reheated in the central kitchen and then transported in heated trolleys
● transported in its chilled state and reheated where it is to be served.

Sous-vide

SOUS-VIDE is a method of cooking and preservation used in restaurants, hotels and industrial catering. The method involves

Key Terms

Season - the period during which a food is locally available.
Preservation - long term food storage.
Shelf life - the length of time that food will remain fresh and safe to eat.
Irradiation - a process involving passing rays from a radioactive or electron beam source through food.
Cook-chill - a process where food is prepared and cooked in bulk then rapidly chilled until required.
Sous-vide - a process where food is vacuum sealed in plastic sachets, cooked slowly and chilled.
Vacuum - a space from which air has been removed.

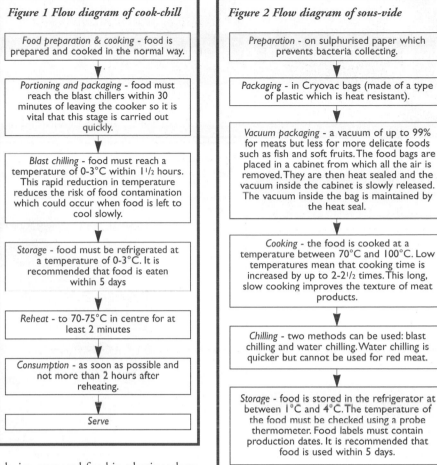

Figure 1 Flow diagram of cook-chill

Food preparation & cooking - food is prepared and cooked in the normal way.
↓
Portioning and packaging - food must reach the blast chillers within 30 minutes of leaving the cooker so it is vital that this stage is carried out quickly.
↓
Blast chilling - food must reach a temperature of 0-3°C within 1½ hours. This rapid reduction in temperature reduces the risk of food contamination which could occur when food is left to cool slowly.
↓
Storage - food must be refrigerated at a temperature of 0-3°C. It is recommended that food is eaten within 5 days
↓
Reheat - to 70-75°C in centre for at least 2 minutes
↓
Consumption - as soon as possible and not more than 2 hours after reheating.
↓
Serve

placing prepared food in plastic sachets, which are then sealed under a VACUUM, cooked slowly and chilled. Figure 2 shows the stages in sous-vide production. The advantages of this method of preservation to the catering industry are:

● it is suitable for most foods
● food can be prepared in advance
● long, slow cooking improves the flavour and texture of food
● shrinkage of food is reduced

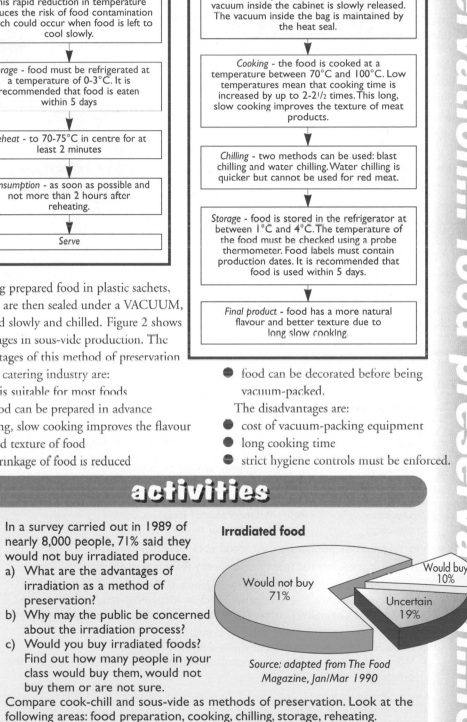

Figure 2 Flow diagram of sous-vide

Preparation - on sulphurised paper which prevents bacteria collecting.
↓
Packaging - in Cryovac bags (made of a type of plastic which is heat resistant).
↓
Vacuum packaging - a vacuum of up to 99% for meats but less for more delicate foods such as fish and soft fruits. The food bags are placed in a cabinet from which all the air is removed. They are then heat sealed and the vacuum inside the cabinet is slowly released. The vacuum inside the bag is maintained by the heat seal.
↓
Cooking - the food is cooked at a temperature between 70°C and 100°C. Low temperatures mean that cooking time is increased by up to 2-2½ times. This long, slow cooking improves the texture of meat products.
↓
Chilling - two methods can be used: blast chilling and water chilling. Water chilling is quicker but cannot be used for red meat.
↓
Storage - food is stored in the refrigerator at between 1°C and 4°C. The temperature of the food must be checked using a probe thermometer. Food labels must contain production dates. It is recommended that food is used within 5 days.
↓
Final product - food has a more natural flavour and better texture due to long slow cooking.

● food can be decorated before being vacuum-packed.

The disadvantages are:

● cost of vacuum-packing equipment
● long cooking time
● strict hygiene controls must be enforced.

activities

1. In a survey carried out in 1989 of nearly 8,000 people, 71% said they would not buy irradiated produce.
   a) What are the advantages of irradiation as a method of preservation?
   b) Why may the public be concerned about the irradiation process?
   c) Would you buy irradiated foods? Find out how many people in your class would buy them, would not buy them or are not sure.

2. Compare cook-chill and sous-vide as methods of preservation. Look at the following areas: food preparation, cooking, chilling, storage, reheating.

Irradiated food

Would not buy 71%
Would buy 10%
Uncertain 19%

Source: adapted from The Food Magazine, Jan/Mar 1990

unit 11 Additives

What are additives?

ADDITIVES can be made from natural or chemical substances. When chemicals are used they are known as artificial additives. These substances are added to foods for two main reasons:

- to preserve food
- to improve the colour, flavour or texture of food.

Do we need additives?

Food additives are an essential part of food processing. They help to ensure:

- that food has a relatively long shelf life
- that food looks attractive
- that food tastes good.

Preservatives keep food safe to eat for longer. These may be added to food in order to prolong its shelf life, e.g. sulphur dioxide is often added to dried apricots to preserve them and keep their colour.

Antioxidants help to prevent fat in food combining with oxygen and becoming rancid. They also help slow down enzyme activity in fruit and vegetables. A natural antioxidant is tocopherol (vitamin E) which is present in some foods and may be added to others.

Colours make food look more attractive. Some colourings are artificial but many are natural or copied from a natural source, e.g. annatto is a yellow colouring made from the seed pods of a Caribbean plant.

Emulsifiers, stabilisers and thickeners improve the consistency of the food. Emulsifiers help fats and water to mix, stabilisers prevent them separating and thickeners add body to food, e.g. locust bean gum.

Flavourings and flavour enhancers improve the taste of food, e.g. acetaldehyde adds an apple flavour to food.

Table 1 Types of additives

activities

1. Look at Table 1. Which types of additive are concerned with food preservation and which are concerned with improving the colour and flavour of food?

2. Match the type of additive in the left hand column with the function in the right hand column.
   - preservatives   - improve the taste of food
   - colours   - stop fats going rancid
   - emulsifiers   - help keep food longer
   - flavourings   - improve appearance of food
   - antioxidants   - help fats and water to mix

3. Why might some people be concerned about additives present in food?

4. This is an ingredients list from a strawberry flavour dessert mix.

   Sugar, Modified Starch, Vegetable Oil (Hydrogenated), Emulsifiers (Propylene Glycol Monostearate, Lecithin), Gelling Agents (Disodium Monophosphate, Sodium Pyrophosphate), Caseinate, Lactose, Whey Powder, Flavourings, Colours (Carmine, Annatto)

   a) Name three additives this product contains.
   b) Explain what function each of these additives performs.
   c) Why is it important that the manufacturer lists all the additives used in this product?

The addition of preservatives allows us to:

- shop less frequently because food has a longer shelf life
- buy foods all year round, that previously were only available in seasons.

However the use of preservatives accounts for less than 1% of additives used. Additives in the form of colourants restore the colour lost in processing and artificial flavours add flavour to food.

Many people would argue that we do not need these additives. But manufacturers say that they produce food that the consumer wants and many people like their strawberry yogurt to be pink or their crisps to taste like prawn cocktail. These requirements are met by using artificial colourants and flavourings.

Are additives bad for you?

A diet which includes a high proportion of processed foods may include additives which do not serve any nutritional purpose and some which may be bad for a few people. Just as some people may be allergic to certain types of food, a small number of people may react badly to additives in food.

- Between 50 and 100 people in every 10,000 may have an allergic reaction to foods such as eggs, milk and fish.
- Between 3 and 15 people in every 10,000 may have an allergic reaction to one or more additives.

The problem is often made worse when people do not know exactly which additive is causing the problem. Even if they are aware that they have an allergy, there are so many additives that pinpointing the culprit can be difficult.

Some additives are thought to be linked to hyperactivity in children. Others provoke asthma attacks in asthma sufferers.

Additives and safety

Since the Food Act 1984 additives have been controlled by the government and only those which have been approved may be used. If a company wants to use a new additive it has to pay for testing by the Food Advisory Committee. This can cost over £1 million. Approved additives are given an 'E' NUMBER and can be used throughout the European Union.

There are about 3,750 additives which may legally be added to our food. The vast majority - 3,500 - are flavourings.

Flavourings are not as tightly controlled as other types of additives because they are used in tiny amounts and in a variety of combinations. Additives must be listed on food labels by type and chemical name or number. Additives, like all ingredients, must be listed on the label in descending order of quantity. The law states that food companies should use flavourings which are 'not injurious to health'.

There is currently no testing on the effect of combining different additives. Nobody knows how these combinations might react together or whether they could be harmful to health.

Know your 'E' numbers

'E' numbers are a form of code, each additive has both a chemical name and an 'E' number code, e.g. E220 = sulphur dioxide, a preservative.

> Colours are in the 100 series
> **E100-E180**
>
> Preservatives are in the 200 series
> **E200-E283**
>
> Antioxidants are in the 300 series
> **E300-E322**
>
> Emulsifiers and stabilisers are in the 400 series
> **E400-E495**

There are many books and pamphlets which give information about additives and the chemical name and 'E' number of each additive.

FOOD LABELLING

Many manufacturers now provide information about the nutritional content of food on the label. Nutrients are listed and the amount per 100g or per serving is given. Some manufacturers tell you what percentage of your daily needs is supplied by the nutrients in the food. However, food manufacturers base this information on the Recommended Daily Amount (RDA) instead of the new Dietary Reference Values (see Unit 7). This is because food labelling is governed by European regulations which are currently based on RDAs. An analysis of nutritional labels can be made using the data supplied and the Dietary Reference Values (DRVs) tables.

Figure 1 Bran cereal label

INGREDIENTS

BRAN ENRICHED WHEAT, SUGAR, HONEY, SALT, MALT FLAVOURING, VITAMIN C, IRON, NIACIN, VITAMIN B₆, RIBOFLAVIN (B₂), THIAMIN (B₁), FOLIC ACID, VITAMIN D, VITAMIN B₁₂.

NUTRITION INFORMATION

		Typical value per 100g	Per 30g Serving with 125ml of Semi-Skimmed Milk
ENERGY	kJ	1350	650*
	kcal	320	160
PROTEIN	g	11	8
CARBOHYDRATE	g	64	26
(of which sugars)	g	(24)	(14)
(starch)	g	(40)	(12)
FAT	g	2.0	2.5*
(of which saturates)	g	(0.4)	(1.5)
FIBRE	g	16	5
SODIUM	g	0.9	0.3
VITAMINS:		(%RDA)	(%RDA)
VITAMIN D	µg	4.2 (85)	1.3 (25)
VITAMIN C	mg	50 (85)	16.3 (25)
THIAMIN (B1)	mg	1.2 (85)	0.4 (30)
RIBOFLAVIN (B2)	mg	1.3 (85)	0.6 (40)
NIACIN	mg	15 (85)	4.6 (25)
VITAMIN B6	mg	1.7 (85)	0.6 (30)
FOLIC ACID	µg	167 (85)	60 (30)
VITAMIN B12	µg	0.85 (85)	0.75 (75)
IRON	mg	11.7 (85)	3.6 (25)

* For whole milk increase energy by 100kJ (25kcal) and fat by 3g.
* For skimmed milk reduce energy by 70kJ (25kcal) and fat by 2g.
Contribution provided by 125ml of semi-skimmed milk - 250kJ (60kcal) of energy, 4g of protein, 6g of carbohydrates (sugar), 2g of fat.

Table 1 Dietary Reference Values for riboflavin mg/day

Age	LRNI	EAR	RNI
0-12mths	0.2	0.3	0.4
1-3yrs	0.3	0.5	0.6
4-6yrs	0.4	0.6	0.8
7-10yrs	0.5	0.8	1.0

	Males	Females	Males	Females	Males	Females
11-14yrs	0.8	0.8	1.0	0.9	1.2	1.1
15-18yrs	0.8	0.8	1.0	0.9	1.3	1.1
19+ yrs	0.8	0.8	1.0	0.9	1.3	1.1

Source: Dietary Reference Values - A Guide, HMSO, 1991

Table 2 Dietary Reference Values for vitamin B₁₂ µg/day

Age	LRNI	EAR	RNI
0-6mths	0.10	0.25	0.30
7-12mths	0.25	0.35	0.40
1-3yrs	0.30	0.40	0.50
4-6yrs	0.50	0.70	0.80
7-10yrs	0.60	0.80	1.00
11-14yrs	0.80	1.00	1.20
15+ yrs	1.00	1.25	1.50

Source. Dietary Reference Values - A Guide, HMSO, 1991

Table 3 Dietary Reference Values for iron mg/day

Age	LRNI	EAR	RNI
0-3mths	0.9	1.3	1.7
4-6mths	2.3	3.3	4.3
7-12mths	4.2	6.0	7.8
1-3 yrs	3.7	5.3	6.9
4-6yrs	3.3	4.7	6.1
7-10yrs	4.7	6.7	8.7

	Males	Females	Males	Females	Males	Females
11-18yrs	6.1	8.0*	8.7	11.4*	11.3	14.8*
19-49yrs	4.7	8.0*	6.7	11.4*	8.7	14.8*
50+ yrs	4.7	4.7	6.7	6.7	8.7	8.7

* About 10% of women with very high menstrual losses will need more iron than shown. Their needs are best met by taking iron supplements.

Source: Dietary Reference Values - A Guide, HMSO, 1991

Activities

1. a) What is the RNI for riboflavin for boys aged 11-14?
    b) What percentage of this requirement is provided by a bowl of bran cereal and milk?
2. How many grams of cereal would a 25 year old man need to eat in order to meet the RNI level for riboflavin?
3. Is bran cereal a useful source of Vitamin B12? Justify your answer.
4. The label states that a bowl of cereal with milk provides 3.6mg iron. What percentage of the RNI for iron does this supply for the following people: a 30 year old man; a 30 year old woman; a 3 year old girl?

Bran cereal

case study ADDITIVES

Sulphur dioxide is a commonly used preservative. It is also the only permitted food additive known to have caused death. Sulphur dioxide is one of a family of additives called sulphites (numbered E220-227), which are known to provoke asthma attacks in some asthma sufferers. For a few highly susceptible individuals, the effect is worse. In the USA, several people have died after suffering asthma attacks brought on after eating sulphite-sprayed food in restaurants. For this reason, the US government has banned the use of sulphites on fresh fruits or vegetables intended to be eaten raw. But sulphites are still widely used as preservatives in packaged and processed food, and they are often used in soft and alcoholic drinks.

Source: adapted from The Food Magazine, July-September, 1991

Sulphured (left) and unsulphured (right) apricots. Sulphur dioxide is commonly used as a preservative in dried fruit. It helps to preserve the fruit and maintain its colour. Sulphur dioxide can be removed from fruit by soaking and cooking but consumers eating raw dried fruit may prefer unsulphured fruit as an alternative.

Activities

1. Why do you think people might choose to buy dried apricots treated with sulphur dioxide rather than unsulphured fruit?
2. Sulphites are known to cause adverse reactions in a very small number of people. Discuss what you think food manufacturers should do about this risk. Who could you contact to put forward your view about this issue?
3. Look through your store cupboard at home. Make a list of all the products you can find containing sulphites (E220-227). Then compare your list with other people in your group. What are the most common items on your lists?

case study EXTENDED LIFE MILK

EXTENDED LIFE MILK

Milk producers are working on a new kind of milk which will keep fresh for up to one month and still taste good. Milk Marque (an independent farmer's cooperative) is testing the new 'extended life' milk at its product development centre for the industry. The milk is being developed for Milk Marque's client, Farm Produce Marketing, who are developing the milk for use in airline catering. The airline wants a milk with all the taste of fresh milk but a longer shelf life. The product must be packaged in 125ml portions to fit on the breakfast trays on board.

UHT milk is already available and lasts for up to 6 months, but it has a bad reputation with some consumers, who say that they do not like the taste. Extended life milk is said to retain all the flavour of fresh milk. The vitamin content is lower than pasteurised milk but higher than UHT milk. But UHT milk can be stored at room temperature and extended life milk, like fresh milk, must be chilled below 8°C.

Fresh Milk from CHESHIRE

Source: adapted from the Independent, 3 February, 1996 and Milk Marque information

TYPE OF MILK	PROCESSING	SHELF LIFE
Fresh milk	heated 72°C - 15 secs.	5 days (refrigerated)
UHT (ultra heat treated) milk	heated 132°C - 1 sec	6 months (unopened)
Extended life	heated 120°C - 1 sec	28 days (refrigerated)
Once opened all milks deteriorate at the same rate.		

Activities

1. Conduct a taste test of fresh and UHT milks, recording reactions to whole, semi-skimmed and skimmed milks.
2. Compare the advantages and disadvantages of fresh, UHT and extended life milk for airline catering.
3. Describe TWO ways that Milk Marque could test consumer reactions to the new extended life milk (see Unit 23).
4. What other opportunities can you identify for marketing extended life milk in the retail sector?

Healthy eating

Food and health

Can eating the wrong foods damage your health? Experts can now prove that eating a poor diet can have serious health effects. We are quite familiar with slogans telling us that smoking can be life threatening. We must now also closely analyse our food intake and consider the long term effects if we want to be as healthy as possible.

Proof of the pudding

Since the late 1970s a number of reports have been published concerning diet and health. These include:

Eating for Health - DHSS, 1978

Proposals for Nutritional Guidelines for Health Education in Britain - National Advisory Committee on Nutritional Education (NACNE), 1983

Diet and Obesity - Royal College of Physicians, 1983

Diet and Cardiovascular Disease - Committee on Medical Aspects of Food Policy (COMA), 1984

Eating for a Healthier Heart - British Nutrition Foundation & the Health Care Council, 1985.

Since the reports have been published, the diet of most people has shown some signs of improvement. The Department of Health and the Health Education Authority have issued guidelines for a healthy lifestyle, shown in Table 1.

Dietary targets

In the early 1990s a series of DIETARY TARGETS was outlined concerned with the health of the nation. The government set up a Nutrition Task Force to help the country

Table 1 8 guidelines for a healthy diet

- Enjoy your food.
- Eat a variety of different foods every day.
- Eat plenty of foods rich in starch and NSP (fibre - see Unit 6).
- Don't eat too much fat.
- Don't eat sugary foods too often.
- Look after the vitamins and minerals in your food.
- If you drink alcohol, keep within sensible limits.
- Eat the right amount to be a healthy weight.

meet these targets. In terms of diet and nutrition, by the year 2005 we should:

- reduce the average percentage of food energy derived from saturated fatty acids by at least 35% (to 11%)

- reduce the average percentage of food energy derived from total fat by at least 12% (to 35%)

- reduce the proportion of men and women aged 16-64 who are obese by at least a quarter and a third respectively.

activities

1. Suggest THREE possible changes that you could make to improve your diet.
2. What are dietary targets and why are they likely to be set by the government?
3. On 21 May 1995 the *Sunday Times* published suggestions for a 'Just For Women' diet. A paragraph is shown below. To what extent do the suggestions meet with dietary targets?

Last week we showed that a good breakfast will set you up for the day, but that does not mean you should skimp on lunch. So this week we explain the importance of the midday meal. Ideally you should have a starter, a main course with vegetables, plus cheese or yogurt. Eat as much as it takes to make you feel full, but remember that bread is not allowed. For drinks, try to restrict yourself to water, weak tea or herbal teas. The occasional half a glass of wine at the end of the meal is not out of the question.

Source: adapted from the Sunday Times, 21 May 1995

Tips for cutting down on fat

You don't have to change the food on your plate to have a healthier diet. The difference is often in the cooking method. Suggestions for reducing FAT are shown in Figure 1.

Fat contains more than twice the calories of carbohydrate and protein.

1g carbohydrate = 4 kcal energy
1g fat = 9 kcal energy
1g protein = 4 kcal energy

This means that you can eat twice the amount of protein and carbohydrates and still not equal the amount of calories contained in fat.

Tips for topping up on NSP

How much NSP (fibre) do you need? The average person eats 11-13g of NSP a day. Ideally, we should be eating 18g daily. Here are 3 ways to get 18g of NSP.

- 4 slices of wholemeal bread, 2 Weetabix, 2 portions of vegetables, e.g. 65g of carrots and 75g of sweetcorn.
- 40g bowl of All Bran, 1 medium sized baked potato with skin, 1 orange.
- 125g baked beans on one slice of wholemeal bread, 50g peanuts and a medium sized banana.

The best sources of NSP are:
- wholemeal bread

- Use kitchen paper to remove excess fat from meat and fried food.
- Cut the visible fat from meat and the skin from poultry before cooking; skim the fat from stews and casseroles.
- If you have chips or roast potatoes, cut them into larger pieces - there is less surface area to absorb the fat.
- Grill, steam or bake food instead of frying.

- Check the fat content of dairy foods such as yogurts, milk, fromage frais.
- Always read the labels on processed food and be aware of the nutrients you are consuming.
- Reduce the fat content by changing to medium fat or low fat cheese.
- Use low fat products, such as margarine or skimmed milk.

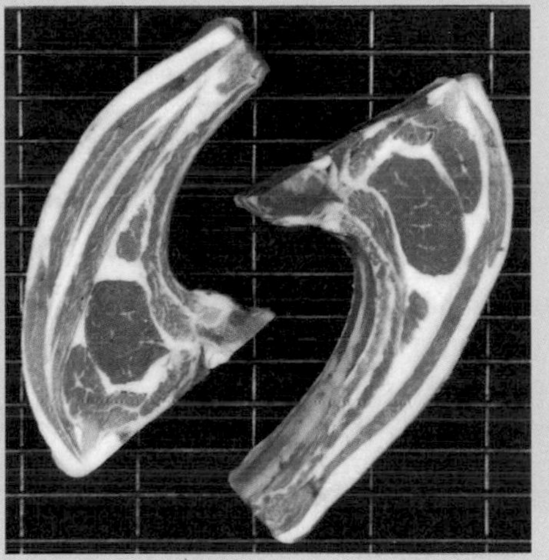

Figure 1 Reducing fat in your diet

- Serve rice with meat dishes.
- Eat wholemeal bread and pasta.
- Wherever possible eat the skins on fruit and vegetables. They are high in fibre and contain vitamins and minerals.
- Use dried fruits as a sweet snack food and carrot, celery or radish as a savoury snack, together with nuts.
- Use wholemeal flour in baking and eat wholemeal cereals.
- Serve fresh fruit or fruit based desserts instead of stodgy puddings.

Figure 2 Increasing NSP in your diet

activities

1. Javed is always hungry and wants to be able to eat more without increasing his calorie intake significantly. Advise him on his choice of food.
2. You are looking for a fat suitable for frying chips. Table 2 gives information about some popular fats and oils.
   (a) Compare the products in terms of fat content and cost.
   (b) Which fat would you use? Explain your choice.

Table 2 Fat content and cost of fats and oils	Olive Oil	Rapeseed Oil	Sunflower Oil	Lard	White Vegetable Fat	Vegetable Ghee
Fat content (g per 100g)						
Saturates	14	7	13	42	23	47
Monounsaturates	70	62	21	42	23	44
Polyunsaturates	11	31	66	9	46	9
Cost	63p (per 100ml)	9p (per 100ml)	7p (per 100ml)	6p (per 100g)	16p (per 100g)	45p (per 100g)

- wheatgerm
- porridge
- wholemeal breakfast cereal
- brown rice
- potatoes
- pulses
- fruit
- vegetables.

Foods high in NSP will satisfy the appetite and also have less calories than sugary or fatty foods. Suggestions for improving the NSP content of your diet are shown in Figure 2.

Tips for reducing sugar

We do not need SUGAR in our diet, but about 15-20% of our calories each day are from sugar. This is about 100g of sugar. Many of us like the taste of sugar, but we really should be reducing our daily consumption of added sugar by about half. Eating too much sugar can lead to tooth decay and can reduce our appetite for healthier foods. Many foods are naturally sweet, such as dried dates, figs, apricots, fresh fruit, fresh vegetables (carrots, pumpkin, sweetcorn) and natural juices. The sugar found in milk is a healthy option. Suggestions for reducing the sugar in your diet are shown in Figure 3.

Tips for reducing salt

The RNI (see Unit 7) for SALT is 4 gms which is the equivalent to one level teaspoon. We are currently eating about 12 gms of salt per day.

Heart disease and strokes are the third most common cause of death in Britain according to a recent report. The saltiness of the British diet is costing over 75,000 lives a year. Apart from the salt we add to our food 70% of the salt in our diet comes from 'ready prepared foods'. The food industry says it adds salt to food to:

- make foods taste better
- preserve foods
- improve the texture.

Getting reliable information from the food industry about the amount of salt

- Limit very sugary foods such as cakes, biscuits, sweets, ice cream, chocolate to one portion per day.

- Sugar substitutes, such as Canderel, can be useful alternatives.

- Drink water or low calorie drinks. Beware though, as many low calorie drinks are acidic and this can damage your teeth.

- Use artificial sweeteners and then eventually cut these out altogether in hot drinks.

- Use concentrated apple juice, dried fruit, desiccated coconut, whole or pureed fruit to help cut down the sugar in baked and fruit dishes.

- Eat fruit, vegetables or sugar free snacks.

Figure 3 Reducing sugar

- Reduce intake of processed food - it usually has a high salt content.

- Do not add salt when cooking vegetables.

- Do not add salt to food before tasting it first and then use very sparingly.

- Use Lo Salt in place of ordinary salt.

- Limit the amount of salted snack foods eaten like crisps, nuts and savoury biscuits.

- Be aware that stock cubes and flavourings often have high salt content.

- Always read the label on processed and ready to eat foods to see if salt has been added.

Figure 4 Reducing salt in your diet

activities

1. Suggest TWO ways in which the NSP content in a pizza could be improved.
2. State FIVE different desserts containing natural sugars.
3. You have been asked to design a packed lunch for a walker. Comment on the lunch you suggest, taking into account the amount of fibre that should be taken daily.
4. Look at the lunches eaten by the three students below.
   (a) Compare the (i) fat, (ii) NSP and (iii) sugar intakes of each of the students.
   (b) Suggest TWO ways in which each student could improve his or her diet.

Kerry A fizzy orange drink
A plate of chips
A chocolate bar

Gurrinder A can of cola
A salad with raw carrots
A jam sandwich on wholemeal bread

Peter Cheese sandwiches on white bread
Apple juice
A low fat yogurt

in ready prepared foods can be difficult. Manufacturers have been reluctant to cooperate with the Nutrition Task Force and this has angered many medical professionals. Until food labelling clearly shows salt content in manufactured and processed foods, consumers may never successfully monitor their salt intake.

Suggestions for reducing the salt in your diet are shown in Figure 4.

The alcohol dilemma

New guidelines for ALCOHOL consumption were issued in December 1995. The new amounts were an increase on previous weekly 'sensible' limits and much controversy surrounded their introduction (see Table 3).

Table 3 Weekly alcohol limits

Old guidelines	21 units (men)
	14 units (women)
New guidelines	28 units (men)
	21 units (women)

1 unit of alcohol = 1/2 pint of beer, one glass of wine or one measure of spirits

These new guidelines are based on scientific evidence which suggests that small amounts of alcohol may help to prevent heart disease, strokes and cholesterol gallstones. Many leading medical professionals fear that this increase may encourage people to drink more than they should.

Nowadays there are many low alcohol and non-alcoholic drinks available. But it is important to read the label carefully. Even low alcohol drinks drunk in large quantities may exceed suggested limits.

Alcohol is packed with 'empty calories' which supply instant energy to the bloodstream, but lack essential nutrients and vitamins. Heavy drinking causes a marked reduction in coordination, leading to slurred speech, clumsy movements and a reduced sensitivity to pain. Long term drinking can lead to distribution of fat on the abdomen - the drinker's 'beer belly'. Alcoholism is an addictive illness and many alcoholics suffer

- Never drink alone.
- Never drink and drive.
- Never neglect a meal in favour of alcohol.
- Keep within recommended guidelines, spread throughout the week.
- Sip your drink slowly and drink smaller measures.
- Do not try to keep up with other people.
- Keep some days completely drink free.
- Pregnant women should avoid alcohol altogether.

Figure 5 Sensible drinking.

Key Terms

Dietary targets - goals set by institutions concerned with improving our diet.
Fat - a nutrient made of carbon, hydrogen and oxygen. The group includes both fats and oils. Fats are solid at room temperature and oils are liquid.
NSP (non-starch polysaccharides) - long, thick walled cells that give strength and support to plant tissue; also known as fibre.
Sugar - a class of water soluble carbohydrates. The sugar we need to cut down on refers to added or non-milk extrinsic sugars (see Unit 6).
Salt - a chemical compound of sodium and chloride.
Alcohol - a chemical substance formed by the fermentation of sugar.

from malnutrition. Prolonged misuse enlarges the liver and can cause a condition called cirrhosis which is the most common cause of liver cancer.

activities

1. Think about your diet. Do you eat much sugar? Make a list of the foods that you eat which contain sugar or to which you add sugar. Compile a table showing where the sugar comes from in your diet.
2. Suggest THREE low salt snack foods for a children's party.
3. In 1995 a range of new products was launched tasting like soft drinks but containing surprisingly large quantities of alcohol. The initial advertising campaign created a huge demand for the product particularly with young people. List some of the reasons why these products might appeal to young people.

Illness and disorders

Illness and disorders

There are some illnesses associated with eating which can affect people's physical and mental health. Some disorders can be triggered by lifestyle and stress. Others may be inherited. Certain drugs can affect appetite and alter eating patterns, e.g. oral contraceptives and steroids.

Obesity

In Britain one in three adults is OBESE. This means that their weight is considerably above average and is causing health problems. Such people have an above average chance of developing medical problems including:
- high blood pressure
- diabetes
- gout
- heart disorders

The only way to overcome obesity is to increase exercise and decrease calorific intake. Crash diets do not work in the long term and they can be harmful to health. Recent research has identified the gene responsible for weight control. The hormone made by this gene can now be manufactured and used in the treatment of obesity.

Anorexia nervosa

ANOREXIA NERVOSA affects mainly girls and young women. Only one in ten anorexics are boys or young men. This disorder is a food phobia covering an underlying mental disturbance. Anorexics have a fear of being fat which leads them to avoid food and become dangerously thin. Anorexia nervosa can lead to:

- extreme emaciation
- tiredness and weakness
- loss of periods (amenorrhoea)
- dry skin
- hair growing on body
- loss of normal hair
- death from starvation.

BULIMIA is closely associated with anorexia nervosa. Sufferers often eat large amounts of food and then make themselves vomit. They may do this several times a day, usually in secret. This repeated cycle of bingeing and vomiting can lead to:
- dehydration
- weakness and cramps caused by potassium loss
- damage to teeth caused by gastric acid in vomit.

Crohn's disease

CROHN'S DISEASE is an inflammatory disease which can affect any part of the gastrointestinal tract. Symptoms are internal pain, fever, diarrhoea and weight loss. The causes of Crohn's are not fully understood. It might be stress, or the highly processed Western style diet. Recent research in Sweden suggests there might be a link between Crohn's disease and measles. Food intolerance is now thought to be an important factor,

Up to 62% of youngsters in gymnastic teams suffer from an eating disorder. In 1994 Christy Henrich, an American world class gymnast died at the age of 22 after battling unsuccessfully for six years against anorexia. She weighed 4 stone 5 lbs (28kg). Her mother said the problem started when a judge at a competition said that Christy would need to lose weight if she wanted to be in the Olympic team that year.

with sufferers reporting symptoms worsening when eating particular foods. There is no known cure and medication is prescribed to calm the inflammation. Extreme cases are treated by surgery. Sufferers may need to take vitamin supplements to counteract their inability to cope with a fully balanced diet.

Coeliac disease

1 in 1,500 people in Britain are affected by COELIAC DISEASE , a disorder of the intestine. The disease tends to run in families and can occur in both adults and children. It is caused by a sensitivity to the protein, **gluten**, found in wheat and rye, but only in small quantities, if at all, in barley, oats, maize

activities

1. Anorexia nervosa affects 1 in 100,000 of the general population, 1 in 100 young middle class women and 1 in 20 young female models, athletes and dancers. What does this tell you about the possible causes of the disorder?

2. Jay is a 16 year old boy with Prader Willi syndrome. In order to control his illness, he is kept on a strict diet. He is never left alone, his parents prepare all his meals and lunch time at school is supervised. Because of this, Jay's weight is fairly normal at 60kg (9½ stone). But Jay is soon going to be an adult when this strict supervision will stop. Devise a diet for one day which would be suitable for a young active male. Suggest some strategies that Jay might use to help himself from overeating. Can you think of any other ways he might be helped to cope?

and rice. Gluten damages the villi (minute hair like projections living in the small intestine) and this can inhibit the absorption of nutrients. Coeliac disease often appears a few months after small children have begun to take solids, such as cereals and rusks containing gluten. The first signs are repeated stomach upsets, followed by bloating, diarrhoea, anaemia and weight loss. By cutting out gluten, the villi can recover. As well as cutting out obvious gluten containing foods, like bread and pasta, people with coeliac disease should also avoid foods containing flour based binders, fillers and modified starch. Instead they should eat plenty of potatoes, rice, pulses, corn and nuts. Corn flour, rice flour, soya or chestnut flour may be used to thicken sauces.

Prader Willi syndrome (PWS)

In Britain 1 in 10,000 people suffer from PRADER WILLI SYNDROME, although the PWS association believes that many cases go undiagnosed. It is a condition in which hunger is never really satisfied. People with PWS will grab food from strangers' plates in restaurants and even eat wall paper, bedding and polish. Sufferers have been known to consume up to 4,000 calories in 2 hours and can become very obese. The cause of PWS is uncertain, but half the sufferers have an abnormality of chromosome 15, i.e. a genetic abnormality.

Allergies

ALLERGENS can produce reactions anywhere in the body, e.g. the nose, lungs, skin and even the brain. When an allergic reaction appears swiftly after eating a particular food, the cause is obvious. A mild allergy can take several hours or even days to produce symptoms. The person experiencing the symptoms does not realise what is happening and it is only when the food is not eaten and the symptoms clear that the culprit food is suspected. Experts say that as many as 3 in every 10 people in Britain are to some degree allergic to or intolerant of certain foods. Allergy related illnesses seem to be on the increase with 1 in 3 children showing symptoms of asthma, eczema or hay fever before the age of 11. The most common foods to produce allergies are, in descending order: milk, gluten, eggs, fish, shellfish, nuts, soya beans and additives.

Dental caries (tooth decay)

Bacteria from food grow on teeth into a sticky film called PLAQUE. If the plaque is not cleaned away regularly, the bacteria break down sugars and starches in food to produce acids which dissolve tooth enamel resulting in dental caries. Figure 1 gives some tips on preventing tooth decay.

Figure 1 How to prevent tooth decay

Danger drinks for teeth - fizzy drinks (even low cal varieties contain high levels of citric acid which can cause tooth erosion), squashes, fruit juices, sweetened tea, coffee or milk drinks. If you must drink these, drink the whole thing at once, preferably with a meal. Constant sipping means teeth are under attack for longer.

Avoid snacking or grazing - these habits ensure food is always present in the mouth and around the teeth which encourages the build up of plaque.

Take positive action against tooth decay when pregnant - eat calcium rich foods together with vitamin D.

Teach young children to care for their teeth - eating a healthy diet and brushing regularly.

If you cannot brush your teeth after a meal, chew sugar free gum - the production of saliva can help to wash harmful acid away.

Key Terms

Obese - having too much body fat. Someone is said to be obese when they weigh 20% more than the maximum for their height.

Anorexia nervosa - an illness which causes people to avoid food, often becoming extremely thin.

Bulimia - people with this disorder eat large amounts of food and then make themselves vomit.

Crohn's disease - an illness causing inflammation of the gastrointestinal tract.

Coeliac disease - an intolerance to gluten, the protein found in wheat.

Prader Willi syndrome - an illness affecting appetite. People with this disorder never seem to feel full.

Allergens - minute particles of matter found in the environment or in food, which the body rejects.

Dental caries - erosion of tooth enamel.

Plaque - a sticky film made up of saliva, food remains and bacteria.

activities

Table 1 Comparing drinks

	% sugar	% acid	pH
Low cal squash	up to 1	0.15-0.4	3.0-3.2
Lemon squash	2-6	up to 0.4	2.6-3.0
Main brand cola	11	0.06	2.4-2.8
Low cal cola	up to 0.2	0.06	2.6-3.0
Ready to drink fruit drink	2-12	0.2-0.5	2.6-3.0

Source: adapted from the Daily Mail, February 1996

1. You are having some friends to dinner. One of them has coeliac disease. Plan a menu that you can all enjoy together.

2. It has been proved that high levels of sugar in drinks can cause tooth decay, and that drinks with a lot of acid (pH less than 5.5) can erode teeth. Look at the table on the left.
   a) Which soft drinks could be harmful to teeth?
   b) Suggest alternatives that are better for dental health.
   c) Harry insists on drinking one can of cola a day. Suggest ways in which he could reduce the risk of damaging his teeth.

TESCO'S HEALTHY EATING CAMPAIGN

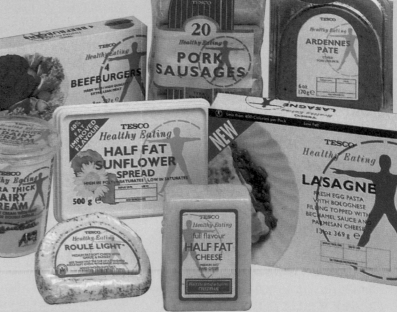

In 1995, ten years after its introduction, Tesco relaunched its Healthy Eating campaign. This campaign was designed by the company to 'allow consumers to care for their personal health'. Tesco produces a Healthy Eating range of products and there is also a series of leaflets available in shops which gives practical help on nutritional matters.

Products which are marked with a Healthy Eating logo will:
- be low in fat and/or
- be high in fibre and/or
- have the right balance of sugar and salt.

Some of the products which bear the Tesco Healthy Eating logo are shown on this page. It is suggested that these products may be healthier alternatives to those of competitors. Tesco says that the Healthy Eating range allows consumers to improve their diet without having to cut out products that they like.

Tesco also provides a nutrition advice service for its customers. This includes leaflets giving nutritional information and suggested recipes which should improve people's diet. There is also a service to answer consumers' questions. Figure 1 shows an example of the type of question asked.

Source: adapted from Tesco Annual Report and Accounts and Tesco leaflets

Figure 1 Tesco nutrition advice service

Q *"I have just bought a bar of Tesco White Chocolate which says 100g (3^1/$_2$ oz) provide: Energy 2253kj/539kcal - but how many calories does it contain?"*

A Calories are the same as kcal or kilocalories, it is just a different way of writing it. So 100g of white chocolate supplies 539 calories and a 25g bar - 135 calories.

Table 1 Nutritional information for 2 spreads

Nutrition Information. Typical Composition 100g (3^1/$_2$ oz) provide:
Energy 1523kj/370kcal,
Protein 2.0g,
Carbohydrate 0.5g (of which sugars 0g),
Fat 40.0g (of which saturates 7.3g, mono-unsaturates 11.2g, polyunsaturates 18.0g),
Fibre 0g,
Sodium 0.6g.

A 15g (1^1/$_2$ oz) serving provides:
5.7mg (57% of the Recommended Daily Allowance for Vitamin E).

This pack contains approx. 17 servings.

NUTRITION	
Typical Values per 100g	
ENERGY	**740kcals**
	3090 kjoules
PROTEIN	**0.6g**
CARBOHYDRATE	**0.8g**
TOTAL FAT	**81.6g**
saturates	46.9g
monounsaturates	28.0g
polyunsaturates	3.0g
SALT	**1.2g**

Healthy Eating
COD FILLETS
IN OVENCRISP BREADCRUMBS

95% fat free

FINEST FISH AVAILABLE TO YOU FROM TESCO

Caught in the clear icy waters of the North Atlantic, this Cod is frozen at its freshest and then breaded under modern factory conditions with traditional care. This product has a Healthy Eating coating, giving a crunchy golden crumb with less than one third of the fat of standard breaded fish.

This Healthy Eating product has been carefully formulated by Tesco to be nutritionally balanced and provides the right proportion of fat, sugars and salt as recommended by leading nutritional experts.

PREPARATION GUIDELINES:
For best results always cook from frozen.
All appliances vary, the following are guidelines only.
Remove from packaging.

To Oven Cook Place on a wire rack on a baking tray. Cook in a pre-heated oven 220°C/425°F/Gas Mark 7 for 25 - 30 minutes, until crisp and golden brown.

Adjust times according to your particular oven.
(For fan assisted ovens cooking times should be reduced. For best results refer to manufacturer's handbook.)
Check food is piping hot throughout before serving.

NOT SUITABLE FOR MICROWAVE COOKING

SERVING SUGGESTIONS:
Serve with Tesco Baby New Potatoes, frozen Petits Pois and a wedge of lemon.

INGREDIENTS:
Cod, Batter (Water, Wheat Flour, Maltodextrin, Salt, Egg Powder, Dextrose, Spices, Onion Powder), Breadcrumbs, Wheat Flour, Vegetable Oil, Salt.

WARNING: THIS PRODUCT MAY CONTAIN SMALL BONES.

STORAGE INSTRUCTIONS
Keep Frozen and use within the following periods:
Ice Making Compartment: 3 days
Star Marked Frozen Food Compartment:
* 1 week
** 1 month
*** or **** Until best before date.
ONCE DEFROSTED DO NOT REFREEZE.

TESCO QUALITY: We are happy to refund or replace any Tesco product which falls below the high standard that you expect. Just ask any member of staff. This does not affect your statutory rights.
Produced in the U.K. for Tesco Stores Ltd., Cheshunt EN8 9SL, U.K. © Tesco '95 0467 UK BB052FE

NUTRITION		
TYPICAL COMPOSITION	Each Fillet (approx. 120g) provides	100g (3^1/$_2$oz) provide
Energy	701kJ/166kcal	584kJ/138kcal
Protein	17.3 g	14.4 g
Carbohydrate of which sugars	16.1 g 1.9	13.4 g 1.6 g
Fat of which saturates	3.6 g 0.7 g	3.0 g 0.6 g
Fibre	0.6 g	0.5 g
Sodium	0.4 g	0.3 g

This Pack contains approx. 5 fillets.

INFORMATION
Each fillet contains:
166 CALORIES • 3.6g FAT

5 018374 058768 >

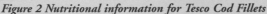
Figure 2 Nutritional information for Tesco Cod Fillets

Activities

1. Suggest FIVE questions that consumers might ask the Tesco nutrition advice service.
2. Explain THREE possible advantages for consumers of Tesco Healthy Eating products.
3. Look at Table 1 which shows nutritional information for a Tesco spread and a margarine produced by another company. Which of the two products would you select as part of a healthy eating plan? Explain your answer using information from the data.
4. Figure 2 shows nutritional information from a 600g packet of Tesco Cod Fillets.
   a) Suggest why someone wishing to improve their diet might buy this product.
   b) The product is going to be used as part of a meal. Suggest a main meal including Cod Fillets that would meet healthy eating guidelines.

PARKWOOD HOUSE DAY NURSERY

Parkwood House in Chester is a nursery for 24 children from 4 months to 5 years old. Every day the nursery serves a morning snack, lunch and high tea. The menu has been meat free since 1989 although fish is served. Some of the children at the nursery have specific dietary requirements: some are vegetarian; some have allergies and are on dairy or gluten free diets. By making changes to basic recipes these children can enjoy the same variety of taste and texture in their food as their friends. For example lasagne can be tuna, for fish eaters or lentil, for vegetarians. Cauliflower and broccoli 'cheese' can be made with soya milk parsley sauce for vegan or dairy free diets. Fruit crumble can be made with rice and soya flour for gluten free diets.

The cook at Parkwood House provides meals based on seasonal produce. This means that the children eat fresh food and it also helps to keep the cost down. Meals based on pulses, fresh vegetables, fish, cheese and dairy products ensure that the nutritional needs of young children are met. The cook will often enhance a meal's vitamin and mineral content with a sprinkling of sesame seeds (for calcium) or wheatgerm (for protein and vitamins E and B group).

The menus at Parkwood House are constantly being changed to provide a varied diet for the children. Meals often reflect an event or project that the nursery is doing. At Chinese New Year everyone dresses up and Chinese food is served.

All the meals are available to buy and are pre-portioned and frozen. Many parents use this 'takeaway' service, confident that their child enjoys the meal at the nursery.

Many of the meals served at the nursery are not what people might expect toddlers to eat, but the children love to try new things. Bean curry and stir-fried vegetables are as popular as cauliflower and broccoli cheese. Part of the reason is the positive attitude at meal times - staff and children sit and eat together and chat about the interesting new foods they are eating. Everyone helps themselves from serving dishes. There is no set time for lunch - everyone sits and chats until the food is gone. There is only one rule,

'If you don't eat your dinner - no pudding!'

Children at Parkwood House learn about food by being directly involved in preparation.

Cauliflower and broccoli 'cheese'

MORNING SNACK

cream crackers, oat crackers, rice crackers with toppings: yeast extract; mushroom pâté; fruit spread; cheese spread

LUNCH

Monday
Potato and watercress soup
Fruit crumble and custard

Tuesday
Tuna and sweetcorn quiche,
jacket potatoes, baked beans
Rice pudding, fruit sauce

Wednesday
Vegetable crumble, mushroom sauce
Apple and pineapple amber

Thursday
Cheese and bean pie, side salad
Banana pudding, natural yogurt

Friday
Lentil shepherd's pie, fresh vegetables
Bread and butter pudding

HIGH TEA

Sandwiches or crackers: with sardine;
yeast extract and beansprout; apple;
egg and cress.
Crumpets, onion and parsley bread,
cheese scones, banana crumblies, fresh fruit

Activities

1. a) Suggest changes you could make to the following recipes to make them suitable for a child on a dairy free diet: macaroni cheese; bread and butter pudding.
   b) What other foods could you include in a dairy free diet to ensure that the child is eating enough protein?
   c) From the menus for morning snack, lunch and high tea, choose a day's food for a child with a milk allergy.
2. a) Suggest changes you could make to the following recipes to make them suitable for a child on a gluten free diet: cheese and tomato sandwiches, tuna and sweetcorn quiche.
   b) What other foods would be likely to contain gluten?
   c) From the menus for morning snack, lunch and high tea, choose a day's food for a child with a gluten allergy.
3. a) Plan a week's menus (morning snack, lunch and high tea) for the children at Parkwood House. Suggest modifications to recipes for children who are: (i) vegetarian and do not eat fish; (ii) those on dairy free diets; (iii) those on gluten free diets.
   b) Write a shopping list for the week and estimate the total cost.
   c) How could a nursery keep the food bill down without compromising the quality of the food?

Food materials

Some definitions

Food technology involves converting raw materials into edible food products. The food materials we use can be divided into the following categories.

PRIMARY FOODS have undergone PRIMARY PROCESSING: basic treatment of raw foodstuffs to make them suitable for either further processing or immediate consumption, e.g. pasteurisation of milk, milling wheat, washing fruit and vegetables and jointing meat.

SECONDARY FOODS which have undergone SECONDARY PROCESSING: further treatment to make them into food products. Flour may be made into bread or pasta, milk may be made into cheese or yogurt, meat can be made into burgers.

A food COMPONENT can be thought of as an individual ingredient within a more highly processed product, e.g. tomato sauce, meat, pasta and cheese are all components of lasagne. Components range from simple cookery aids, such as cornflour, vinegar, herbs and spices to pre-manufactured products like pizza base mix, frozen pastry and canned pie filling. Table 1 gives some examples of components. Bicarbonate of soda is a versatile component with many uses around the home (see Figure 1).

A COMPOSITE food is made of different component parts. Some of the parts may have undergone primary processing (e.g. the meat in lasagne) and some may have undergone secondary processing (e.g. the pasta, tomato sauce and cheese in lasagne). Consumers have the choice of purchasing basic ingredients and making dishes at home or buying ready made composites (these are often known as convenience foods).

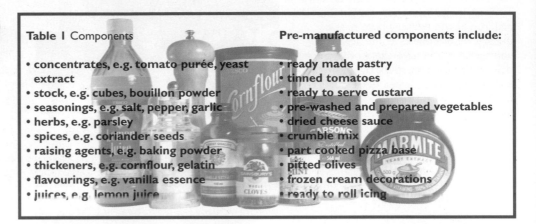

Table 1 Components

- concentrates, e.g. tomato purée, yeast extract
- stock, e.g. cubes, bouillon powder
- seasonings, e.g. salt, pepper, garlic
- herbs, e.g. parsley
- spices, e.g. coriander seeds
- raising agents, e.g. baking powder
- thickeners, e.g. cornflour, gelatin
- flavourings, e.g. vanilla essence
- juices, e.g. lemon juice

Pre-manufactured components include:

- ready made pastry
- tinned tomatoes
- ready to serve custard
- pre-washed and prepared vegetables
- dried cheese sauce
- crumble mix
- part cooked pizza base
- pitted olives
- frozen cream decorations
- ready to roll icing

Using food as a material

Food products are made by combining ingredients in different proportions and using a range of different techniques (see Unit 15). Food materials can be prepared using a variety of processes and equipment (see Unit 18). When food materials are cooked, they react to heat in different ways (see Units 1-5 and Unit 17).

Using components

When a recipe is made, slight variations in ingredients, proportions, techniques and cooking methods can result in changes in the finished dish. In a domestic setting, this is acceptable. A family may enjoy the variety of outcomes. When food is mass produced, however, it is important that there are as few changes as possible. Customers expect consistency and manufacturers want to maintain the quality of their product.

In addition to carefully controlling the production process (see Units 28 and 29), manufacturers can use standard components to achieve a consistent outcome. Table 2 shows some of the advantages and disadvantages of using pre-manufactured food components. Standard components can also be useful for the domestic cook. Figure 2 suggests several questions to ask when deciding whether to use ready made food components.

activities

1. What are the components of a pizza?
2. Which ingredients have undergone primary processing?
3. Which ingredients have undergone secondary processing?

Table 2 Using pre-manufactured food components

ADVANTAGES
- guaranteed quality
- consistent results
- saves time
- little or no skill required to use them
- some have a relatively long shelf life
- can be used as part of more complex dishes

DISADVANTAGES
- may contain ingredients consumer wishes to avoid, e.g. artificial colourants
- could be expensive
- may contain added fat, sugar or salt
- could have poor proportions, e.g. little meat compared to sauce in pie fillings
- flavour, colour and texture may not be as good as fresh equivalent

Key Terms

Primary foods - raw materials which have undergone primary processing to make them into edible food commodities.

Secondary foods - food commodities which have undergone secondary processing to make them into food products.

Primary processing - basic treatment which turns raw materials into food commodities.

Secondary processing - further treatment which converts commodities into food products.

Component - part of a food product.

Composite - food product made from different component parts.

Figure 1 *Bicarbonate of soda*

Bicarbonate of soda (bicarb) is a weak alkaline sodium salt and the main ingredient in baking powder (the others are cream of tartar and a starch filler). When bicarbonate of soda is subjected to moisture and heat it gives off carbon dioxide which helps food to rise. It can also be used in the following ways.

- A paste of bicarb and water makes a great homemade toothpaste.
- Add a pinch to egg whites before beating for extra height in your meringues.
- A pinch of bicarb in water, sipped slowly, is an excellent remedy for indigestion.
- Mix ½ tsp bicarb with ½ pint of milk as an alternative to buttermilk in recipes.
- Soaking time for pulses can be halved if you add a little bicarb to the soaking water.
- A pinch in a vase of water keeps flowers fresher longer.
- Use bicarb dissolved in water to remove smells from a fridge.
- Smear on a paste of bicarb and water to reduce the itching of insect bites.

Source: adapted from the Daily Mail, 28 July 1995

Figure 2 *Choosing pre-manufactured food components*

Can it be easily stored?

Do I like the taste?

Will it save me time?

Is the colour and texture acceptable?

Is it good value for money?

Does it perform as well as or better than available alternatives?

What ingredients are used and are they acceptable to me?

Is it a multi-functional product?

Is it easy to use?

activities

1. The catering trade make extensive use of pre-manufactured food components (see case study on p. 68). Suggest reasons why this is the case.
2. a) Investigate the range of stock products available (e.g. cubes, powders, liquids, pastes).
   b) Suggest dishes that can be made with each type of stock.
   c) What are the advantages of using ready made stock rather than preparing your own?

Measurement and proportions

Imperial and metric measurement

Britain has traditionally used the IMPERIAL system of measurement but since the 1970s the METRIC system has gradually been adopted. On 1 October 1995 - 'metrication day' - it became illegal to sell pre-packed foods in pounds and ounces rather than kilos and grams. Loose goods, such as vegetables and meat, must be sold by metric weight from 1 January 2000. Table 1 gives some imperial/metric conversions.

Measuring equipment

When measuring by weight, scales are used. These range from traditional scales using loose weights to digital scales, capable of weighing accurately to fractions of a gram. Equipment available for measuring by volume ranges from measuring bowls and jugs (usually marked in fluid ounces and millilitres) to cups and measuring spoons (see Figure 1).

Table 1 Metric and imperial measurements

IMPERIAL	EXACT METRIC EQUIVALENT	FOR EASY CONVERSION
WEIGHT		
1oz	28.33g	25g
4oz	113.3g	100g
8oz	226.6g	200g
12oz	339.9g	300g
1lb	453.3g	500g
2lb	906.6g	1kg
VOLUME		
1³/4 pt	994ml	1 litre
1pt	568ml	500ml
¹/4 pt	142ml	150ml

Figure 1 *Cups and measuring spoons*

CUP SET
1 cup (250ml)
¹/2 cup (125ml)
¹/3 cup (80ml)
¹/4 cup (60ml)

MEASURING SPOON SET
1 tablespoon (15ml)
1 teaspoon (5ml)
¹/2 teaspoon (2.5ml)
¹/4 teaspoon (1.25ml)

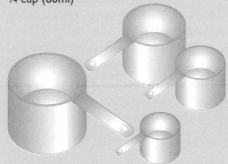

Cups can be used to measure larger quantities of both dry and liquid foods. Measuring spoons are useful for measuring small amounts of ingredients, such as spices or liquid flavourings. When using cups or spoons, dry goods should always be levelled off with a knife, unless the recipe specifies a 'rounded' or 'heaped' measure.

activities

1. How were manufacturers and retailers affected by 'metrication day'?

2. Why might some people have been concerned about the changeover?

3. An elderly relative gives you a shopping list. Convert the imperial measurement into the most appropriate metric measure. Use Table 1 to help you.

   - ¹/2 lb Cheddar cheese
   - 1lb carrots
   - 5lb potatoes
   - 4oz wine gums
   - 1pt milk

From 1 October, the law demands that pre-packed foods are sold in metric units. The imperial measurement may still feature, but the metric measure must be dominant. For anyone educated since schools went metric, 'metrication day' holds no fears. Others are concerned. One shopper said: 'They'll be putting up prices without people realising it.' No retailer admits that it would be rounding up prices but it was commonplace after decimalisation in 1971. Retailers may also pass on conversion costs to their customers. Sainsbury is spending more than £1 million on conversion charts and leaflets for distribution in stores. The National Association of Shopkeepers said: 'New weighing equipment will have to paid for somehow, and the only way will be to increase prices'.

Source: adapted from the Observer, 3 September 1995

Correct proportions

When designing a recipe, the components must be combined in the right PROPORTIONS if the finished product is going to succeed. For example, if a can of baked beans contained more sauce than beans, customers would be very dissatisfied. Consistent results are necessary to give satisfaction, fulfil legal obligations and ensure a quality product.

Pastries

A wide variety of pastries can be made, each suitable for a different purpose. Varying the proportion of fat to flour and using different fats produces different results (see Table 2). Generally a soft plain flour is used for short crust and suet crust,

In a large-scale food production unit, ingredients are weighed using digitally calibrated scales. They are fed direct from storage hoppers into food preparation equipment (on wheels for easy movement).

while a strong plain flour (with a higher gluten content) is used for flaky pastries. Salt improves flavour and strengthens the gluten.

Short crust pastry

The proportions used are half fat to flour. The fat may be all margarine or butter; all white shortening or lard; or half

---

Figure 2 Proportions in bread making

Many breads are made using yeast. Fresh yeast probably gives the best flavour, but it is not always easily available. Alternatively, dried yeast can be used, or the easy blend variety which is fast and easy to use. The resulting doughs are very similar. Sweet yeast doughs require more fat and sugar which slows down the action of the yeast. The proportions for bread are:

- 500g strong flour: 120g fresh or 1 level tbsp dried yeast
- 500g strong flour: 1 pack easy blend yeast for quick rising
- 750g strong flour: 1 pack easy blend yeast if there is more time.

---

activities

1. The scales in the picture both register a weight of 1lb. Why does the McCain portion of chips look bigger?

2. Why would a retailer selling McCain French Fries get 'more portions per pound'?

3. If you were the manager of a fast food restaurant, which chips would you choose for your business? Explain why.

POUND FOR POUND YOU GET MORE FROM McCAIN: Don't worry, your eyes are not deceiving you. When you buy McCain French Fries you really do get more for your money. McCain French Fries have a consistently longer cut than the competition. This means more portions per pound, which in turn means a lower cost per portion.

Source: adapted from McCains advert

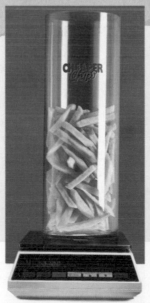

white and half yellow fat. Using different combinations will alter the flavour, colour, texture and ease of handling during preparation. Sugar can be added for a sweet pastry or finely grated cheese for a savoury base. The fat is rubbed into the flour with the tips of the fingers. Cold water (1 tsp per 25g flour) is added to bring the dough together.

Flaky or rough puff pastry

The proportions used are three quarters fat to flour. The fat should be a mixture of butter or margarine and lard or white shortening. Only a quarter of the fat is rubbed in and then ice cold water is added. Seven tbsps of water per 200g of flour is used together with 2 tsps lemon juice to form a soft dough. Because of the low fat content in the initial stages, a large amount of water has to be used to make the dough. Fat is then introduced into the dough by rolling and folding. This pastry needs to rest in the refrigerator to allow the gluten to soften before rolling.

Suet crust pastry

The proportions used are half fat to flour.

Figure 3 Biscuits

Biscuits are made using either the rubbing in or the creaming methods. The proportions are half fat and sugar to flour in both methods. Biscuits can be piped, rolled, dropped in spoonfuls on the baking tray, or pressed into a tin before baking. The mixture is usually bound together with a little egg. Plain soft flour is most suitable for biscuit making. A moderate oven should be used. Biscuits are soft when they come out of the oven and become crisp as they cool. A crisp biscuit in the oven is a burnt biscuit.

Table 2 Pastry proportions

Pastry	Ratio	Fat	Flour	Water	Special points
Short crust	1:2	100g	200g	8 tsps	All yellow fat All white fat Combination
Rough puff	3:4	150g	200g	7 tbsps	+ 2 tsps lemon juice
Suet crust	1:2	100g	200g	7-8 tbsps	Grated suet
Choux	2:3	50g	75g	8-9 tbsps	Boiled fat water & egg
Hot water	3:8	75g	200g	5 tbsps	Boiled fat & water

Table 3 Cake proportions

Method	Ratio	Flour	Fat	Egg	Caster sugar	Example
Creaming/ All in one	equal	100g	100g	2	100g	Victoria sandwich
Rubbing in	8:4:2:3	200g	100g	1	75g	Rock cakes
Whisking	1:2:1	50g	–	2	50g	Swiss roll
Melting	8:3:2:8	200g	75g	1	50g sugar 150g syrup	Gingerbread

This pastry requires more water than short crust as the suet is dry and is not rubbed into the flour in the same way as short crust.

Choux pastry

The proportions used are two thirds fat to flour. This pastry is made by boiling the fat and water together, adding the flour and then beating in egg. The water creates enough steam to make a light, crisp pastry. The finished dough must be piped or spooned onto a baking tray. It cannot be rolled.

Hot water pastry

The proportions used are 75g lard to 200g flour with 5 tbsps water or milk and water. The liquid and fat are boiled together and the flour beaten in. When cool enough, the pastry is moulded rather than rolled.

Cakes

There are several basic methods of cake making (see Table 3). Each has its own merits and produces a different type of cake. All methods use a raising agent.

Creaming method

The main ingredients are self raising flour, butter or margarine, caster sugar and eggs in

Table 4 Basic white sauce proportions

Method	Ratio	Milk	Flour	Fat	Type	Use
Roux/ All in one	16:1:1	250ml	15g	15g	Pouring	Vegetables/ steamed puddings
Roux/ All in one	10:1:1	250ml	25g	25g	Coating	Fish/vegetables Other savoury dishes
Roux/ All in one	5:1:1	250ml	50g	50g	Binding	To bind ingredients e.g. fish cakes

equal proportions (a medium egg weighs approximately 50g).

All in one creaming method

The same ingredients as the traditional method. All the ingredients are beaten together in one bowl and baking powder is added to help the mixture rise.

Rubbing in method

The main ingredients are self raising flour (or plain flour and baking powder), butter or margarine, caster sugar and egg. The ingredients are incorporated by rubbing the fat into the flour. The proportion of fat to flour is half fat to flour.

Whisking method

No fat is added to this mixture so the resulting sponge stales very quickly. The raising agent is air which is incorporated into the mixture by whisking together the eggs and the sugar, before folding in the flour with great care. The proportions are double the weight of egg to flour and caster sugar (e.g. 3 eggs, 75g plain flour, 75g caster sugar).

Melting method

The basic ingredients are flour, butter or margarine, brown sugar, treacle or golden syrup, egg and milk. Because there is such a high proportion of sugar the fat and sugar must be gently melted before adding the flour. The raising agent is bicarbonate of soda. This method of cake making is always cooked at a lower temperature due to the high proportion of sugar.

Basic white sauce

The basic white sauce (see Table 4) has many uses and can be made successfully by the all in one method for those who find the roux method difficult. Milk, flour and butter or margarine are combined in the following proportions.

- Pouring sauce:
  250ml milk / 15g flour / 15g fat.
- Coating sauce:
  250ml milk / 25g flour / 25g fat.
- Binding sauce:
  250ml milk / 50g flour / 50g fat.

A pouring sauce should cover the back of a wooden spoon and pour off in a thin stream. A coating sauce should cover the back of a spoon and pour rather like a curtain. A binding sauce is a very thick sauce which has the ability to hold ingredients together, e.g. in fish cakes.

Roux

This may be used for both white and brown sauces (see p. 13 for method).

All in one sauce

The sauce may be prepared by placing all the ingredients into a saucepan and stirring vigorously as the saucepan heats. The sauce should combine and thicken without lumps forming.

Key Terms

Imperial - a system of measurement standardised in Britain in 1215 and almost unchanged since then.

Metric - a system of measurement, based on the number 10, designed by mathematicians in 17th century France.

Proportions - the relative quantities of ingredients in a recipe, e.g. the proportion of fat to flour in short crust pastry is half fat to flour.

Ratio - the relative quantities of ingredients in a recipe, expressed in numbers, e.g. the ratio of fat to flour in short crust pastry is 1:2.

activities

1. Cook a small batch of short crust pastry using the following methods: a) by hand; b) food processor; c) mixer.
Compare the samples commenting on flavour, texture and ease of preparation.

2. Continental pastries include pâté sucré and filo. Suggest TWO dishes where each could be used.

3. Suggest a variety of ingredients which could be added to a standard shortbread recipe to create a new range of biscuits for children.

4. Prepare a cheese sauce using the roux method, the all in one method and a packet mix. Compare for best results and value.

5. Which pastry is used for: pork pies; chocolate éclairs; apple pie?

BRAMLEY'S COFFEE HOUSE

Bramley's is a licensed coffee house in Ormskirk, serving up to 80 people. The busiest time is lunchtime, especially on market days. Bramley's specialises in baguettes, salads, jacket potatoes, hot meals and cakes. All the food is made on the premises, except gateaux, croissants and ice cream. Because the kitchen and food storage area are quite small, the manager of Bramley's orders food on a twice-weekly basis. Although this means that he cannot take advantage of the lower prices of products bought in bulk, it does mean that the stock rotation is good and food is always fresh. Low stocks mean that Bramley's occasionally runs out of an ingredient and a member of staff has to go out to buy it. On the other hand, there is very little waste. Products in jars and tins are opened as necessary, frozen goods are thawed in small quantities and dried goods are rehydrated or used directly in recipes as they are needed.

These are just some of the products found in Bramley's stock cupboard.
- *Bouillon mix: vegetable, chicken or beef.*
- *Canned products: tuna, kidney beans, butter beans, sweetcorn, chestnuts, tomatoes, cherry pie filling, pineapple chunks.*
- *Jars and cartons: salad dressing, garlic purée, blueberry chutney, custard, mayonnaise, cumberland sauce, mango chutney.*
- *Dry goods: pre-cooked sponge layers, digestive biscuits, baking powder, salt, ground white pepper, cornflour, sultanas, chopped mixed nuts, desiccated coconut, dried parsley, lasagne verde, part-baked croissants.*

Consistency of quality is important in Bramley's. Recipes are written on cards and must always be followed accurately. Standard components, such as canned pie filling, are used. This ensures that whoever is cooking, the finished result will be consistent in terms of flavour, colour and appearance.

Cherry and almond pie is a favourite at Bramley's. Canned cherry pie filling is used for several reasons:
- *availability - fresh cherries have a limited season*
- *cost - fresh cherries are very expensive*
- *time - stoning fresh cherries takes a long time*
- *consistency - the quality of the pie is maintained.*

Activities

1. Which products, found in Bramley's stock cupboard, might be used in the following recipes: sticky toffee pudding and custard; tuna and bean salad; vegetable lasagne; beef and chestnut casserole; tiramisu; tomato and basil soup; fruit and nut flapjacks?
2. Choose THREE products from the stock cupboard. For each product, answer these questions.
   a) How is it useful?
   b) Which recipes could it be used for?
   c) Are there any alternatives to this product?
   d) Suggest some new recipes that might be designed using the products you have selected. Ensure that you consider people with special dietary needs in your designs.
3. What are the advantages and disadvantages of using standard components instead of fresh alternatives?
4. a) Which products would need to be bought on a daily basis?
   b) How could Bramley's avoid waste of fresh produce?
5. Describe how stock rotation should be organised. Explain the various storage areas which should be used and give examples of food products which could be placed in each area.

MEASUREMENT AT BRITISH BAKERIES

British Bakeries manufacture Hovis, Mothers Pride and Nimble bread in different manufacturing sites across Britain. The bread making process (see Figure 1) is virtually the same in each site ensuring consistency and quality in bread sold throughout the country. In order to achieve this consistency, it is vital that the measurement of ingredients and the proportions used are carefully controlled. Most bakeries now have a computerised process control system which controls the product from mixing to slicing. Table 1 shows the effects of changing the proportions of ingredients. Figure 2 shows the ideal proportions of ingredients for white and wholemeal bread.

Figure 1 The bread making process

MIXING (1)

flour
water   } measured by weight to nearest 0.2kg

yeast
vinegar*   } measured by volume

*Vinegar is used in the summer to inhibit mould.

ALL THESE MEASUREMENTS ARE CONTROLLED BY COMPUTER SOFTWARE LINKED INTO THE MIXER

↓

MIXING (2)

salt — by hand using a Stevens weighing scale - a highly accurate computerised scale.

improvers — The recipe and key criteria are programmed into the scales and actual weights are constantly monitored against targets.

↓

DIVIDING
Dough divided into portions to achieve finished bread weight (FBW) of either 800g or 400g. Portions typically weigh either 895g or 450g. Weighed using Stevens scales or automatic checkweighers.

↓

COOKING

↓

CHECKING HEIGHT
The height of each loaf is checked using a measuring stick. Each type of loaf has a target height. The acceptable height for a loaf is between 5mm less than and 7mm more than target height.

↓

SLICING
Loaves are sliced, bagged and the final weight is checked to comply with the Federation of Bakers' Code of Practice.

Table 1 Changing proportions

INGREDIENT	MORE	LESS
flour	tight dough which may not rise properly, resulting in reduced volume	softer dough, stickier to handle, increased volume
water	as less flour, and also reduces crumb colour	as more flour
salt	reduced volume, flavour affected	increased volume, flavour affected
yeast	too much gassing (only suitable for Danish or Nimble bread, where a more open texture is desired)	dough will not rise properly resulting in reduced volume
improvers	a complex composite of enzymes, ascorbic acid, E472(e)(an emulsifier and stabiliser), soya flour and filler - proportions of each ingredient are especially formulated for each new harvest	

Activities

1. Why is it important that the breadmaking process is the same in each of British Bakeries' manufacturing sites?
2. Name a stage in the breadmaking process where measurement by:
   a) weight; b) volume; c) height takes place.
3. Accurate measurement of ingredients is important to ensure that the correct proportions are used. What might happen if too much of the following were used:
   a) yeast; b) flour; c) salt?
4. At the end of the production run a bakery discovers that the average finished bread weight is low.
   a) How could the bakery remedy this problem?
   b) Which part of the process would be affected?
   c) What changes would need to be made?

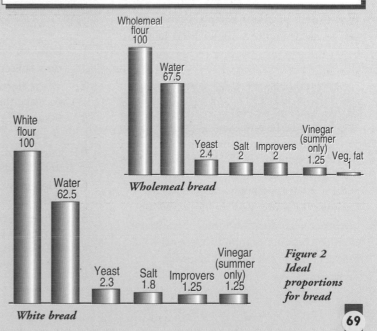

Figure 2 Ideal proportions for bread

Adapting recipes

Why change a recipe?

When using a recipe, it makes sense to follow the instructions precisely. The ingredients, proportions (see Unit 15) and methods suggested in the recipe will have been tried and tested. By following them accurately, you can be sure of a reliable result. Occasionally, however, there may be reasons to adapt a recipe, for example when:

- working on a limited budget
- making a recipe vegetarian or vegan
- avoiding certain foods because of allergy or intolerance
- an ingredient is unavailable
- catering for family likes/dislikes
- reducing the kilocalorie content
- improving the nutritional balance.

It is useful to know how ingredients can be substituted to alter recipes, and how proportions can be varied to alter the nutritional balance of a dish. When changes are made the colour, flavour, texture and nutritional value of the finished dish will be altered. Table 1 shows some products and alternatives that can be used. Figure 1 shows what happens when the proportions in a recipe are altered.

Developing food products

Food manufacturers are constantly adapting their products or adding to their range to make it more appealing to customers. We often see the words 'new' or 'improved' on labels but what does this mean? Reasons for altering a product or introducing a new product tend to fall into the following categories:

Table I Substituting ingredients

Food	Substitute	Notes
Cream	Low-fat cream Fromage frais Quark Crème fraîche	May take longer to whip. Will not whip, flavour change.
Butter	Low-fat spreads	Less flavour, some not suitable for frying. Softer texture, difficult to make pastry. Methods may need to be adapted, e.g. using a fork for pastry making.
White flour or pasta	Wholemeal varieties	More liquid is needed as bran absorbs water. Colour will be darker. Texture of finished dish will be coarser.
Cheese	Natural low fat varieties e.g. Edam and cottage cheese Vegetarian alternative Reduced fat cheeses	Flavour may be less intense. Texture may change.
Whole milk	Skimmed or semi-skimmed	Less creamy result especially in dishes such as custards. May have more watery appearance.
Sugar	Artificial sweeteners Natural alternatives (fruit, honey)	May have 'aftertaste'. Fruit will affect colour and texture.
Salt	Low sodium salt	Unlikely that there is any change.

- improving the nutritional value of the dish by reducing or removing fat, sugar and salt, increasing the proportion of NSP or adding vitamins and minerals

- launching a new range which may appeal to certain groups of people, for example, yogurts for babies and toddlers or low cost meals for one person.

activities

1. How could you adapt this recipe for someone on a limited budget?

2. What ingredients would you need to change to make this dish suitable for a vegetarian?

3. How could you make the meal appealing to a child?

4. Suggest two ways of reducing the fat content in this recipe.

5. Suggest two ways of adding colour to the dish.

6. What effect would the changes you have suggested in questions 1-5 have on the finished dish? Consider colour, flavour, texture, nutritional content.

These are the ingredients for a shepherd's pie:

- 500g minced lamb
- 1 onion, chopped
- 2 tbsp dripping
- 1 tbsp flour
- 250ml stock
- 1 glass red wine
- 1 tsp dried herbs
- 1kg potatoes, mashed with
- 50g butter and
- 5 tbsps whole milk
- seasoning

Figure 1 Changing proportions

REDUCING FAT
Result less moist.
Less flavour.
Product will stale more rapidly.
Paler colour.

INCREASING FAT
Result may be greasy.
Darker colour.
Flavour may be improved.

REDUCING SUGAR
Less flavour.
Paler colour.
Poorer keeping quality.
Capacity to rise may be reduced.

INCREASING SUGAR
Baked mixtures become very soft
during baking then hard on cooling.
Increased cooking time.
Sugar crystals may form in some foods.
Darker colour.

REDUCING SALT
Less flavour.
Can create differences in texture,
e.g. salt makes meat protein bind
together in sausages.
May reduce keeping qualities.
May reduce capacity to rise in bread.

ADDING WATER
May make baked products hard.
Creates bulk in products e.g.
margarines, poultry.
Encourages mould growth.

Market research takes place before recipe development in order to identify what people want to buy (see Unit 22).

With some food products (e.g. sausages, meat pies and fruit drinks), the ingredients are regulated by law. Manufacturers can only adapt their recipes within the guidelines laid down (see Figure 2).

Figure 2 Pork sausages

activities

A burger-type product usually consists of the following:
- meat, vegetables, fish, or protein alternative e.g. Quorn
- a binding ingredient
- flavourings
- possibly a coating.

1. Which of the above components influences:
a) texture
b) flavour
c) nutritional value?

2. Name a variety of meats which could be used in burgers.

3. What types of fish would be suitable for burgers?

4. Suggest some flavouring ingredients which could be used.

5. Suggest a suitable coating for a fish or vegetable burger.

6. Why might a non-vegetarian choose a Quorn burger?

7. Draw up a specification (see Unit 22) for an economy product. You may wish to consider the following points:

- type of main ingredient
- proportion of main ingredient to filler
- size of burger
- number of burgers per pack
- source of ingredients.

Pork sausages must contain at least 65% meat, however the meat may come from several different parts of the pig, including tail, head and tongue and up to half of it can be fat and connective tissue. More expensive sausages may contain a higher proportion of meat. Cheaper pork sausages contain rusk (baked and crushed flour dough) which bulks out the sausage by swelling up with fat and water. Other permitted additives are sugar, colourings, flavour enhancers, nitrates and nitrites (to preserve the sausage and give it its characteristic pink colour).

Heat transference

Heat is a form of energy. When heat is applied to food, it changes both the chemical properties and the physical appearance of the food (see Units 1-5). During the cooking process changes are likely to take place to the colour and texture of the food. For instance, meat will shrink during roasting because heat forces moisture to the surface where it evaporates. In moist methods of cooking, water soluble nutrients and flavour pass from the food into the cooking water (see Unit 6). As grilled food cooks some of the fat melts and drains into the grill pan. Fried food tends to absorb the fat in which it is cooked.

There are three basic methods of transferring heat: CONDUCTION, CONVECTION and RADIATION (see Figure 1). When cooking food two or sometimes three of these methods are used together.

Conduction

All matter is made up of vibrating molecules. When energy (heat) is applied to these molecules they vibrate faster, collide with their next door neighbour and pass the energy on in the form of a chain reaction. In a saucepan the heat is applied at the base and the energy is passed from the nearest molecule to the furthest point. Heat will always travel from the warmest to the coolest point. Conduction takes place both in the cooking container and in the food itself.

Certain materials are better conductors of heat than others. Metal conducts heat better than wood. Materials which do not conduct heat very well are called insulators. The saucepan should be very good conductor,

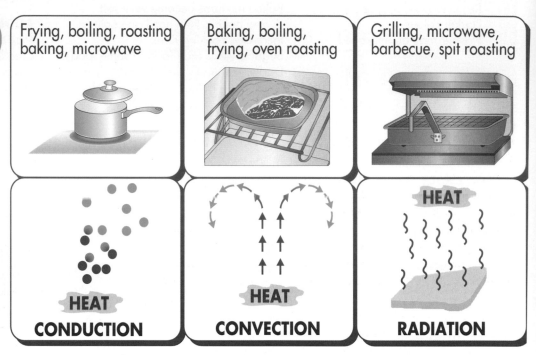

Frying, boiling, roasting baking, microwave

Baking, boiling, frying, oven roasting

Grilling, microwave, barbecue, spit roasting

HEAT CONDUCTION

HEAT CONVECTION

HEAT RADIATION

Figure 1 Heat transference

however its handle should be a very good insulator.

Convection

Convection takes place in gas and liquids. As molecules are heated they expand and so becomes less dense (lighter). These lighter molecules float upwards while denser (heavier and colder) molecules sink down to replace them. Convection takes place when using liquids, for example when food is boiled or stewed or where food is fried in oil. It also takes place in ovens as the air circulates around the food.

activities

A food manufacturer offers the choice of grilling, oven baking or barbecuing a product (see label on the right).

1. What do you think the product might be?

2. Which is the quickest method of cooking?

3. What kind of heat transference takes place with each method of cooking?

COOKING INSTRUCTIONS: For best results, cook from frozen and follow instructions carefully.
TO GRILL: Pre-heat grill to medium setting and cook for about 12 minutes, turning occasionally.
TO OVEN BAKE: Pre-heat oven to 220°C/425°F, Gas Mark 7. Place on a baking tray and cook for 15 minutes. For fan assisted ovens, reduce cooking time according to manufacturer's handbook.
TO BARBECUE: Wait until the coals turn white. Grill for 10-12 minutes turning occasionally.

Table 1 Energy efficiency in the kitchen

- Gas cookers are cheaper and use less energy than electric cookers.
- Microwaves use very little energy.
- Toasters usually use less energy than a grill.
- Only boil as much water as you need in a kettle.
- Use a pressure cooker.
- When the oven is on, try to cook several dishes at once.
- Choose the correct size pan for the rings on the hob.
- When boiling, don't use more water than is necessary; turn heat down once boiling; cover pan.
- Choose appliances with a low wattage.

Source: 'Save Energy, Save Money', Centre for Alternative Technology, 1993

Table 2 Power consumption

APPLIANCE	CONSUMPTION (watts)
electric cooker	12,000W
kettle	2,500-3,000W
grill	2,000W
toaster	1,000-3,000W
microwave	600-1,000W
food mixer	120-700W

Source: 'Save Energy, Save Money', Centre for Alternative Technology, 1993

Radiation

Radiation is the direct transfer of energy from the heat source to the food. There are many types of radiation waves, e.g. X-rays and radio waves. In cooking, 3 types of wave are used: visible red, infra-red and microwave. In the case of the first two the radiated waves fall on the surface of the food and heat the surface. The centre of the food is heated by conduction. Certain substances absorb radiation better than others, for example, glass absorbs very little and the wave will pass straight through.

Visible red radiation (e.g. a grill or barbecue) has a short wave length.

Infra-red radiation (e.g. an infra-red hob, plate or lamp) has a slightly longer wave length. These radiation waves penetrate about 1 cm below the surface so this method is quicker than conventional grilling.

Microwave radiation uses much longer wave lengths and can penetrate food up to a depth of about 4 cms. This makes it a very fast method of cooking. In a microwave oven the magnetron converts electrical energy into microwave energy.

Food cooked solely by radiant heat is often thin and cooks rapidly due to the intense nature of the heat, e.g. toast. Thicker foods, e.g. steak, are initially sealed (browned) by grilling the outside using intese radiant heat. The cooking process is completed by continuing with the radiant heat on the outside yet cooking the centre of the food by using conduction, which is a less intensive form of heat.

Microwaves cannot pass through metal so the waves travel in straight lines until they reach the wall of the oven where they are reflected back into the oven space. Metal cooking containers should not be used as they will affect the electromagnetic waves and may damage the oven.

Cooking methods

Food can be cooked by dry heat, moist heat or a combination of both (see Table 3 on p. 74). The method we choose to cook foods depends on:

- ingredients available
- facilities and time available
- flavour, colour, texture and volume required
- the skill of the cook
- dietary requirements.

We should also consider the benefits and costs of different methods. This could include the financial cost, convenience, performance, sensory appeal, nutritional benefits and environmental cost (see Tables 1 and 2). For example, the costs of barbecuing may be that it takes longer to cook food than a grill, and it may make a lot of mess. The benefits could be the enjoyment gained from cooking and eating in the open air and the taste of the chargrilled food.

Boiling

Food is immersed in boiling water (100°C) and then, for most dishes, the temperature is reduced to simmering point (85-99°C). Continuous boiling can cause foods to break up, e.g. potatoes. Vegetables, herbs and spices can be added to the boiling water to improve the flavour. The cooking liquid is not served with the food, but may be used in a sauce.

Water soluble vitamins can be destroyed by the intense heat and may be lost in the cooking water, if it is not used for a sauce.

Poaching

Food is cooked in water brought to the boil and then lowered to simmering level. Poached foods generally require short cooking times. The pan may be open or closed and the food may be in direct contact with the water. Special poaching pans for eggs may be used, where the eggs are protected from the water in small

activities

1. Which cooking methods are most useful for a diet that aims to be low in fat?

2. What are the benefits and costs of:
   a) microwave cookery;
   b) moist methods of cooking;
   c) stir frying;
   d) casseroling?

3. In order to reduce both environmental and financial costs, it makes sense to try to save energy in your cooking methods. Using the information in Tables 1 and 2, design a 'Save Energy' poster for a kitchen wall.

Table 3 Cooking methods

METHODS	USES	HEAT TRANSFERENCE
MOIST METHODS		
BOILING	vegetables, starchy foods (e.g. pasta or rice), tough cuts of meat, jam making, reducing sauces and syrups	conduction through base of saucepan → convection currents in liquid transfer heat to food → conduction through food
POACHING	foods which fall apart easily (e.g. fish, eggs)	conduction through pan → convection in steam → conduction through food
STEAMING	fish fillets, vegetables, suet or sponge puddings	conduction through pan → convection in steam → conduction through food
PRESSURE COOKING	foods which take a long time (e.g. suet puddings, pulses and stewing beef).	conduction through pan → convection in steam → conduction through food
STEWING/ CASSEROLING	tougher cuts of meat, curry, goulash, chilli, ratatouille, fruit	conduction through pan → convection in steam → conduction through food
COMBINATION METHODS		
POT ROASTING	tougher cuts of beef, lamb, small pork joints, poultry	conduction through pan → convection in steam → conduction through food
BRAISING	meat, especially large or tough joints, vegetables because it enhances their flavour, rice	conduction through pan → convection inside the pot → conduction through food
DRY METHODS		
BAKING	flour based foods (e.g. bread, cakes and pastries), meat (covered with pastry or breadcrumbs), fish, fruit and vegetables	conduction through pan and oven shelf → convection from circulated heat in oven
ROASTING	meat, fish and some vegetables	conduction through pan and oven shelf → convection from circulated heat in oven
GRILLING	meat (tender, small and regular shaped cuts are best), poultry, fish, shellfish, vegetables, food products (e.g. fish cakes, burgers), finishing dishes with a golden crispy topping	Radiated heat penetrates 1mm into the food → conducted heat travels from the surface to the centre of the food, also from the hot grill bars to the food
SHALLOW FRYING	lean, tender cuts of meat (e.g. sirloin, fillet and rump), burgers, offal, vegetables, fish, shellfish and eggs	conduction from source → cooking surface and through fat
DEEP FRYING	fish, shellfish, meat, poultry, Scotch eggs, doughnuts, vegetables (e.g. potatoes, onion rings), vegetables and fruit coated in batter	conduction from source → cooking surface and through fat
BARBECUING	small even sized cuts of meat (e.g. chops, steaks), sausages, burgers, fish, vegetables such as peppers and corn on the cob, kebabs	Radiated heat penetrates 1mm into the food → conducted heat travels from the surface to the centre of the food, also from the hot grill bars to the food
MICROWAVE	foods which benefit from rapid cooking (e.g. fruit and vegetables), foods which benefit from even cooking (e.g. custard), foods which do not require browning (e.g. chocolate and ginger cakes), food that does not need a crisp surface texture (e.g. soups and pasta dishes)	radiated heat penetrates the surface of the food → conduction through food

dishes. This is not considered to be true poaching, but should be called moulded eggs or oeufs moules.

Steaming

Food is cooked in steam rising from boiling water. Food may be in direct contact with steam, or protected by a container which is heated by the steam but is not in the water. A tightly fitting lid is necessary with a steamer and water must be topped up regularly.

Pressure cooking

Water temperatures range from 100-120°C. The amount of water used is usually half that used in boiling. By increasing the pressure within the closed pan, higher temperatures can be achieved. This reduces the time needed to cook the food by a quarter to a third, e.g. potatoes cook in about 5 minutes, and a beef casserole in about 20 minutes. Increased heat is likely to destroy vitamin C, but the reduced water and cooking time conserves the vitamin, making little difference overall to the nutritional balance.

Stewing/ casseroling

Food is cooked in a small amount of liquid at simmering point. Liquid is part of the dish to be served and contributes to the overall flavour. The method requires long slow cooking. A stew is prepared and completed on top of the stove. A casserole is prepared on the hob and completed in the oven.

Pot roasting

Meat is browned initially, then cooked in a covered container which retains the steam from the meat, giving a moist finish to the meat.

Braising

Food is cooked in a container which is closed for all or most of the time. There are

A commercial steamer unit. The water level can be checked/adjusted by means of a spout at the side. The base can accommodate up to 3 steamer pans or poacher cup/pudding basin frames allowing several dishes to be cooked at once.

three separate stages in braising.
- A selection of root vegetables (e.g. leeks, carrots and onions) is prepared and placed in the braising dish. This is called a **mirepoix**.

- The joint is browned either in a hot oven or frying pan, then laid on top of the mirepoix, and a liquid, either water or a good stock poured over until the meat is $2/3$ immersed.

activities

1. Suggest appropriate cooking methods for the following dishes, giving reasons for your choice.
a) frozen pizza; b) homemade lasagne; c) fish cakes; d) chips; e) broccoli.

2. Identify a method of cooking which matches each of these statements.
a) This method is very fast but food could be brown on the outside before it is cooked inside.
b) This method involves the use of water but the food does not touch it.
c) This method can result in the loss of water soluble vitamins so cooking time needs to be minimal.
d) This method involves considerable browning and flavour development through the Maillard Reaction (see Unit 1).

Braised meat

- The dish is covered with a lid, brought to the boil on the stove and then transferred to the oven to complete the cooking at simmering point.

Vitamin loss is great with vegetables cooked using this method.

to prevent drying out. The high temperatures increase shrinkage and loss of juices in meat.

Water and fat soluble vitamins in meat are lost as they leach out of the joint.

Baking

When food is baked, it is mainly cooked with a dry heat which can be easily and accurately controlled, inside an oven. Most baked foods require a container to help them retain the required finished shape. The food is never in direct contact with a sauce or cooking liquid. Occasionally, moisture may be created by placing a pan of water in the oven to aid the crust on bread, or to prevent a crème caramel from curdling during baking.

Cooking times and temperatures vary widely according to the type of dish being baked and its size. e.g. meringues are baked at a very low temperature and bread is baked at a very high temperature.

Roasting

Food is cooked by dry heat in a hot oven or on a spit. Small amounts of fat are used

Grilling

A fast method of cookery using intense heat up to 1000°C from an electrical element, gas flame or fire fuelled with charcoal or wood. The heat source can be above and/or below the food. It is a simple method using few additional flavourings. Little or no additional fat is used. Some fat contained within food drips away.

Shallow frying

Food is cooked in a small amount of fat or oil. Either high or low temperatures can be used depending on the required outcome. Frying pans usually have shallow sides with a heavy base. Solid surfaces called griddles can also be used. Food tends to absorb fat especially if the food breaks up or the temperature is too low. Coatings of flour or breadcrumbs can reduce this. Small pieces of food can be shallow fried, at very high temperatures in a wok. This is called stir frying. The advantages of this method of cooking are that food is cooked extremely rapidly, which preserves the colour, flavour, texture and vitamin content of the food, and that relatively little fat is needed for stir frying, which keeps the energy value low. See Unit 4 for more information on shallow frying.

activities

1. What kind of heat transference takes place with wok cooking?
2. Why should you have prepared all the ingredients before you start cooking in a wok?
3. You are preparing the following components for a stir fry recipe:
   • chicken breast
   • mange tout
   • carrots.
   Explain how you would prepare each ingredient, giving reasons.

WOK TIPS
- Use a single-handled wok - it is easier to shake pan with one hand while stirring with the other.
- Chinese cooks use thin, carbon steel woks. They conduct heat well and are very durable.
- Have all the ingredients ready prepared before you start cooking. Cut meat, fish and vegetables into small pieces, varying the size and shape according to the type of food.
- When cooking in a wok, keep heat constantly high. Heat the wok first before adding oil. Heat for another minute then add whichever flavourings you are using (e.g. onion, garlic, ginger or spices). Cook for a few seconds. Add the rest of the ingredients and cook for a few minutes only until just done. You can add ingredients in batches if some take longer than others to cook. Add soy or other sauce.
- Wash the wok in hot water. Do not use soap. Dry well to avoid rusting.

Source: adapted from the Observer, 8 October 1995

Barbecued meat and vegetables

taken as the dripping fat can cause flaring and the heat source is obviously not as easily controlled as on a conventional grill. Although some fat is required to keep the food moist and to prevent sticking to the barbecue rack, in general low fat meats should be used with visible fat trimmed away and low fat marinades and sauces should be used.

produces heat. Heat is retained within the food at the end of the cooking period and adjustments need to be made for this as the food continues to cook outside the microwave oven. It is important to follow carefully the cooking instructions given in a microwave cookery book or on a food package. Insufficient cooking can result in harmful bacteria still being present, which may cause food poisoning (see Unit 9). Overcooking can lead to tough and dry food.

Food cooked in a microwave resembles steamed food in appearance and texture. Some foods are more successfully cooked in the microwave than others. Fish and vegetables respond well but pastry dishes tend to be soggy and pale in colour. Various developments in microwave technology have made it possible to combine the functions of a microwave with a conventional oven to overcome these problems (see Unit 20). Water soluble vitamins are retained due to the small amount of liquid used and the rapid cooking time.

Deep frying

Food is immersed in a container of fat or oil at a temperature of between 165°C and 190°C. The food is usually coated with flour, breadcrumbs or batter (except chips). The food cooks quickly, goes brown and becomes crispy. The food absorbs some oil which increases its energy value. Fat soluble vitamins may be lost but water soluble vitamins are retained as there is no water in the process. See Unit 4 for more information on deep frying.

Microwave cookery

Microwaves penetrate into the food where they cause water molecules within the food to vibrate, producing friction which in turn

Barbecuing

This method is the same as grilling but is carried out in the open air over an open flame. The use of charcoal gives a different flavour to food. The food can be basted with a marinade or sauce to prevent drying. It should be turned frequently. Care must be

Conduction - a method of heat transference where energy passes from one molecule to another.
Convection - a method of heat transference which takes place in liquids and gases, where warm molecules rise, allowing cool molecules to fall closer to the source of heat and be heated.
Radiation - a method of heat transference where energy is passed from one place to another by electromagnetic waves.

activities

the microwave symbol   the power output

800W

D

the heating category for small packs

To help people to determine accurate microwave cooking times, the Ministry of Agriculture, Fisheries and Food (MAFF), in partnership with manufacturers, retailers and consumer groups, has developed a voluntary labelling scheme for microwave ovens and food packs. The symbol on the left appears on microwaves manufactured since 1992. The symbol includes three pieces of information:
- the microwave symbol, to show that the oven has been labelled under the new scheme
- the power output of the oven (in watts)
- the heating category (a letter A-E).

Most packaged foods suitable for microwaving will give heating instructions according to the power of the oven or, for small food packs, the heating category.

1. Why is it important to cook food thoroughly in a microwave?
2. Why do consumers need to know the power output and heating category of their microwave oven?
3. The instructions on a fish pie suggest that it should be reheated for 6 minutes in a 750W microwave oven. What might happen if the pie is cooked for:
   a) 6 minutes in a 650W microwave oven
   b) 6 minutes in a 800W microwave oven
   c) 4 minutes in a 750W microwave oven?

Mixing, cutting, forming and shaping

Food preparation

When food is prepared it often undergoes one or more of three **manipulative processes:**

- mixing (e.g. beating an egg white)
- cutting (e.g. grating cheese)
- forming and shaping (e.g. rolling pastry).

All tools and equipment used in the preparation of food (as opposed to the actual cooking of food) will fulfil one or more of these functions. Figure 1 shows a range of the tools and equipment available. When preparing food, it is important that the correct tool is selected in order to:

- complete the task in a safe, hygienic and efficient way
- achieve a consistency of finish
- achieve a quality outcome.

Mixing

There are many ways of combining foods, e.g. stirring, whisking, kneading and rubbing in. In many cases, the choice of equipment

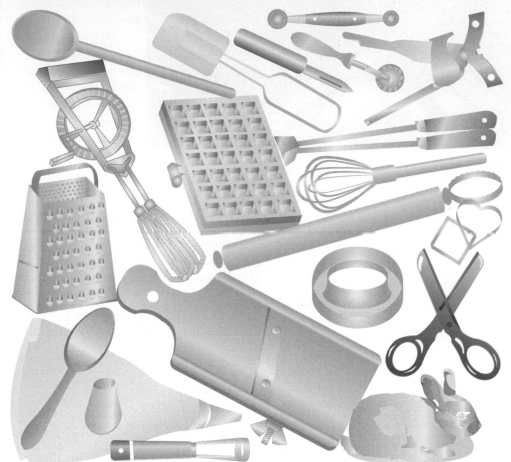

Figure 1 Tools and equipment

activities

The dishes on the right involve a combination of manipulative processes. Draw a similar chart to Table 1 and fill in the details for each dish.

1. State which recipes involve mixing, cutting or forming and shaping. Fill in each task in the appropriate column.
2. Give examples of equipment which could be used for each task . Figure 1 might give you some ideas. If there are several alternatives, choose the one that you think is most appropriate. You should be able to explain why you think the piece of equipment you have chosen will produce the best outcome.

- **butterfly cakes**
- **meringues**
- **pizza**
- **cheesecake**
- **cream of tomato soup**
- **trifle**
- **chicken vol-au-vents**
- **scones**
- **jam tarts**

Table 1 Manipulative processes and tools

DISH	MIXING PROCESS	CUTTING PROCESS	FORMING/ SHAPING PROCESS
Butterfly cakes	Creaming mixture: electric mixer	Cutting out top of cake: paring knife	1. Baking cakes: bun tin 2. Filling with butter cream: piping bag & nozzle
Meringues			

Figure 2 *Food preparation machines - a Kenwood Chef, made for the domestic market and a heavy duty catering model, the Crypto Peerless Euromixer.*

- bowl size - 4 litres
- capacity - 2.7kg cake mix
- table top model
- variable speed control
- hinged action to allow bowl removal

- bowl size - 30 litres
- capacity - 11.5kg cake mix
- floor standing model
- variable speed control
- emergency cut-off switch

Figure 3 *Professional knives including specialist knives (e.g. for boning, carving and cutting frozen foods) and cleavers. These knives are expensive due to the high degree of precision in manufacture. Handles may be colour coded (see Unit 19). A domestic range of knives is usually smaller and less expensive.*

used is a matter of personal preference. In some cases, however, choosing the right tool for the job is important. For example, when incorporating flour into a whisked sponge mixture a metal spoon will produce a more satisfactory outcome than a wooden spoon. This is because it has a thinner edge and cuts through the mixture cleanly, destroying few air bubbles. The mixture will retain air and when it is baked it will have a light texture. A wooden spoon, on the other hand, is a better choice for mixtures that need creaming, e.g. butter and sugar in a Victoria sandwich.

Mixing tools include spoons, spatulas, whisks (balloon, rotary, spiral and electric hand whisks), food mixers (see Figure 2), blenders and food processors.

Cutting

Cutting tools and equipment include knives (see Figure 3), graters, zesters, cheese slicers, mandolins, vegetable peelers, shaped cutters (for pastry, biscuits or aspic), egg slicers, scissors, electrical food slicing machines, potato chippers and food processors. Different cutting tools and equipment will give varying results. For example, for a consistent finish, a knife would not be the best choice for slicing cheese. The results could be irregular with slices varying in thickness, shape and length. A cheese slicer will produce an outcome which is more consistent, and in commercial terms more cost effective. When a very large quantity of sliced cheese is required an electric food slicer might be an appropriate piece of equipment to use. When using tools and equipment with cutting blades, safety guidelines must be followed (see Unit 19).

- Only trained personnel over 18 to use this type of machine (listed under Dangerous Machines Order 1964)
- Stainless steel anodised finish for easy clean
- Emergency stop button
- Hopper can only be removed when slicer is in safe position
- Variable thickness possible
- Rear blade guard

Industrial food slicers

activities

1. Study this illustration of the industrial slicers and draw up a list of rules which you would display beside one of these machines. Include in your list safe usage, cleaning and maintenance .
2. Why do you think that items of industrial equipment are composed largely of stainless steel?
3. Suggest reasons why industrial machines are often operated by push buttons.
4. Explain the need for an emergency cut-off button.
5. Why do you think that there is more emphasis on aesthetic appeal in the design of domestic machines compared to their industrial equivalent?

Forming and shaping

Equipment used to form and shape food includes piping bag and nozzles (see Figure 4), rolling pin, mould (jelly, dariol, ramekin), cake tin (loaf, bun, Victoria sandwich, savarin ring, flan ring), sausage maker, mincer, pasta maker, burger press. Some pieces of equipment will give a more decorative finish than others. For example, the creamed potato on top of a shepherd's pie can be finished with either a fork or a piping bag and nozzle. The fork will roughen the surface, introducing lines and possibly a lattice pattern. A piping bag with a nozzle will produce more sophisticated patterns, swirls and effects with the same mixture. In terms of quality of outcome the piping bag gives a more professional finish.

Labour saving equipment

Machines are able to perform repetitive tasks efficiently, accurately, safely and with a

Figure 4 Piping bags can be used with different nozzles to give a range of effects. Food materials that can be piped include: icing, whipped cream, butter cream, choux pastry, potato, vegetable purées.

activities

Food processors are multi-functional food preparation machines that can be useful in a domestic or an industrial kitchen. The domestic model on the left includes a food processing bowl and a blender. The industrial model below can produce up to 150kg of sliced, diced, grated, shredded or chipped fruit, vegetables or cheese per hour.

1. Find out what functions a domestic food processor performs.
2. What are the advantages and disadvantages of using a food processor?
3. Design a menu for a special occasion meal, using several different functions of a food processor.

consistency of outcome. Equipment such as food processors can certainly save time and effort if a large quantity of food needs to be prepared or if a specific appearance is needed. However, there is little point setting up a food preparation machine if all you require is one roughly chopped carrot - a basic vegetable knife would suffice.

Labour saving equipment is very important in an industrial setting where large quantities of food need to be produced within a specified time. Food preparation machines help catering outlets to produce food with the required uniformity of appearance, taste and texture.

Catering equipment

Catering equipment can be divided into 3 categories:
- Large equipment (e.g. ranges, sinks, tables, boiling pans, fish fryers - see Unit 20).
- Mechanical equipment (e.g. mixers, mincers, peelers, dishwashers).
- Utensils and small equipment (e.g. pots, pans, bowls, knives and whisks etc.)

In the catering industry some of the aesthetic design of domestic equipment has to be sacrificed to meet standards of hygiene and safety. Machines are often made of stainless steel and have large illuminated controls, as well as an emergency cut-off switch. There are machines not usually found in the home, e.g. a cream making machine that makes 80 litres of cream per hour; a twelve slice toaster capable of producing 500 slices of toast an hour; or a potato peeling machine which peels 25 kilos (56 lbs) of potatoes in 3 minutes.

Most catering equipment is operated by an electrical motor which is larger and more powerful than its domestic equivalent. It is also more likely to have sharper blades, operate faster or be capable of achieving higher temperatures than equipment found in

the kitchen at home. It is therefore vital that such items should only be operated by people who have received the necessary training or who are working with somebody who is properly trained.

These machines are useful provided that they satisfy a commercial need. A large piece of equipment is expensive and must provide value for money. Table 2 shows some of the factors to be considered when a business is deciding whether to purchase equipment.

Table 2 What to consider when buying equipment	
Cost	Can the business afford it? Is there an equivalent model available at a cheaper price?
Legal requirements:	
Safety	Can the machines be legally operated, i.e. with trained staff of an appropriate age?
Hygiene	Does the machine conform to current hygiene regulations?
Capacity	Will it produce the desired quantity of food to meet deadlines?
Speed of operation	Will it produce the desired outcome in the time available?
Ease of use	Can staff operate the equipment safely and efficiently?
Value for money	Does having such a machine actually save time, effort, money or staffing?
Outcome	Does the machine produce what you and your customers want?

Table 3 Catering equipment

- automatic potato peeler
- juice extractor
- blender
- hand-held blender
- mincer
- food processor
- sandwich toaster
- slicer
- espresso machine
- mixer
- pasta machine
- sausage making machine

activities

1. Name a variety of food outlets which would find an automatic potato peeler useful.

2. Select four items from Table 3 which you think would be particularly useful to a public house which is starting to offer a lunchtime menu to its customers. Explain your choice.

3. A small food outlet has to justify its expenditure on three items of equipment to its accountants.

Make a good case for purchasing industrial quality machines rather than the cheaper domestic equivalents.

4. A small butcher's shop has decided to manufacture its own sausages. The process involves, mincing, chopping, mixing and shaping. What machines would need to be bought to manufacture the sausages?

Safety in industrial kitchens

It is the dual responsibility of employers and employees to ensure that premises and equipment are safe and well maintained to prevent accidents. All employees need to be given appropriate training to enable them to prevent accidents, to report hazards and to comply with instructions to reduce risks. This unit looks at the safe, hygienic and efficient use of tools and equipment. Unit 30 deals with the law in relation to safety in the workplace.

Kitchen equipment

Equipment selected for industrial use must conform to European Union safety directives. Equipment must carry the CE mark which indicates that the required safety standards have been met.

All equipment should be safe, properly maintained and used correctly for the purpose for which it is intended. Some materials will need regular disinfection to maintain the highest hygienic standards. Particular care should be paid to any surface which will come into direct contact with foodstuffs. It is for this reason that food grade stainless steel (containing 18% chromium and 8% nickel) is often the preferred material in industrial kitchens as it is durable and easy to clean. Equipment used in any kitchen, domestic or industrial, should be designed so that it is hygienic and safe. The design of the working area is another important factor (see Unit 30). Accidents occur when there is overcrowding or when the location of equipment has not been carefully considered.

Table 1 Design of kitchen equipment

Equipment should:
- protect food from contamination by foreign matter such as nuts, bolts and washers
- have few joints, holes and crevices where dirt and bacteria can be trapped
- have surfaces which are smooth and impervious
- be hard wearing and therefore long lasting
- be easy to move and disassemble for thorough cleaning and disinfecting
- be made of a material which will not rust e.g. stainless steel
- be non-toxic and non-absorbent
- be resistant to heat
- be resistant to cracking, chipping and pitting.

Table 2 Knives and blades

KNIVES
Knives are one of the most important tools in the kitchen and it is vital that they are correctly used to avoid both accidents and cross-contamination.
- Use the correct knife for the job.
- Keep knives sharp.
- Cut on a board not on a table or in the hand.
- Use different knives for raw and cooked food, or wash knife thoroughly between uses. Colour coded knives help avoid cross-contamination.
- Clean knives using a sanitiser or bacterial wipe and keep handles grease-free at all times.
- Do not leave knives in a sink of water as someone could put their hands into the water and cut themselves.
- Clean knives immediately after use keeping the blade facing away from your hands and body.
- Pass a knife by offering the handle to the other person.
- Store knives correctly, either in a knife block or knife roll.
- Do not attempt to cut frozen food: the cut is likely to be ragged; extra pressure will need to be applied and should the hand slip an injury will be much worse.
- When transporting a knife carry with the blade pointing down and the blunt edge facing in the direction you are walking.
- Keep knives in good order. If they are damaged in any way they should not be used as the risk of an accident is increased.
- Use appropriate metal mittens when jointing meat.

BLADES
Some machinery has a guard to protect the operator from injury from a moving blade.
- Ensure that the guard is in place before use and not tampered with during use.
- Turn the machine off at the mains before removing the guard for cleaning purposes.
- Never leave a machine unattended with the guard removed.

Table 3 Chopping boards

Chopping boards must be:

- non-absorbent - preferably made from polyurethane or other materials which can be sterilised (soft wood boards may absorb water containing bacteria; hard wood and plastic boards can be thoroughly cleaned)
- stain resistant and capable of withstanding regular cleaning using chemicals
- non-toxic and low odour
- capable of withstanding heavy usage without going out of shape.

Table 5 Colour coding in the catering industry

In order to prevent cross-contamination, many pieces of catering equipment are now available in different colours, to be used for different tasks. Chopping boards are available in plain white polypropylene with a coloured edge or in a solid colour. Flexible colour-coded cutting mats are also available. Knives can be purchased with coloured handles.

Table 6 Avoiding injury from burns and scalds

- Ensure that clothing offers sufficient protection and is correctly worn.
- Carry hot substances using two hands and appropriate pads and cloths.
- Remove metal utensils from boiling pans - they will conduct the heat and could burn the hands.
- Do not allow pan handles to protrude over the edge of the cooker - they could be knocked over.
- When using moist methods of cooking lift lids carefully to avoid steam in the face.
- Do not overfill pans of liquid as they may boil over when heated.
- To avoid burns from spitting fat, wet food should never be put into a deep fat fryer.
- Fire extinguishers and blankets should be properly maintained and serviced.

Table 4 Electrical and mechanical equipment

- Equipment listed under the Dangerous Machines Order 1964 should be especially well maintained. Users must be of a suitable age and have appropriate training. Machines in this category are: mincing machines; slicing and shredding machines; chipping and chopping machines; rotary bowl choppers; mixing machines.
- Ensure a machine is in good working order before use.
- Only one person should operate a machine at any one time.
- Always use the correct attachments for the piece of equipment - NEVER use hands to force food through mincers and processors.
- NEVER place hands into a bowl with a rotating blade, paddle, whisk or hook.
- Some pieces of large equipment may require safety notices to be displayed on the machine or close by.
- Some equipment may not be cleaned by employees under 18 years old.
- Keep operating and cleaning instructions near to the equipment.
- All large equipment, whether free-standing or table top, should be stable and secured where appropriate.
- Electrical equipment should be fitted with the correct plug and fuse.
- Purchase equipment from reliable manufacturers.
- Fryers should have efficient thermostats and must never be overfilled.
- Microwaves should be checked regularly to ensure that there is no radiation leakage from the seals around the door.
- Monitor regularly all low temperature equipment. Readings taken should be recorded and appropriate action taken should any piece of equipment rise above prescribed levels. Foods stored in poorly maintained equipment could be injurious to health.
- Ensure that seals around fridges and freezers are sound. Should a seal become perished or damaged the low temperature will not be maintained. Seals should be regularly cleaned and disinfected.
- Walk-in fridges and freezers should have a handle which operates from the inside.
- From the 1 January 1996 gas-fuelled equipment must be fitted with a fuel cut-out mechanism. This directive should avoid the risk of gas explosion should the pilot light not ignite properly.

activities

1. Choose any item of equipment pictured in Unit 18. Evaluate its design in relation to the criteria in Table 1.

2. Look at Table 2.
   a) Why should a metal mitten be worn on a butcher's non-cutting hand?
   b) Why is it a good safety practice to keep knives well sharpened?
   c) What should you remember when cleaning knives?

3. a) What is the purpose of colour coded catering equipment?
   b) Design a poster, without words, to help kitchen staff, whose first language may not be English, remember which colours to use for specific tasks.

4. The preparation of pan-fried lamb cutlets with a redcurrant sauce requires the following processes:
   - separating cutlets from the saddle of lamb
   - frying cutlets for a short time at high temperatures
   - adding alcohol to the hot pan to flavour the sauce
   - arranging the cutlets on a plate and pouring sauce over them.
   a) What hazards could occur at each stage?
   b) How could the task be completed in a safe, hygienic and efficient way?

5. An Indian restaurant has agreed to accept students on work experience. They want to run a safety training programme for the students. Outline the possible content of such a course, using the following headings:
   - food preparation
   - cooking - equipment used in Indian cookery
     - cooking methods and associated risks
   - transporting food from kitchen to dining area
     - serving customers.

case study — THE HOTWICH

Green Meadow Foods has launched Britain's first hot sandwich which can be warmed in a microwave. The product was designed to fill the gap in the winter sandwich market, when sales fall by 20% compared to the summer. The Hotwich is a hot sandwich snack, using ciabatta bread, and is initially available in two varieties: Milano (smoked ham and cheddar cheese) and Sorrento (sun dried tomato pâté, onions and mozzarella cheese).

The problem with heating bread and other baked products in a microwave is that they often become soft and lose texture. Green Meadow Foods have designed a special packaging sleeve, with a metallic liner, which helps the bread to keep its crusty texture when reheated by microwave. The Hotwich can also be reheated in a conventional oven.

Source: adapted from the Sunday Times, 14 May 1995 and Green Meadow Foods product information

INSTRUCTIONS

Keep Chilled. Store at 0-4°C

MICROWAVE HEATING (Microwave heating based on 700 Watt or Category B Ovens).
Remove sandwich from plastic film, retain cardboard sleeve. Replace sandwich in sleeve and heat on high power (100%) for 2½ minutes. Leave to stand for 1-2 minutes in sleeve before eating.
CAUTION: CONTAINER AND SANDWICH WILL BE EXTREMELY HOT.

CONVENTIONAL OVEN HEATING
Pre-heat oven to 200°C, 400°F, Gas Mark 6. Remove Hotwich from outer sleeve, do not remove from bag. Place Hotwich in bag on a baking tray, place in top part of oven and heat for 16-18 minutes. Carefully remove from bag. Allow to rest for 1 minute before eating.
CAUTION: SANDWICH WILL BE EXTREMELY HOT.

Activities

1. a) What happens to sales of sandwiches during the winter months? Why?
   b) Why might people buy a Hotwich rather than a sandwich during the winter?
2. a) What problem did Green Meadow Foods encounter when trying to design a sandwich product that could be heated in a microwave?
   b) What solution did the company find to this problem?
3. A petrol station sells a range of hot and cold snacks and drinks. Customers choose and heat their own snacks. The manager wants to add the Hotwich to the snack range.
   a) What TWO pieces of equipment must the petrol station have in order to sell this product?
   b) Design a list of simple instructions to be displayed next to the Hotwich stand so that customers know how to heat the product.

case study — DANGEROUS MACHINES

CASUAL WORKER TRAPS ARM IN BREAD MACHINE

A casual worker in a bakery suffered 3 broken fingers and deep cuts in his hand when his arm became trapped in a bread roll making machine. He had not been trained how to use the machine safely.

The safety guard had been removed from the machine to allow staff to lubricate the rollers manually. The automatic lubricator had broken down.

The worker was told to use his fingers to lubricate the rollers. He did so, while the machine was still running.

The firm had been asked several times by the Health and Safety Executive to set up a Health and Safety policy, but had failed to do so. They were fined £10,000 for failing to train the worker and £2,000 for operating a machine without a safety guard.

Source: adapted from Health and Safety Executive newsletter, August 1994

DANGEROUS MACHINE

1. Only trained operators are allowed to use this machine.
2. Operators under training may only use this machine under skilled supervision.
3. Only persons over the age of 18 are allowed to operate or clean this machine.
4. Check that the guards are in place before operating.
5. Before commencing to clean or dismantle this machine, the operator must check that power has been switched off or the power plug removed.
6. Switch off when not in use.

Dangerous machine safety sign

Activities

1. List THREE reasons why this accident occurred.
2. What precautions do you think the company should take to prevent accidents of this type in the future?
3. Design a safety poster to be displayed near the bread roll making machine.

MAKING PASTA

Traditionally, pasta is made with durum wheat semolina. Durum wheat has a particularly hard grain, with a high gluten content. When this semolina is mixed with water, it forms a dough which is ideal for making pasta. However, the dough is almost impossible to roll out by hand, and machines must be used to do this job. Pasta can also be made with soft flour but eggs must be added to produce a dough with extra strength and elasticity that can be kneaded and rolled by hand.

Figure 1 Making pasta by hand

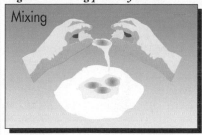

Mixing
Kneading
Rolling
Cutting

The eggs are mixed into the flour. The dough is kneaded for a long time, until it has a silky texture. The dough is then rolled out very thinly (this also takes some time). The pasta is then cut into shapes.

Figure 2 Making pasta in a factory

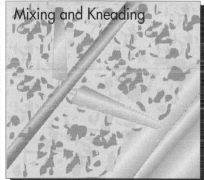

Mixing and Kneading
Rolling

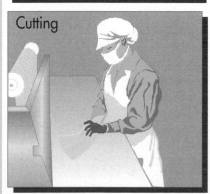

Cutting

Semolina and water, and sometimes eggs, are mixed and the dough is kneaded by stainless steel paddles. The dough then passes between metal rollers, until it is the right thickness. The pasta is then cut into shape. Alternatively, the dough is forced through perforated plates to form different shapes. The pasta is then vacuum packed or dried.

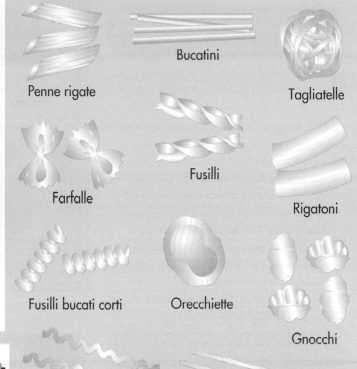

Penne rigate
Bucatini
Tagliatelle
Farfalle
Fusilli
Rigatoni
Fusilli bucati corti
Orecchiette
Gnocchi
Fusilli bucati lunghi
Spaghetti

Figure 3 There are over 150 different pasta shapes available

Activities

1. What are the properties of durum wheat?

2. Draw a flow chart of a factory pasta making process.

3. Compare the process of making pasta by hand and in a factory. What equipment is used at each of the following stages: mixing; kneading; rolling; cutting/shaping?

4. a) Why do you think there are so many different shapes of pasta available?
   b) Choose THREE shapes and suggest a sauce that would go well with each.

Large equipment

The industrial kitchen

Unit 18 looked at some of the smaller types of equipment used in food preparation. This unit focuses on the larger equipment used for cooking, refrigeration, dishwashing and waste disposal in an industrial kitchen.

In a catering kitchen the storage, preparation, cooking and serving of food is a technological system which requires careful control to maximise efficiency and maintain profits. The equipment chosen must be appropriate for the business. For example, a large, busy restaurant must assess the number of customers it hopes to serve in a day and choose equipment which can meet this demand efficiently.

Combination ovens. The models shown here allow racks of food to be rolled into the cooker direct from the preparation area.

Choosing equipment

Unit 18 looked at some of the questions that should be asked before buying a piece of equipment. All of these are relevant when deciding whether to purchase a large piece of equipment and, in addition, there are some other factors which should be considered.

- Size and weight - can the floor support the equipment?
- Fuel supply - is there an appropriate power supply? Some catering equipment is so large and consumes so much energy it requires a special 3 PHASE electrical supply. This is a very expensive outlay and is only to be found in factories, production lines and very large hotels.
- Water and drainage - if needed, are they available?
- Noise - is the level acceptable?
- Maintenance - are spare parts and servicing available locally?

Gastronorm containers

activities

GASTRONORM containers are used in the catering industry. They are available in several standard sizes. Most large equipment, such as ovens and refrigerators, is designed to accommodate different combinations of these containers. The diagram below shows how different arrangements of gastronorm container can be used in a space.

1. What are the benefits of an industry standard catering container?

2. A counter service café has a bain-marie wide enough to fit 4 full size gastronorm containers. Draw a plan showing what size and combination of containers they should use to serve the following menu:
   - gammon steaks with pineapple
   - vegetarian cottage pie
   - chips, new potatoes, peas, corn on the cob
   - cranberry relish, gravy, cheese sauce
   - bread and butter pudding.

- Ventilation - will additional ventilation be required? Large equipment can create a lot of smoke and/or steam, which must be removed from the kitchen. Ideally the whole air in a kitchen should be replaced 10-20 times an hour, using an extraction system.

Cooking equipment

The style and function of industrial cooking equipment can be very different from that in a domestic kitchen. In a large kitchen there will be one or more RANGES, which comprise oven and hob. In addition, there may be grills, fryers, hot cupboards, bain maries, steamers, bratt pans, boiling pans and microwaves.

Conventional oven

Zones of heat exist within an oven with the top being the hottest and the bottom being the coolest. In general the middle shelf relates to the oven setting. Conventional ovens are at their most economic when you can make use of the different temperature zones. They are often used in a domestic environment, and can be fuelled by gas or electricity.

Convection oven

Hot air is circulated around the oven using a fan. This regulates the heat within the oven ensuring even and rapid cooking. Additional blasts of air can be provided by a power blower. Cooking time and temperature are reduced, which economises on fuel. The cooking process reduces evaporation of liquid keeping shrinkage to a minimum.

Combination oven

A convection oven with the addition of increased humidity in the form of water or steam jets. Combi-ovens are controlled by microprocessor systems, usually with digital displays and with built in cooking programmes for a consistent end result.

Microwave oven

A microwave oven cooks food using high frequency electromagnetic waves (see

The Falcon 350 is a modular combination of ovens, hob, grill and fryers, which can be adapted according to the size and needs of the kitchen.

Unit 17). Industrial microwaves are far more powerful than their domestic counterparts. Domestic microwaves have a wattage of 650-1,000 watts. Industrial microwaves have a wattage of 1-2 kilowatts (1,000-2,000 watts), enabling the ovens to cook food far more quickly. Some models have automatic defrosting systems, browning elements and programmable controls. Others combine a microwave and convection oven. The advantage of this is that the colour and texture of food is improved. Metal cooking pans can also be used without damaging the appliance.

Microwaves are used for cooking, re-heating or thawing foods. They can be found in both the cooking and service areas of a catering outlet.

Hobs

There are two main sources of energy for hobs: gas or electricity.

With a gas hob, a naked flame is applied via a burner. The amount of gas released is regulated by the control knob. The advantage of gas is that the heat applied to the cooking utensil is virtually instantaneous.

There are several kinds of electric hob.

- **The radiant ring** which glows red when on full heat. It consists of an electric element in the form of a spiral tube.

AMANA CONVECTION EXPRESS
- 1,000W microwave plus 2,200W convection heat
- compact unit, ideal for pubs, clubs and restaurants
- 24 memory programme and touch pad controls
- stainless steel construction
- runs off 13 amp plug
Source: Lockhart catering catalogue and Bradshaw Microwave Ltd

- **The disc ring** is very common in parts of Europe. This is a spiral ring covered by a flat top.
- **Ceramic hobs** have a smooth flat surface. The radiant rings are situated under the surface of the hob and transmit heat through the hob to the base of the cooking pot.
- **Halogen hobs** also have a smooth flat surface and are heated by special tungsten halogen light filaments rather than the traditional spiral ring.
- **Induction hobs** have a solid top plate made from VITROCERAMIC material which only provides heat when in contact with the base of a pan. These hobs rely on a magnetic field to conduct the heat. They have many advantages: they save energy; cook up to 50% faster; are clean, hygienic and safe; and do not generate as much heat in the kitchen. However, these hobs are very expensive and require special cooking pans as any non-magnetic material such as aluminium or copper will not work.

Steamers

Steaming ovens are used for bulk steaming of meat, fish, vegetables and puddings and for any products that may require a moist cooking environment.

There are three types of steamer: atmospheric, pressure and pressureless.

- **Atmospheric** - water in the cooker is heated by gas or electricity to give off steam. Water is continually pumped into the cooker to provide a constant source of steam.
- **Pressure** - the steam in this type of oven is used under pressure which speeds up the cooking process.
- **Pressureless** - sometimes known as a convector steamer. It works rapidly and contains a convection system which removes air from the oven, making the steaming action more efficient. It can also incorporate a controlled defrost facility.

Bratt pan

A large shallow tilting pan which is moved by the action of a wheel. It is made of cast iron steel or stainless steel with a hinged cover and is thermostatically controlled. It can be heated by gas or electricity. Bratt pans are used for frying, poaching, stewing, boiling and braising (see Case Study on p. 94).

Boiling pan

A large free-standing pan with a lid which has a direct water filling valve and a draining outlet. The pan may have an outer and an inner wall filled with water for indirect heating, similar to cooking in a bain marie. Boiling pans are made of aluminium or stainless steel with a capacity up to 40 litres and are heated by gas or electricity. Many are fitted with a tilting device so that they may be emptied safely and easily. Boiling pans are used for large batch vegetable cooking, soups, stews, stocks, sweet and savoury sauces and milk puddings.

Hot cupboards and bain maries

Hot cupboards are large stainless steel storage containers, which may be floor

The wide shallow design of bratt pans ensures even cooking.

activities

Figure 1 How induction hobs work

Induction hobs heat almost twice as fast as conventional hobs. As heat is only generated within the cooking pan, the hob remains cold. This means that there is no risk of burning, any food spills will not stick to the hob and the hob can be cleaned easily. The temperature is instantly controllable, reducing from boil to simmer immediately and switching off automatically when the pan is removed. Power used is proportional to the size of pan. Induction hobs use, on average, 50% less energy than conventional hobs.

Source: adapted from Lockhart catering catalogue, 1995 and Bonnet brochure

1. Look at the photograph of the induction hob and Figure 1. Explain why the egg cooks on the pan side but remains raw on the hob side.
2. What are the advantages and disadvantages of induction hobs?
3. Which catering outlets would find an induction hob useful? Explain why.
4. Match the following statements to the type of hob (gas burners, radiant/disc rings, ceramic, halogen, induction).
   This type of hob....
   - *can accommodate several pans on a flat surface*
   - *is fast and easily controlled*
   - *particularly suits pans with different sized bases*
   - *relies on pans having solid flat bases*
   - *produces instant heat*
   - *is easy to clean.*

standing or mounted on wheels. They can be used to keep plates or food piping hot until required. Hot cupboards may have a bain marie mounted on the top. This is a large, shallow container of hot water into which gastronorm containers can be placed. This is an ideal way of keeping food at the correct temperature until it is served.

Deep Fat Fryers

Fryers can be used for any type of fried food. The heat source can be from the top, the bottom or both. They can be heated by gas or electricity and are thermostatically controlled.

Pressure fryers cook food in an air tight pan which is a quick and safe method because the oil can be heated to a lower temperature and still fry efficiently.

Hot air rotary fryers are designed to cook foods like battered products and frozen chips in 4-6 minutes without any oil.

Computerised fryers automatically control cooking temperatures and time, basket lifting and product holding times. Information is fed from the oil to the computer through a probe. The computer will take into consideration the 'recovery rate' of the oil, i.e. the amount of time taken for the oil to return to the programmed temperature after cold food has been added to the fryer.

Contact grill

This type of grill has two heating surfaces which face each other and the food lies between them. It is sometimes known as a double-sided or infra grill. It is heated by electricity and cooks very quickly. Contact grills are used for steaks and other similar thin pieces of meat and fish which require rapid cooking.

Fry plates/griddles

These are solid metal plates heated from below which reach the required temperature rapidly. Griddles can be used for individual portions of meat, hamburgers, eggs and bacon. Some griddles may have zone heating allowing parts of the cooking surface to be switched off so that energy can be reduced at less busy times of the day.

A medium duty Zanussi deep fat fryer. The food is cooked in two, independently controlled, frying wells. The oil is drained away into the unit base. The range includes both gas and electric fryers.

Griddles with a chromed polished surface give off less radiant heat which saves energy.

Barbecues

Any food which can be grilled can be cooked on a barbecue. Barbecues may be fuelled by electricity, gas or charcoal. Charcoal takes about an hour to reach the required temperature. With gas or electric barbecues the heat source is instant and controllable. A chargrill combines the rapid cooking of a grill and the flavour achieved through traditional barbecuing.

Refrigeration

Correct refrigeration is crucial in the food industry. All food is perishable and fresh food can be at risk if it is not refrigerated. Table 1 gives guidelines for using a refrigerator wisely. These apply both to domestic and commercial kitchens. See Unit 9 for more guidance on the hygienic storage of food.

The size and type of food operation will dictate the size and capacity of the refrigeration equipment required. A caterer may wish to chill food in a chill unit; store food for a short period of time in a refrigerator or deep freeze for longer periods of time.

Chillers

Chilling can take place in a room or in a cabinet. This method is used for storing fruit, salads, some cheeses and prepared cold dishes.

Ice cream conservators

Ice cream must be kept at a temperature below -17°C. Purpose built conservators and display cabinets are available for storage and attractive presentation.

activities

Here are some profiles of different catering businesses

1) A riverside restaurant with a patisserie, outdoor terrace and café. It serves full lunch and evening menus as well as providing sandwiches and snacks. The restaurant caters for 770 covers daily.

2) A nursing home which is situated in a converted Georgian house. The clients have a range of dietary needs. The home caters for 54 covers daily.

3) A fish and chip shop café serving four varieties of fish, chips, pies, sausages, vegetables and drinks. The shop caters for 300 covers daily.

These equipment packages are available.

a) 2 fryers with twin baskets
   1 fryer with single basket
   1 grill
   2 microwaves

b) 1 undercounter boiler/steamer
   1 oven, hob and grill range
   1 oven and grill range
   2 hot cupboards

c) 1 microwave
   1 oven and grill range
   1 hot cupboard and bain marie

1. Suggest the most appropriate package for each outlet.

2. Which of the outlets would consider speed of cooking to be a top priority?

3. Which of the outlets might consider a conventional oven to be inappropriate to their needs?

Table I Fridge sense

- Keep fridge temperature between 1°C and 4°C.
- Check temperature regularly.
- The coldest part of the fridge is at the top - ideal for perishable foods like cheese and cooked meats.
- The least cool part of the fridge is at the bottom, in the chiller drawers - ideal for delicate salad leaves and fruit.
- Cool cooked food within 1½ hours before refrigerating.
- Defrost frozen food in the fridge.
- Raw or defrosting meat or fish should be kept at the bottom of the fridge so that it cannot drip onto other foods.
- Store raw and cooked foods separately.

Both refrigerators and freezers work in the same way. A motor circulates a refrigerant which carries heat away from a sealed box. Chemicals called chlorofluorocarbons (CFCs) used to be the refrigerant until it was discovered that they damaged the earth's ozone layer. Nowadays hydrofluorocarbons (HFCs) are used but there is still concern that these contribute to global warming. Greenpeace urges consumers to buy fridges and freezers containing only hydrocarbon gases.

This Cinders portable barbecue is fuelled by Calor gas rather than charcoal, making it easier to control and clean.

Refrigerators

Refrigeration is a method of preservation where food is stored for short periods of time at temperatures below 8°C. This temperature is stipulated by the Food Safety (Temperature Control) Regulations 1995.

An industrial kitchen will usually have a variety of refrigerators.

- Separate fridges for raw and cooked produce.
- Counter model fridges - especially useful in busy kitchens and serveries as an 'on the spot' store for ingredients and menu items or for holding food which is ready to serve to the customer. This type will often be located at the point of sale.
- Specialist refrigeration, e.g. designed to hold bottles of wine at a temperature best suited to the product.

Commercial refrigerators have many more adjustable shelves than their domestic equivalents. They are designed to accommodate the storage of standard size gastronorm trays and pans. They are made of stainless steel and the doors open to 90° for easy loading and cleaning. The refrigeration unit is usually mounted on top of the appliance. They have a thermometer visible from the outside and may have sensors which will sound an alarm if the temperature rises to an unacceptable level. Newer models aim to conserve energy. Most have an automatic defrost device.

Freezers

Industrial freezers hold frozen food at a much lower temperature than their domestic counterparts; the temperature range is between -18°C and -29°C. They may have single, double or triple doors with the motor fitted to the top of the appliance. Doors can be hung on either side, so that they can open either way. They have magnetic catches and are lockable. Factories and very large scale operations may have walk-in freezer units.

activities

1. What is the correct operating temperature of a commercial freezer?

2. Why is it necessary to reduce the temperature of cooked food very rapidly before storing in a freezer?

3. What are the advantages to a restaurant of being able to cook-freeze food prepared on the premises?

Cook-freeze is a method of food preparation using a blast freezer and a deep freeze. Many large kitchen operations now have their own cook-freeze food production units. Dishes are prepared and then rapidly frozen using a blast freezer in which low temperature air is passed over the food very quickly. A blast freezer is capable of holding 20-400 kg of food. This process reduces the temperature of the food to -20°C. Food is then transferred to a deep freeze which maintains a temperature of at least -18°C, where it is held for a maximum of 6 months until required. This method allows storage of food cooked on the premises as well as ready frozen foodstuffs.

In large catering operations cold rooms may be used. These walk-in refrigerators can be built to any size, and can incorporate dual compartments running at different temperatures.

and are operated by hand. The glass is pushed onto a revolving brush and washed with hot detergent water. The item is then rinsed and sanitised.

About 500-600 items can be handled in one hour.

Cabinet dishwashers look more like domestic dishwashers. They contain large square racks which hold a variety of items. Unlike domestic dishwashers, however, they operate very quickly, each batch taking only 2-3 minutes.

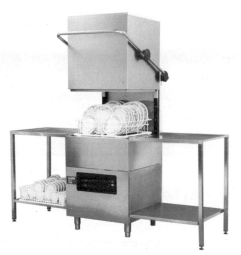

The Classic Hydro 850 dishwasher is a pass-through machine that can be operated in straight line or corner layouts. Timed cycles (60/120/180 seconds) or continuous wash can be used. Wash temperature is 55°C followed by a fresh water rinse at 85°C.

Dishwashers

Dishwashing can take two forms:
- hot water and sterilising rinse
- low temperature and bleach.

Pass-through dishwashers operate using sprays, which are angled above and below the dishracks. Racks are loaded with crockery and move through each section of the dishwasher where they are washed, rinsed and sanitised. FLIGHT dishwashers also carry the crockery through the machine but instead of baskets crockery is loaded onto a conveyor belt fitted with plastic or metal pegs. Flight dishwashers are particularly suitable for large scale operations handling 3-4,000 dishes per meal time.

Brush dishwashers are used for glassware

Waste disposal units

Food waste must be removed quickly from food preparation areas to avoid unpleasant smells and possible contamination of fresh food. Waste disposal units are operated by electricity and will accept many different types of waste. They grind the food, mix it with water and then dispose of it down the drain. Free standing units and units designed to be integrated into a work top are available. For solid waste hydraulic

compactors are available. These reduce glass, paper, plastic and tin waste to a fifth of its volume and seal it in strong hygienic bags. Many types of waste can be recycled (see Unit 25).

Key Terms

3-phase - a powerful electrical supply needed to run very large pieces of equipment.

Gastronorm - a standard size container used in the catering industry.

Range - a combination of oven and electric hot plates or gas burners.

Combi-oven - a combination of oven and steamer in one unit.

Vitroceramic - a mixture of pottery and glass, used to make hobs.

Flight - a large dishwasher, where crockery is loaded onto a conveyor belt fitted with plastic or metal pegs instead of baskets.

activities

1. a) What is a flight dishwasher?
    b) Name TWO other catering operations where a flight dishwasher might be particularly appropriate.

2. Suggest reasons why Treliske Hospital requires a thermal disinfection rinse in its dishwashing system.

3. How does the thermal disinfection rinse destroy micro-organisms?

Treliske Hospital in Cornwall has just installed a new flight dishwashing system, designed to achieve unprecedented standards of cleanliness. The new machine cost about £35,000. It has an extra rinse built into its cycle which guarantees thermal disinfection. Normal machines achieve the standard of sanitisation, which means that glass and tableware are clean, but does not necessarily ensure that micro-organisms are destroyed. The thermal disinfection rinse ensures that the surface temperature of wares reaches 90°C for one second, 80°C for 1 minute or 71°C for 3 minutes. This will remove all harmful organisms found in a food service environment. Treliske Hospital is the first in the NHS to specify thermal disinfection as a standard. It remains to be seen if other health authorities will follow suit.

Source: adapted from Food Service Management, July 1996

Presentation

Whether in the home or in a restaurant first impressions play an important part in how successful a meal is going to be. Family tradition often dictates the way a room and table is decorated for special occasions such as Christmas or a bar mitzvah.

Environment

At home, meals can be eaten in almost any room which is convenient and many people eat their meals in front of the television. In the summer people often eat outside. A celebration will stimulate the participants to create a memorable meal. In restaurants, presentation is even more important. The size of the restaurant, the atmosphere, the way the tables are set, the china, cutlery and glass used are all important factors influencing a customer's decision about where to eat. In a small restaurant, the atmosphere may be very intimate. Diners may be seated close together and could be aware of what other people are eating and whether they are enjoying themselves. In a larger restaurant, the atmosphere may be more formal. There may be more privacy but it could feel less friendly. In winter, a restaurant with an open fire seems warm and friendly, while in summer a restaurant with an outside eating area or an air conditioned dining room may well be more popular.

The table

In France, guests in Bed and Breakfast often find themselves eating 'en famille' with everyone sitting around one large table. In a public house or inexpensive cafe, tables may be close together and the place settings might be quite simple, with table mats and cutlery

wrapped in paper serviettes. In a more formal restaurant, tables will be covered with large cloths which hang well down the legs of the table and are then topped with smaller cloths which can easily be changed if they become soiled. The tables will be laid with place settings including cutlery, glassware, china and napkins. Flowers and candles

A table setting

complete the presentation. The quality of the table setting indicates the importance placed on presentation by the restaurant and helps to establish the important first impression. However, unless the environment, the table, the food and the service are all equally good, customer satisfaction will not be achieved.

Service

Buffets

The length and shape of the tables can vary according to the occasion. The food may be self service or served to the guests from the table display. Food may be elaborately decorated and presented on 'mirror' serving dishes. Buffet meals may include hot or cold dishes.

Table service

Customers sit at tables and are personally served. The food may be presented to the diners ready plated, partially plated with vegetables served at the table, or there may be 'silver service' - where the whole meal is served to the customer at the table.

At very expensive restaurants, the ratio of servers can be as high as one server to two customers. Wine is ordered from the **sommelier** (wine waiter). Smaller restaurants employ fewer waiters who look after several tables at once.

activities

For the following design activities, you should include your own illustrations. Each element of your design should be clearly explained.

1. Design the table setting for a Christmas dinner. The family only have white crockery. How will you make the setting festive?

2. Suggest a suitable menu and appropriate tableware for a summer

wedding buffet. Design the shape of the buffet tables using three rectangular tables of 2m x 1m. Plan where you would position each of the dishes, cutlery, plates, floral arrangements and napkins. Design an appropriate colour scheme.

3. Design a colour scheme and china for a new wholefood cafe.

Creating a lattice topping for an apple tart.

Food presentation

Shape, size and FINISH is often governed by tradition. Food can be 'finished' (completed) by glazing either before or after cooking and presented with a GARNISH (see Figure 1), if savoury or DECORATION, if sweet. Presentation skills and traditions are widely different across the world, e.g. the Chinese have presentation skills which turn their meals into a complete art form.

Some traditional finishes

Apple pie is made from sweet shortcrust pastry which covers the apples but may not have a pastry base - this is to prevent the pastry absorbing the water from the apple as it cooks. An alternative to the plain pie is to use pastry to create a lattice, leaving small gaps for the fruit to show through. Traditionally, sweet pies and tarts do not have additional pastry decorations. Before presentation caster sugar may be shaken over the cooked pastry.

Cornish pasties are made from short

crust pastry. A circle of pastry is cut out and filled. The edges are KNOCKED UP and then fluted using the back of a knife to create the traditional shape.

Steak and kidney pie is made from flaky pastry. It is served in a deep oval dish. The pastry is knocked up and completed with large flutes. The dish should be completed with pastry leaves and roses and glazed with an egg wash to give a shiny brown finish.

Hot cross buns are made with a sweet yeast dough. After proving, they are completed by piping a mixture made of flour, oil and water, in the shape of a cross. After baking, while still hot, the buns are glazed with a cold sugar syrup.

Glazing

A GLAZE is a smooth shiny coating added to dishes to give an attractive finish. Both sweet and savoury dishes can be glazed. There are several different methods of glazing.

Egg wash - a mixture of beaten egg and milk brushed onto pastry or dough immediately before cooking gives a shiny golden finish.

Egg yolk mixed with a little oil - gives an excellent brown finish to Duchesse potatoes

Egg white - brushed over a sweet pastry and sprinkled with caster sugar gives a crisp, sweet, light golden finish.

Milk - brushed over scones and pastry aids browning, but does not add shine.

Sugar and water - boiled together to make a light syrup and left to cool, may be brushed over hot sweet buns immediately after cooking to give a shiny sticky glaze.

Apricot jam and redcurrant jelly - can be warmed and used to cover French apple tart and other open flans.

Arrowroot - this starch dissolves into a clear liquid which will cover fruit flans and set lightly. The syrup in which the fruit was cooked is often used to make this glaze, adding flavour and colour.

Aspic - the savoury equivalent of arrowroot; a clear jelly made of stock and gelatine. Useful for cold dishes with elaborate decorations which need to be kept in place. The jelly gives a smooth shiny finish to the dish. It can also be chopped up to give a glinting, quivering bed on which food can be presented.

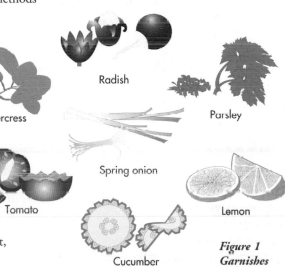

Figure 1
Garnishes

Watercress, Radish, Parsley, Tomato, Spring onion, Lemon, Cucumber

Key Terms

Finish - **completing the presentation of a dish.**
Garnish - **enhances the appearance of a (usually savoury) dish.**
Decoration - **enhances the appearance of a sweet dish.**
Knocked up - **two layers of pastry are sealed together using a light chopping action with the back of a knife.**
Glaze - **a smooth shiny coating added to dishes to give an attractive finish.**

activities

The dish on the right is served as a main course in a restaurant.

1. Why is a sauce needed with this poached salmon dish?
2. What nutritional benefit is there when using watercress as a garnish?
3. What vegetables would you select to complement the soft texture of this meal?
4. Suggest a dessert with a piped decoration which could be served following the salmon dish.

Bratt pans are used in large catering kitchens, such as those in hotels, restaurants, hospitals, ships and company canteens. Their wide shallow design is ideal for even cooking of large quantities of food. They have a tilting action which enables food or water to be easily removed from the pan.

The Elro tilting pressure bratt pan combines the functions of four different appliances:

• normal bratt pan
• pressure bratt pan
• tilting boiling vessel
• pressure boiling and steaming appliance.

It is a versatile piece of equipment enabling chefs to fry, braise, boil, steam, pressure steam and pressure stew in one appliance. The Elro bratt pan is controlled by a microprocessor for fully automatic frying, boiling and steaming. For example, if the automatic steam function is selected, the temperature will rise to 108°C, then reduce to the cooking temperature. After the pre-set steaming time, an acoustic signal will be heard, indicating that the power has been turned off by the control system. The steam will then be condensed through the cooling system of the lid.

Source: adapted from Elro product information

The Elro tilting pressure bratt pan is controlled by a microprocessor. The actual temperature of the pan is displayed at the top and the remaining cooking time is shown underneath. Controls for boiling, steaming, frying and automatic programme setting are at the bottom.

• Solid, totally flat pan base.
• Integral pouring spout in front edge of pan.
• Designed with hygiene in mind.
• Energy efficient.
• The latest in microprocessor control.
• Compatible with gastronorm containers.
• Replaces several pieces of conventional equipment; saving space and money.
• Retains the nutritional value, shape, colour and taste of food.

Activities

1. Name the cooking methods for which the Elro tilting pressure bratt pan is suitable.
2. Why does the pan have a wheel on the side?
3. What are the advantages of the steaming process being controlled by a microprocessor?
4. Elro say that their bratt pan is 'designed with hygiene in mind'. What design features of a piece of catering equipment help to maintain hygiene standards?
5. The catering manager of a hospital kitchen wants to purchase this piece of equipment. What reasons should be given to the finance director to persuade him or her that it is a worthwhile investment?

HEATHCOTES BRASSERIE

Heathcotes Brasserie is a modern, informal restaurant with the emphasis on quality food at relatively inexpensive prices. The Brasserie does not operate a dress code and there is no need for reservations, except on special occasions like Mothers' Day or Christmas. The atmosphere inside is bright and modern, with a 60ft wall mural dominating the room. There is plenty of light and tables are laid in a simple, functional style. Gentle jazz music plays in the background. The staff are friendly and polite, ready to chat or tell you more about the food. The menu, which changes every 3 months, combines modern British dishes with influences from the Mediterranean. All food is served ready plated. In the kitchen, staff specialise in their own areas: pastry, vegetables or main courses but Max, the head chef, personally finishes each dish before it leaves the kitchen. Each dish is beautifully presented so that it is as pleasing to the eye as the tastebuds.

The interior of Heathcotes Brasserie, showing the decor and table setting.

STARTERS

SALAD OF BLACK PUDDING
with crushed potatoes, bacon, garlic and baby onions

PRESSED TERRINE OF HAM HOCK AND CHICKEN LIVER PARFAIT
wrapped in Cumbrian ham with Cumberland sauce

TERRINE OF GOATS' CHEESE
olive tapenade, tomato vinaigrette

RAVIOLI OF PEAS
and broad beans with tarragon

ONION, STILTON AND LEEK TART
with walnut pesto

Some dishes served at the restaurant.

Activities

1. a) What kind of image is Heathcotes Brasserie trying to present to customers?
   b) How does the environment, table setting and service contribute to this image?
2. What are the advantages of serving food to customers ready plated?
3. What is meant by the following terms: parfait; terrine; ravioli; pesto?
4. Choose one of the starters from the menu extract and draw what you think it should look like on the plate. You may decorate the dish with an appropriate garnish if you wish.
5. A restaurant wants to open a cellar café, appealing to young people, serving good quality food in an informal atmosphere. Advise the restaurant on its decor, table settings and menu.

Product development

Product and market orientation

Some companies are PRODUCT ORIENTATED. They make products and then try to convince people to buy them. Other firms are MARKET ORIENTATED. They try to find out what consumers want before they develop products. Most food manufacturers fall into this second group.

The market

When a large food manufacturer decides to produce a new product, it could cost millions of pounds to research, develop and market. The company wants evidence that the product will sell well before investing this kind of money.

First, the company needs to identify its TARGET MARKET or GROUP. These are the intended users of the product.

Target market

It is essential for companies to identify the people most likely to buy their product. Table 1 shows the socioeconomic groups in Britain. Over 50% of the population are in groups C1, C2 and D. Only 3.5% of the population make up group A. If a company wants to make the greatest number of sales, it makes sense to target groups C1, C2 and D. If the other socioeconomic groups also purchase the product, this will be a bonus for the company. Other companies may design products to appeal to specific groups. For example, a luxury dessert may be aimed at the higher earners in groups A and B, while another company might specialise in frozen meals for elderly people, who are likely to be in group E.

Companies should also consider the age group of the target market. Young people with few family responsibilities have the greatest disposable income and many consumer goods are aimed at this section of the population.

Identifying the target market helps the company to decide:

● how the product should be designed
● what it should cost
● how it should be advertised
● where it should be sold.

Identifying needs

Influenced by a changing economic, technological and social environment consumers change their ideas about the products they want to buy. In order to be successful, food manufacturers must identify changing consumer needs and new trends and develop products to meet these. This can be done by expanding an existing market or by developing a completely new and original product. Manufacturers aim to produce goods with 'added value' - products which will generate consumer interest and which are different from goods already on the market.

Market research

Manufacturers respond to the results of MARKET RESEARCH which measures demographic trends, purchasing and consumption habits. Food manufacturers may carry out their own research, employ a market research company, or they may use the results of work conducted by government

---

Table I Socioeconomic groups

Group A - higher managerial, administrative or professional
Group B - intermediate managerial, administrative or professional
Group C1 - supervisory or clerical, and junior managerial, administrative or professional
Group C2 - skilled manual workers
Group D - semi-skilled and unskilled manual workers
Group E - state pensioners, casual workers, unemployed

Source: Institute of Practitioners in Advertising

---

activities

1. At which market are Boots aiming their rehydration drinks?

2. Suggest ONE way in which Boots could find out more about the needs of this market.

3. a) What alternative drinks are available for consumers in this market?

b) How do Boots offer 'added value' with this product, i.e. in what ways does it differ from what is already available?

BOOTS REHYDRATION DRINKS

Although plain water is useful, sports enthusiasts prefer a drink that can be absorbed by the body faster. Boots Isotonic drinks are formulated to be in balance with the body's own fluids. As a result they are absorbed quickly to help prevent dehydration and fatigue. They also replace salts lost through perspiration and their specially selected levels of carbohydrate 'top up' the energy reserves in the muscles.

Source: adapted from Boots information leaflet

departments or independent organisations. There are different ways of finding out what people want from their food (see Table 2). One method is the **hall test**. Market researchers stand in the street or a hotel lobby and ask people a series of questions to determine if they are in the target market for a particular product. If they are, the researcher will invite the person to come in to a hall and answer further questions. Participants could be asked to comment on illustrations of a product or new packaging, or they might be asked to look at and taste a new product.

Products and brands

Products are foods which have undergone secondary processing (see Unit 14), e.g. chocolate biscuits. Brands are products made by a particular company and known by their trade name, e.g. Hob Nobs. A product is a tangible item, but a brand is a marketing concept. Some brand names are well known around the world, e.g. Coca-Cola. Other companies sometimes try to imitate the most popular brands. Many supermarkets have produced their own label products which are similar to the brand names, but are often sold more cheaply. The manufacturers of the original brand may challenge another company if the logo, colour or design of their product resembles the original brand too closely.

Changing products and brands

To remain successful, companies must be able to change their product or brand image in response to new trends, developing technology or changing market needs. This may mean modifying existing recipes (see Unit 16) or developing new products. With popular brands the image may need to change to reflect the needs of each new

> **Table 2** Market research methods
>
> *DESK RESEARCH* - the collection and analysis of information from company records and different media (e.g. trade journals, magazines and television).
>
> *CONTINUOUS SURVEYS* - the regular collection of information about purchasing and consumption habits from a sample of households.
>
> *QUALITATIVE RESEARCH* - identifying motivation, attitudes and reactions through in-depth personal interviews and group discussions.
>
> *QUANTITATIVE RESEARCH* - obtaining data from large groups of people.
>
> Data can be collected by personal interviews, telephone interviews, self-completion tests, hall tests or group discussions.
>
> *Source: adapted from Market Research Society leaflet*

generation. This may mean altering the logo, packaging and advertising.

What do consumers want?

There are many different issues affecting people's choice of food. Unit 8 looks at some of these factors. When developing new products, it is important for manufacturers to consider the variety of views consumers may have (see Figure 1 on p. 98).

● Quality of the product - a major concern for many consumers; often

activities

After 54 years in a red, white and blue can, tomorrow Pepsi Cola goes blue. Every single can of Pepsi around the world will change on the same day. It is one of the most expensive marketing moves ever, including a £2 million commercial featuring a famous model and a tennis champion, and a press conference on board Concorde which has been painted blue for a year to publicise the change. Why go to all this trouble and expense? The answer is the marketing war between Pepsi and Coca-Cola. Although both drinks consist of sugar, water and bits of vegetable with a few E numbers thrown in; there is not, as blind tasting has revealed, a great deal of difference between them. But Pepsi only manages a third of Coca-Cola's total global sales.

Source: adapted from the Guardian, 1 April 1996

1. Pepsi and Coca-Cola are brands of cola drink. Name some brands of the following products: biscuits; breakfast cereals; baked beans; coffee.

2. Why is it important for Pepsi to change its brand image?

3. The main market for soft drinks is people aged 16-24. Do you think the change to blue Pepsi, and the accompanying publicity campaign, would appeal to this market? Why?

4. The article claims that Pepsi and Coca-Cola taste remarkably similar. Conduct a blind tasting (see Unit 23) to find out if this is true.

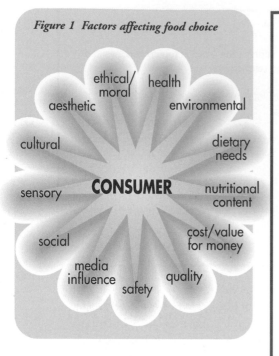

Figure 1 Factors affecting food choice

ethical/moral, health, aesthetic, environmental, cultural, dietary needs, **CONSUMER**, nutritional content, sensory, cost/value for money, social, media influence, quality, safety

linked to cost and ideas about value for money.

● Nutritional content - many people aim for a healthy diet. This has opened up new food markets for manufacturers, e.g. low salt, sugar and fat free food.

● Cost and value for money - this remains top priority for many families, particularly those on low incomes.

● 'Green' issues - some consumers avoid eating meat or fish, others avoid additives and pesticides, preferring to buy food grown organically. Some consumers make buying decisions based on ethical concerns, for example avoiding companies which conduct animal testing, or which are involved in the arms trade.

● Cultural and regional preferences - attitudes towards food vary depending on what you were brought up to eat.

● Media influence - advertising is very powerful in encouraging consumers to try new products. Products may be associated with a particular image or specific characteristic for, e.g. a healthy food, an energy giving food, a versatile or convenient food.

Consumer expectations

When a consumer buys a food product, he or she expects that it will:

Figure 2 Functional foods

Low Fat Horlicks contains vitamins which the label says help to 'protect your body from some of the harmful effects of today's stressful lifestyles'. The product is 56% sugar.

Pact contains Omega 3 fats which the pack says 'help maintain a healthy heart'. The product is 60% fat, of which 15% is saturated.

Toffee Treat's label says 'each serving provides 58mg calcium'. On this basis, an 11 year old girl would need 14 servings for a day's calcium, which would also give her 190g sugar.

● be edible
● meet certain quality standards (see Unit 29)
● meet advertising and nutritional claims.

If the product meets expectations, a consumer will probably buy it again. This is why it is important that manufacturers communicate the right messages to consumers.

Functional foods

Some food manufacturers have developed products which they claim have specific health benefits (see Figure 2). These foods are known as

FUNCTIONAL FOODS or NUTRACEUTICALS. In 1996, the Food Commission examined 700 of these products and found many of the foods to be of poor nutritional quality. In the majority of cases the claim to improve health was not based on the food product itself but on the supposed benefits of an added ingredient. Any food that makes a specific health claim needs a licence under the Medicines Act. None of these 700 functional foods had one. The Food Commission is concerned that:

● consumers could be confused by misleading claims

activities

1. How might the screening of the documentary affect sales of the soft drink?
2. As a consumer of the drink, what would you do?
3. How should the soft drink manufacturer respond to any customer complaints?

A manufacturer launches a new soft drink, with a massive advertising campaign. The drink is very successful. Two months after the launch, a television documentary reveals that the manufacturer's parent company is involved with arms dealing in the Middle East.

- functional foods may contain other ingredients, such as sugar or salt, that should be limited in the diet.

Consumer power

Food products are designed to appeal to particular target groups. Different products compete against one another for consumer attention so it is vital that all those involved in the design, production, marketing and distribution of products understand what consumers think of them.

Consumers make their views known to food manufacturers in a variety of ways. Some customers may write to companies, with questions or suggestions. Most large manufacturers have customer relations departments which deal with queries and complaints. Some consumers may participate in market research. But the most important power that a consumer has is the ability to buy or not to buy a product.

The design process

The development of new products is a long process of research and consultation between designers, producers and consumers (see Figure 4). The exact process by which a product is designed, tested and marketed varies from company to company and the details are usually a closely guarded industrial secret. The rest of this unit looks at the key stages in the development of a product and discusses some of the issues a company may have to consider.

It is in a company's interests to listen to consumer views.

Figure 3 Olestra

It is every slimmer's dream - fat without the calories. A new product, called olestra, a fat free alternative to fat, has been launched in the USA. But there are concerns about this new product. The US Center for Science in the Public Interest, a non-governmental organisation, has suggested that all olestra containing foods bear the following label.

NOTICE

This product contains olestra. Olestra can cause diarrhoea, loose stools, faecal urgency, nausea, gas and bloating. Olestra can cause underwear staining, anal leakage, greasy bowel movements and oil in toilet. Symptoms should go away within 48 hours after you stop eating olestra foods. If symptoms persist call your doctor. Olestra also reduces the absorption of nutrients, and vitamins A, D, E and K have been added to compensate.

Figure 4 Designer, producer and consumer

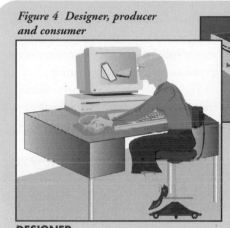

DESIGNER
A person who creates ideas for new food products including the image of the product and its appropriate packaging. The designer may also be involved in the adaption or refinement of an existing product based on information gained from market research.

PRODUCER
The company who manufactures, packages and distributes the product.

CONSUMER
The purchaser or user of a food product.

Figure 5 on p. 100 shows a flow diagram of the stages in product development. You will find it useful to follow the same sequence of steps when designing your own food products, even though you are working on a much smaller scale.

activities

1. Look at Figure 2.
   a) Why are these products described as 'functional' foods?
   b) Who do you think is the target market for each product?
   c) The Food Commission says that some functional foods make 'misleading claims'. Why is the information given misleading?

2. A slimmer in the USA buys a packet of crisps containing olestra and suffers some of symptoms described in Figure 3.
   a) Why might slimmers feel that their expectations of the product had not been met?
   b) Why might the manufacturer of the olestra containing product be reluctant to include the notice suggested by the US Center for Science in the Public Interest?

Computer aided design

Designers often use computers to help them design products. COMPUTER AIDED DESIGN (CAD) allows designers to make two or three dimensional models of a product or its packaging. The company can then discuss the designs, use the pictures in market research tests and make modifications - before a product is even made. This could save time and costs. CAD can be used in the design of individual items, batches or mass produced goods (see Unit 28).

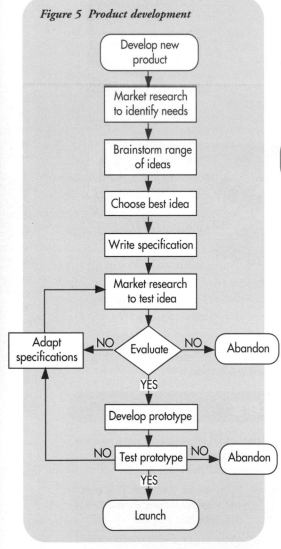

Figure 5 Product development

- Develop new product
- Market research to identify needs
- Brainstorm range of ideas
- Choose best idea
- Write specification
- Market research to test idea
- Evaluate → NO → Abandon
- Evaluate → NO → Adapt specifications
- YES
- Develop prototype
- Test prototype → NO → Abandon
- YES
- Launch

The brief

Once a manufacturer has identified the needs of consumers, a BRIEF is issued. This is a statement which explains clearly what kind of product is to be designed. Examples could be:

- develop an easy to eat meat product with a European flavour
- develop a new vegetable product which can be quickly and easily cooked and has a healthy image.

The company's product development team will brainstorm a range of alternative products in response to the brief. This could result in up to 100 suggestions for products which all conform to the requirements of the brief. For example, in response to the briefs above the team could have included some of the following suggestions:

- for the meat product - meatballs in a spicy Hungarian sauce, kebabs with a Greek yogurt based dip or veal escalopes with a lemon flavoured crunchy coating
- for the vegetable product - oven-roasted ratatouille, red peppers stuffed with spinach and ricotta, or mushroom and walnut crêpes.

Product development

The range of ideas suggested by the product development team are then screened to find out whether they are economically viable, technically possible and likely to generate sales.

Eventually, the best ideas are narrowed down to one and the product development process begins. The company will need to consider many questions at this point. For example, if specialist machinery is required for a particular process the company must decide if the estimated profit returns will cover the costs of new equipment. It may be more cost effective to adapt an existing range rather than develop a completely new one. For example, a large piping machine used for delivering the exact amount of cream within a gateaux could also be used to pipe meringues or potato. Sometimes developments in technology suggest new product ideas. For example, Cadbury developed a new production process capable of extruding chocolate into different shapes without the use of moulds. As a result of this technological breakthrough, the 'Spira' bar was developed.

Cadbury's 'Spira' has a unique shape and texture, made possible by a new chocolate extrusion process.

Other issues that companies may have to consider include:

- availability and cost of ingredients
- energy use of production process
- health and safety implications of new production process
- recruitment of new staff or training of existing staff
- suitable packaging.

The specification

A SPECIFICATION is written for the chosen product. This is a document which gives detailed requirements of the final design. A specification could include:

- exact quantities of ingredients
- production techniques to be used
- quality standards for the production process
- final size, shape, texture and volume of the finished product
- nutritional value of finished product.

activities

1. Brainstorm a range of ideas in response to ONE of the following briefs:
   a) design a delicious, nutritious snack for young children
   b) design a winter packed lunch for an office worker
   c) design a luxury dessert with a sophisticated image.

2. Discuss the ideas and select one idea to go forward for product development.

3. Write a specification for your product including the following points:
   - ingredients needed
   - production method
   - packaging or presentation.

Specifications are often extremely detailed. This level of precision is needed so that the food manufacturer can ensure a product which is always consistent. During development and production, there is constant evaluation of the product to check that it meets the specifications. If it does not, modifications may need to be made.

Testing the product

A PROTOTYPE is made which is an example of what the final product will be like, including packaging. A limited quantity is produced for testing purposes. This testing may take place in a controlled market research environment or the product may be put on general sale in a selected region of the country. This testing procedure is known as a feasibility trial or test market. The results help the company to decide if any final changes need to be made to the product.

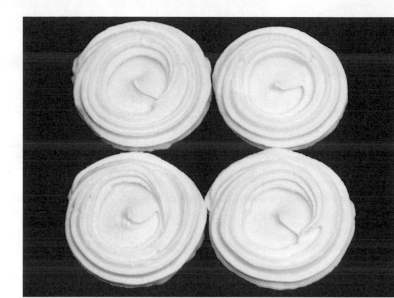

The specifications for a meringue shell may state how much air should be incorporated into the egg foam. During production, the meringue mixture is weighed before baking to check both the volume and the weight. These must match the amount set out in the specifications. If the sample is too heavy more whisking is needed, if it is too light the mixture has been whisked too much. The precise height and diameter of the cooked meringue shell is also stated in the specifications. To ensure standard results the diameter of the piping tube and force to extrude the mixture must remain contant. The final product is measured to check the dimensions.

Launching the product

Before the launch, the product is advertised to generate consumer interest. Companies often run 'teaser' advertisements before the product becomes available in the shops. These are intended to stimulate interest and have the effect of encouraging people to look out for the new product and buy it as soon as it is launched.

Timescale

The development of a new product can take a long time. For example, the first stages in the development of Cadbury's 'Spira' were in 1984 and the product was launched nationally in 1989. Other products can be developed in as little as 28 weeks (see Birds Eye Case Study on p. 102). The company will set deadlines for the different stages of development and for the product launch and each department within the company must structure their work accordingly by creating realistic work schedules. If deadlines are not met money will be lost and there is a risk that competitors may develop similar products thereby dividing the market. For more information on planning work, see Unit 26.

Key Terms

Product orientated - **a business which develops products using little or no market research which it hopes will be successful in the market.**
Market orientated - **a business which develops products which have been researched and designed to meet the needs of consumers.**
Target market/group - **the intended users of a product.**
Disposable income - **the amount of money a person has to spend after all essentials have been paid for.**
Market research - **the collection, analysis, intrepretation and presentation of information about consumption of goods and services.**
Demographic trends - **information about the changing population of a country such as the birth rate and the number of people of a particular age.**
Functional foods - **foods which claim to have specific health benefits.**
Nutraceuticals - **a functional food. The name implies that the product is a cross between a food and medicine.**
Computer aided design - **the use of computers in the design of a product.**
Brief - **a clear statement of design intention.**
Specification - **a detailed description of the final design of a product.**
Prototype - **a sample of the product, based on the specifications and including packaging.**

activities

1. Why do you think a yogurt for babies would be a profitable development for a company?

2. Describe a market research test that could be carried out in order to establish the viability of baby yogurt.

3. Design either the packaging or the TV advert for baby yogurt stating the main marketing points of convenience, health and purity.

A yogurt company has asked its product development team to design a new yogurt for babies.

PRODUCT DEVELOPMENT AT BIRDS EYE

case *study*

Birds Eye is the largest frozen food company in Britain. It developed the frozen pea in 1938 and the fish finger in 1955. Since this time it has developed hundreds of other frozen products to add to its range.

Country Club Cuisine range was launched in 1991. Research had shown that over 60% of the population were either cutting out or reducing their red meat consumption. The two key reasons behind this trend were:
* health concerns over the high fat levels in red meat
* wider availability of vegetable products.

Birds Eye already had an established reputation for providing frozen vegetables and felt that adding vegetable based meals to its range was a market innovation which would provide customers with added value.

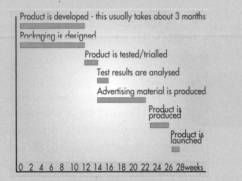

Figure 1 A Gantt chart shows the time-scale for developing, producing and launching a new product.

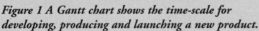

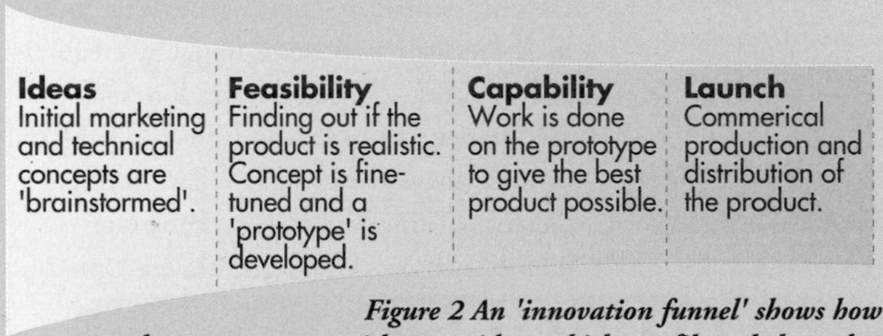

Ideas	**Feasibility**	**Capability**	**Launch**
Initial marketing and technical concepts are 'brainstormed'.	Finding out if the product is realistic. Concept is fine-tuned and a 'prototype' is developed.	Work is done on the prototype to give the best product possible.	Commerical production and distribution of the product.

Figure 2 An 'innovation funnel' shows how the process starts with many ideas which are filtered through a number of stages, becoming fewer and more focused, eventually narrowing down to one idea.

MARKET RESEARCH
Observation of consumer trends and the collection and monitoring of consumer views is the starting point in the development of new foods.

↓

BRIEF
A brief is issued asking a Concept Chef to explore many types of product. Up to 70 dishes may be invented including pies, pastries, pasta dishes and curries. From this large selection a basic concept is agreed - this determines the shape and form the product will take and the variety of flavours and/or fillings which will appear in the range.

↓

SAMPLES
Sample products are made, photographed and shown to the general public in order to test visual appeal. From the results of the visual testing 12-15 dishes go forward to the next stage of development.

↓

MARKET RESEARCH
Further research gives the development team an idea about who will buy the new product. The target group could be health conscious adults, children, teenagers etc. Identifying this group helps Birds Eye to decide what the product should look like, taste like and how much it should sell for.

↓

PRODUCT DEVELOPMENT
A name for the product is established and samples are created. Further testing takes place. Samples are cooked in volunteers' homes to see how they perform in various types of cooker. Families taste the product and supply Birds Eye with detailed information about their views. Final major adjustments are made at this stage.

↓

SPECIFICATION
When the final specifications for the product have been agreed they are written down and must be carefully adhered to by the manufacturers. The specifications ensure that every product made is identical in terms of size, quality, thickness, colour, flavour, texture and performance on the plate. The product specifications are top secret.

↓

MANUFACTURING DEVELOPMENT
The final recipe is scaled up from a kitchen product devised by a chef to a product made with tons of ingredients in a factory. There are many considerations at this point. Are the ingredients available all year round? Are the ingredients fragile? Will imported products be required? Factory trials are conducted to test suppliers and distribution. Hygiene is tested several times a day by the chemistry laboratory in order to prevent bacterial infection on the production line. The laboratory also determines the nutritional content of the product to be printed on the label.

↓

PRODUCTION
Many tons of a new product are made in preparation for the launch.

Figure 3 Flow chart showing how a product is developed

Activities

1. Why is it important that the development of a new food product starts with collecting the views of consumers?
2. Why did Birds Eye decide to develop a vegetable based meal product?
3. How did Birds Eye find out which meal idea would appeal to consumers?
4. What advantages are there in collecting information from people who have cooked the product in their own homes during the testing period?
5. The flow chart, innovation funnel and Gantt chart are three ways of looking at the product development process.
   a) Which model shows how long each stage of the process takes?
   b) Which model explains in detail what happens at each stage?
   c) Which model shows how lots of ideas are narrowed down to the launch of one product?
   d) Suggest how one of these models could be useful in planning your own work.

THE WONDER BEAN?

The soya bean is a versatile and nutritious food. It is the only vegetable food containing all 8 indispensible amino acids, making it a protein of high biological value. It contains as much protein as steak without any of the saturated fat. Soya also contains important minerals like iron, calcium and phosphorus (see Table 1). It can be grown very cheaply (see Unit 6) and can be made into many different products: soya 'milk', 'cheese', flour, tofu, textured vegetable protein (TVP) and soy sauce. The cooked beans can be eaten in stews or mashed into burgers. Raw beans can produce fresh bean sprouts. Soya products are an ideal food for anyone, but of particular value for vegetarians.

Table 1 Nutritional content of soya

100g provides:	Dried beans (raw)	Raw sprouts	Soy sauce	Tofu	Soya milk	Fortified soya milk	Soya flour
Calories	403	46	171	72	33	64.6	421
Protein (g)	34.1	6.2	10.6	7.8	3.4	3.2	37.1
Carbohydrate (g)	33.5	5.7	23.3	2.5	2.3	7.1	30
Fat (g)	17.7	1.4	4.7	4.2	1.5	3.5	20
Fibre (g)	4.8	0.76	2.4	0.08	-	-	2.4
Minerals							
calcium (mg)	226	47.6	71	125	20.9	146	200
phosphorus (mg)	554	66.7	312	125	50	45.8	557
iron (mg)	8.4	1.05	1.8	1.9	0.82	0.8	8.4
sodium (mg)	5.0	-	2941	6.7	-	-	1.4
potassium (mg)	1677	-	335	42	-	-	1714
Vitamins							
A (IU)	80	76.2	58.8	0	40.9	37.5	114
B1 (mg)	1.1	0.2	0.06	0.06	0.08	0.08	0.9
B2 (mg)	0.31	0.2	0.1	0.03	0.03	0.03	0.31
B3 (mg)	2.2	0.76	0.6	0.08	0.18	0.2	2.1
B6 (mg)	-	-	-	-	-	-	0.6
B12 (µg)	-	-	-	-	-	1.7	-
C (mg)	-	13.3	-	-	-	-	-

Source: adapted from Kitty Campion, Vegetarian Encyclopedia, 1995

Activities

Working in groups, design a new frozen food product using tofu or TVP. Use the checklist below to help you. Draw up a specification for your product (see Unit 22). You may use text, graphics and original artwork in your specification. Present your ideas to the class.

CHECKLIST
• What is the purpose of your product?

The market
• Who are the intended users of your product?
• Who else might buy it?
• What are the dietary needs of these people?
• How will you find out what your intended market wants from a food product?
• What other products exist to meet the needs of this market? Is there a gap in the market?

The product
• What ingredients will you need? Are they available all year round? What will be their cost?
• What will the product look like - size, shape, colour?
• What will it taste like?
• What will be its nutritional value?
• What system will be used to manufacture the product?
• What energy use will be required? Can this be reduced?
• What controls will you need to ensure a consistent, quality product?
• What are the health and safety issues associated with the manufacture of your product?

Packaging
• What kind of packaging is necessary - to protect the product and attract buyers?
• What are the financial and environmental costs of the packaging?
• Does the product need to be cooked by the consumer? If so, what cooking instructions need to be included on the packaging?
• What other information needs to be included on the label?

HOW TOFU IS MADE
Soya beans are washed and ground to a paste. The fibre is removed (this is **okara**, which can also be used to make soya products such as pâtés and burgers). The remaining mixture is heated to produce soya milk. Calcium sulphate is added to coagulate the milk and the curds are pressed to give tofu. Tofu is available in original, smoked and marinated forms. It can be used for savoury or sweet dishes such as: kebabs, stir-fries, casseroles, burgers, salad dressings, fruit fools and sweet tarts.

Source: adapted from Cauldron Foods product information

HOW TVP IS MADE
Soya beans are hulled and the oil is extracted. The remaining beans are ground up to make soya flour. This is mixed with water and formed into different shapes - chunks, mince or flakes. TVP has a sponge-like texture and a bland taste and needs to be flavoured before adding to dishes. As well as being an excellent source of protein, vitamins and minerals, TVP adds substance and bulk to vegetarian dishes. TVP can be used for many types of dish, for example: lasagne, cottage pie, pasties, burgers and sausages.

Source: adapted from The Vegetarian, magazine of the Vegetarian Society, Autumn 1995

Tofu

TVP lasagne

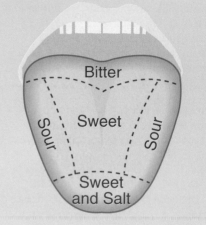

Figure 1 How we taste

Use your senses

The qualities of food that affect our organs of sense are known as ORGANOLEPTIC qualities. We are also affected by the AESTHETIC qualities of food. These are the features of food that appeal to our sense of beauty and taste.

Sight

When we look at food we can determine its colour, size, shape, age and quality.

Pictures of foods are often enough to stimulate our taste buds. The colour of food is also important. The recognition of specific flavours often relies on the food being coloured as expected. For example we expect chocolate flavoured products to be brown. Artificial colours are frequently used to enhance the colour of food. See Unit 11 for more information on colourings.

Hearing

Although not as important as the other senses, our sense of hearing is involved in our appreciation of food. The sounds made during preparation and cooking (e.g. cutting a fresh apple or frying chips) sharpen our appetite and give information about the crispness or crunchiness of a dish.

Smell and taste

When we eat, our senses of smell and taste work together to allow us to appreciate the flavour of food. Smell indicates freshness, ripeness and individual characteristics. When our sense of smell is reduced - for example, when we have a cold - it affects our ability to taste.

Different taste buds on the tongue detect salty, sweet, sour or bitter flavours. They are

The aesthetic appeal of a meal lies in its shape, form, colour and composition. The organoleptic appeal of the same dish comes from its tempting aroma, fresh look and delicious flavour.

concentrated in different areas of the tongue (see Figure 1). A substance must first dissolve in water in order for it to have a flavour. When food is mixed with saliva in the mouth, its flavour is developed. The number of taste buds we have decrease with age - babies and children have more than adults, making them more sensitive to strong flavours. We are most sensitive to taste when the temperature of food is between 22°C and 41°C. Sensitivity is reduced when the food is hotter or cooler than this.

Touch

We use our hands to touch food and

confirm its texture, consistency and ripeness. We also do this indirectly, using a utensil such as a wooden spoon or a knife. When we put food in our mouth, our brain receives many messages in addition to flavour, e.g. texture, consistency, moistness, dryness, chill, heat. These qualities of food are known as MOUTH FEEL.

Sensory profiling

MMR Sensory is a market research company. It carries out SENSORY PROFILING for food manufacturers, using highly trained taste

activities

1. a) Using the SENSORY DESCRIPTORS on the right describe the characteristics of the following foods. Use words from the list and add ideas of your own.
    - jelly, blue cheese, sponge cake, raw carrot, lemon mousse, toffee, curry, crisps, rice pudding, fried fish, shortbread, tofu.
    b) Which sense is easiest to describe? Which is the most difficult?

2.. Suggest THREE dishes which have a combination of textures within them e.g. lemon meringue pie.

3. Which food aroma do you enjoy the most - and which do you like the least?

SENSORY DESCRIPTORS

crunchy, crisp, fresh, tangy, creamy, strong, smooth, lumpy, peppery, salty, yellow, sweet, sour, bitter, acidic, brown, watery, thick, chewy, sticky, tart, slimy, bland, tough, bright, juicy, dry, moist, sharp, crumbly, shiny, spongy, oily, greasy, hot, spicy, cool, dark, light, heavy.

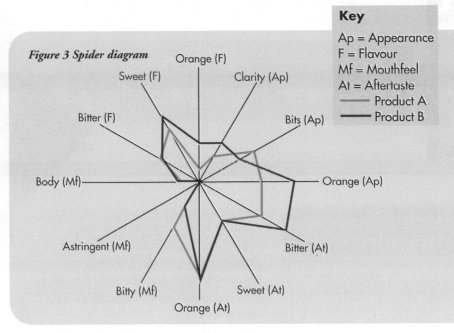

Figure 3 Spider diagram

Key

Ap = Appearance
F = Flavour
Mf = Mouthfeel
At = Aftertaste
—— Product A
—— Product B

Labels: Orange (F), Sweet (F), Clarity (Ap), Bitter (F), Bits (Ap), Body (Mf), Orange (Ap), Astringent (Mf), Bitter (At), Bitty (Mf), Sweet (At), Orange (At)

panels to describe the sensory characteristics of a product. Products are compared with other similar goods on the market. This helps manufacturers to determine the strengths and weaknesses of their product. There are several types of sensory test that *MMR Sensory* could use (see Table 1).

The taste panel

About 10 people take part in a sensory profile panel. Members have normal ability to perceive taste, odour, colour, etc. The most important quality is to be able to describe the sensory characteristics of the samples evaluated.

Familiarisation

When the panel begins work on a new product, e.g. orange squash, the members

first familiarise themselves with all the types of orange squash available. The method of assessing the drinks is standardised, e.g. dilute 1 in 5 with still bottled water. This standardisation is important to remove any variables which could affect the results.

Vocabulary development

The next stage is to build up a large vocabulary of words to describe the appearance, odour, flavour, mouthfeel and aftertaste of orange squash. Tasters compare different orange squashes and note down differences, e.g. level of sweetness, amount of body, etc.

Attribute rating

The next stage is the formal rating of products. This is a BLIND TASTING. Each panellist works individually in an environmentally controlled booth, where lighting is controlled so that visual differences between products are masked. The panellist is asked to test a product and

rate it on 30-60 attributes, e.g. sugary taste, viscosity, 'bits' in the squash, etc. The taster rates each attribute using a mouse and VDU linked to a central computer. Each panellist rates all of the products three times to ensure consistent results. No more than three products are rated in each session to avoid fatiguing the palate.

Data analysis

All the data is analysed on computer. There are several methods of analysis. 'Spider diagrams' (see Figure 2) are a useful way of comparing the sensory characteristics of different products. The ratings for each attribute are plotted onto the legs of the spider and joined up to produce a web. The shape of this web is known as the sensory profile of a product. A manufacturer might try to achieve a sensory profile similar to another product which is the market leader. The spider diagram will pinpoint areas where the product may need to be modified.

activities

Figure 2 shows the sensory profile of two orange squashes. Product A is the market leader.

1. Which product has a more orangey flavour?

2. Which product has more bits in it?

3. Which product has a more bitter taste?

4. The manufacturer of Product B would like to make its orange squash more like Product A in the hope that this will increase sales. What modifications should be made to Product B?

Disassembly

Packaging includes a variety of pieces of information about a product.

Product information

Information about a food product can be obtained by reading the labels or packaging (see Unit 25). For example, you could find out its net weight; how many units the package contains; the storage life; nutritional information; price and ingredients. The ingredients are given in weight order, the greatest first. However, the weight of each ingredient is not given.

What does disassembly mean?

We DISASSEMBLE a food product to find out more information about it. By carefully taking apart a product and weighing the individual ingredients you will find out more about the composition and proportions of a food product.

Who uses disassembly?

When designing a new product a food manufacturer might disassemble similar products made by other companies to find out more about the competition it faces. The food company would then analyse and evaluate the results before launching its own product.

Trading standards officers disassemble products to check that manufacturers are meeting legal requirements and packaging claims.

Disassembly is also a useful activity for students of nutrition or food technology. Products like sandwiches, fruit cake, ready meal products, pies and pasties can be quite simple to disassemble. Some products, however, are impossible to disassemble in a classroom. For example, you could disassemble a can of minestrone soup but it would be impossible to disassemble a can of tomato soup.

Recording results

Before disassembling a product you should design a PRO FORMA or template to help you record your results. This is a sheet that lists the procedures that you need to carry out and the questions that you want to answer. This could be as simple as the example in Table 1 or more complicated like the pro forma in Table 2. Using a pro forma ensures that the same method of analysis is used for each sample. This allows you to compare like with like in your evaluation. Your pro forma will vary depending on what you want to find out, but may include questions about the following areas:

- sensory characteristics of product
- choice of materials
- suitability of ingredients

Table I Simple pro forma

PRODUCT	APPEARANCE	TEXTURE	FLAVOUR

- proportions of ingredients
- production processes
- quality of product
- whether product meets intended purpose
- value for money.

Maintaining quality

When developing new foods manufacturers must consider the profit they hope to make. It is also vital that quality standards are maintained to protect the company's reputation. The ingredients allowed in some

activities

Kim and Aran want to set up a business making sandwiches and selling them through a range of local outlets. In order to help them make decisions about the products they might make and sell, they decide to carry out a disassembly of products currently available. Their aims are to find out which sandwiches are likely to sell well and which offer the best value for money.

1. Design a pro forma that will help Kim and Aran to assess the sandwiches.

2. Carry out the disassembly activity on a selection of sandwiches using the pro forma you have designed.

Table 2 Pro forma for chicken product disassembly

1. *Look at the product in its package.*
   - Why might the product appeal to children?
   - Examine the list of ingredients on the package and comment on the quality of ingredients.
   - What kind of meat is used?

2. *Defrost 100g of the product and remove the crumb. Record the weight of the core and crumb. Examine the core.*
   - What is the proportion of crumb to core?
   - Describe the appearance of the core.
   - Is it chicken meat or a chopped and shaped mixture?

3. *Place the core in warm water and stir.*
   - Describe what happens.
   - What conclusions do you draw from the results of this test?

4. *Weigh two 100g portions of the product and then cook according to the manufacturer's instructions*
   - With the first portion, remove the crumb. Record the weight of core and crumb.
   - What is the difference between these weights and the uncooked weights?

5. *With the second portion carry out a sensory test.*
   - What are your impressions of the product's aroma, texture and taste?

There are many breaded chicken products on the market aimed at children.

composite dishes are governed by legislation (see Unit 16). Many products previously covered by legislation have now been deregulated and some people believe that the quality has suffered.

While it is not illegal to vary the proportion of ingredients within a composite dish (as long as the product is not governed by legislation), it is illegal to mislead the consumer by inaccurate or vague information on the label.

An example of consumer confusion could arise in the case of a Shepherd's Pie. Because the word 'meat' does not appear in its name, it is not covered by the regulations specifying minimum quantities of meat allowed in a product. Manufacturers must only declare the meat content on the label if it is less that 10%, so a Shepherd's Pie may have an extremely low meat content of only 11 or 12%, without declaring this.

Key Terms

Disassemble - to take apart.
Pro forma - a standard sheet designed to record answers to the same questions for a number of different samples.

activities

1. a) Why are public analysts concerned about the quality of some food products?
   b) Which products feature in their report?

2. a) Write a set of instructions for the disassembly activity carried out by the newspaper on a packet of Chicken Kievs.
   b) Why are the results of this disassembly activity disturbing?

3. Carry out a disassembly of a breaded chicken product designed for children. Your aim is to find out information about the quality of ingredients; nutritional value and value for money and to determine which product is most suitable for the market. Table 2 suggests some procedures you could carry out and questions you could ask.

The association representing scientists at Britain's public food laboratories has published a report accusing the food industry of lowering standards. These are some of their results.
- The average meat content of potted meats has fallen from 95-80% in 10 years.
- Fish in many breadcrumb coated products is being replaced by water, cereal, emulsifiers and phosphates.
- Sliced meat may be described as roasted when it has been boiled, then flavoured.
- Shaped chicken products may consist almost entirely of mashed chicken skin, water and soya protein.
- Economy burgers may contain added rind, gristle and fat.
- Breaded scampi may have added water to increase bulk and weight.

Trading standards officers say that people are confused and often deliberately misled about the products they buy. The *Observer* analysed a packet of Chicken Kievs. After defrosting for an hour, the breadcrumb skin came off to reveal a centre of reconstituted mashed chicken skin moulded into the shape of a chicken breast, flecked with fragments of muscle meat. When this was stirred in warm water the product virtually disintegrated.

Source: adapted from the Observer, 21 July 1996

Why do we package food?

Food which has been processed needs to be packaged effectively so that it remains in prime condition for the consumer. A package should perform 4 functions.

- It must **protect** the food from: physical damage such as knocks and breakages; deterioration through high or low humidity and temperature change; contamination from odours, insect attack and mould growth; physiological changes within the product itself. The packaging must ensure that the product remains fresh from when it is opened until the whole pack has been consumed.
- It must **contain** the food to avoid loss through breakage or theft.
- It must **give information**. By law food labels must include information about contents, weight, nutrition, price, use by and best before dates plus storage advice. In addition they can include serving suggestions and a customer guarantee.
- It can be used for **marketing**. The pack displays the product on the shelf. The right package draws attention to the product and helps to persuade the customer to buy.

The label

Most pre-packed food must give the following information on the label:

- name of food
- list of ingredients, unless nothing added
- instructions for use
- storage instructions
- USE BY or BEST BEFORE dates.

- a lot or batch mark
- name and address of manufacturer
- a statement that the food has been irradiated or contains irradiated ingredients (if applicable).

Table 1 identifies the information found on a Tesco corn flakes package and gives reasons for including each element.

Table 1 Information on Tesco corn flakes package

INFORMATION	REASON
Product name	Identification of food
Fortified product	Health awareness
Illustration	Reinforces name
Weight	Legal requirement
e symbol	European standardisation
Storage instructions	Legal requirement
Composition of package	Environmental awareness
Guarantee	Manufacturer's reputation
Address	Legal requirement
Bar code	Stock control, pricing
Nutrition information	Health awareness
Ingredients	Legal requirement
Suitability for vegetarians	Special needs awareness
Best before date	Legal requirement/quality assurance
Batch code	Identify date of manufacture
Money saving coupon	Encourage brand loyalty
Description of product range	Encourage wider sales

activities

1.
a) What information must now be included on a sandwich label?
b) What are the reasons for including this information?

2.
a) What problem are sandwich makers facing as a result of the 1996 Food Labelling Regulations?
b) How have Breadwinner Foods addressed this problem?
c) Can you suggest any other solutions?

The new Food Labelling Regulations which came into force on 1 July 1996 include sandwiches for the first time. Labels on sandwiches must show the name and address of the makers, the use by date, the storage instructions and the name of the sandwich. All ingredients must be listed, plus the breakdown of individual ingredients if they make up more than 25% of the sandwich. Bread will almost certainly make up more than 25% of a sandwich, so all the bread ingredients must be listed. All this information can take up a lot of space. Describing a tuna mix and cucumber sandwich, for example, takes more than 40 words. Sandwich makers are concerned that the whole pack could end up covered with labelling, with the customer unable to see the product. One company, Breadwinner Foods, has invested in new machinery, costing £75,000, which will print ingredients on a clear label positioned on the top and bottom of the sandwich pack.

Source: adapted from Food Service Management, July 1996

Use by and best before

Food labels contain information about when the food should be eaten. Packs are marked with use by or best before dates. Food that goes off quickly (e.g. yogurt, meat pies, ready meals) is marked with a use by date. It is essential to eat the food by this date. There could be a risk of food poisoning if the food was eaten after this date - and it probably would not taste very nice either. Other foods (e.g. cereals, dried and canned goods) are marked with a best before date. Food is not necessarily dangerous after this date, but the quality may start to deteriorate.

Primary and secondary packing

Packaging falls into two categories.

PRIMARY PACKAGING is the box or wrapper in which the product is sold and should protect and display the product to its best advantage. There may be several layers of primary packaging.

SECONDARY PACKAGING is the extra packaging required for distribution e.g. several bottles of sparkling water may be over wrapped with heat sealed plastic to provide additional protection or baked beans may be packed in boxes of 48, loaded onto a pallet and over wrapped in heavy duty plastic for protection, security and convenience of transportation from the factory to the point of sale.

Materials used for packaging

Cans

Tin cans used for food are made of steel coated with a surface of tin to protect the steel from rusting. Modern cans are light and the walls are thin with ridges and lips which add strength to the structure. The inside of tins containing acidic food, like fruit, is often lacquered on the inside to prevent tin dissolving in the acid. Steel has been partly replaced by aluminium, a strong lightweight material which is expensive to extract and use. The recycling of aluminium cans has become an important industry. Cans are easily stacked on the supermarket shelf but are heavy to transport

Glass

Bottles and jars may be made of glass. The advantages of glass are that it:
● is cheap to produce
● is easy to clean and sterilise - and so can be recycled many times
● reveals contents effectively
● can withstand internal pressure of products such as fizzy drinks and champagne.

Bottles can be secured in a variety of ways including the fitting of TAMPER PROOF seals. The disadvantages are the fragility of the product and that glass is heavy to transport.

Paper and cardboard

This is a common type of packaging because it is: cheap; lightweight; easy to print on; easily disposed of or recycled. Paper and card can be treated to fulfil particular functions:
● greaseproof paper used for fatty products,
● waxed bags containing cereals
● plasticised cartons for liquids.

Cardboard containers are sturdy and rigid and can be produced in many shapes and sizes to suit varying products. Brick shaped containers known as tetrapacks are easy to store and are used widely for liquids.

Plastic

This was not used widely as a packaging material until the 1960s. Plastic containers come in a wide range of sizes and shapes, e.g. a preformed tray for chocolate eclairs, a supportive band around a frozen gâteau, a vacuum pack of cheese or a heat resistant tray for a cook-chill meal. Many modern plastics carry a triangular recycling sign and lettering such as PET to identify the type of plastic.

Technological developments in the use of plastics has led to MODIFIED ATMOSPHERE PACKING (MAP). This is a form of food preservation achieved by packaging the food in a hermetically sealed pack with a combination of three gases: oxygen; carbon dioxide and nitrogen. The foods are packaged in peak condition and the modified atmosphere inside the pack lengthens the shelf life of the product. Colour deterioration is inhibited until the pack is opened. The clear pack allows consumers to see the product. Some products packaged in this way are: salads,

activities

1. a) Give an example of a food packaged using each of the materials described above.
    b) State why you think the manufacturer has selected this type of material.

2. Orange juice can be packaged using different materials.
    a) List the packaging materials that can be used.
    b) Explain the advantages and disadvantages of each material.

An example of modified atmosphere packaging.

fresh pasta, sliced bacon, portions of meat and fish, poppadoms and part baked breads.

Combined materials

Plasticised aluminium foils which combine strength with the ability to create an air tight environment are used for crisps, coffee and drinking chocolate.

Choosing the right packaging

When assessing what type of packaging is going to be appropriate for a product, food manufacturers must consider a range of factors:

- rate of decay of product
- fragility of product
- whether product needs to be visible
- ease of use
- weight
- cost
- recyclability.

Environmental issues

Most people are concerned about the environment. As a consumer you can help to protect the environment through your spending decisions. Manufacturers are responding to consumer pressure to produce products which are less harmful to the environment.

Food manufacturers may be contributing to environmental problems by using

manufacturing processes which cause pollution or use up more energy than is necessary. They may also use too much packaging on their products (see Table 2) which causes the following problems:

- increased fuel costs in distribution
- extra domestic waste
- problems of collection, disposal and pollution.

With packaging, environmental groups say that our first concern should be to **reduce** the amount of waste created. We can do this by using reusable shopping bags, rather than taking new bags at the checkout, refusing extra unnecessary layers of packaging and writing to manufacturers who we think have over packaged their goods.

The second priority should be to **reuse** as much as possible. Ways of doing this include: saving jars to make jam; collecting yogurt pots, egg cartons and cardboard for primary schools or playgroups and buying refill packs.

After reducing and reusing, we should think about **recycling**. Consumers can help to protect the environment by recycling household waste in special bins provided by

the local authority. It is estimated that about half of our waste material could successfully be recycled. Table 3 shows the materials which can be recycled. In addition, we can choose to buy recyclable goods or products in recycled packaging.

Marketing

Packaging is an important way of communicating with customers. The right package can improve sales by:

- attracting attention to the product
- helping to persuade the buyer that it is value for money
- creating product familiarity and brand loyalty.

Research has revealed that a product on a supermarket shelf has ¹/₅ second to identify itself to a customer as the shopper's glance sweeps down the shelves.

In a product display the pack colour is noticed first, then the shape and finally the detail. Many products are identified subconsciously. For instance a Mars bar is an easily recognisable product due to its characteristic style of graphics and the colour

activities

1. What does the article tell you about the special needs of the elderly and infirm?

2. Make a list of action points for packaging manufacturers headed, 'Considering people with special needs'.

3. Environmental groups advise people to 'reduce, reuse, recycle'. Suggest ways that you could reduce, reuse and recycle the packaging in your household.

4. 'Food products are over packaged'.
   a) Do you agree with this statement?
   b) What might be some of the disadvantages of using several layers of packaging?
   c) How could you tell manufacturers what you think about this issue?

I had a 2kg weight on my left ankle, a 1kg weight on my right wrist, a blurred pair of spectacles, a pair of ear plugs, 2 surgical rubber gloves on each hand and a swimming arm band on my left arm. Then I went shopping. This is what it's like if you have recently had a stroke, your sight is failing and you've got arthritis. The project, run by Age Concern, aimed to teach food retailers and manufacturers about the special needs of the elderly and infirm. My first task - find a pack of spaghetti; how long does it take to cook? I found the packet but could not read the small print instructions. Next - locate a jelly; how long does it take to set? The information on the jelly pack was difficult to read, even without my fuzzy glasses. Too much space was given over to non-essential information like a recipe and a colour picture. After this, I was asked to open some products. It was almost impossible with some of them. Cheese with impenetrable plastic covers. Sauce bottles with unyielding screw tops. Milk cartons which spilt their contents all down your shirt.

Source: adapted from The Times, 18 February 1995

Table 2 Packaging

- Packaging accounts for at least 50% of household rubbish.
- Some packaging is necessary to protect the product and convey information.
- One third of packaging is not necessary and is only used to increase product sales.
- 5% of Britain's energy is used to make packaging.
- Consumers pay £10 out of every £65 shopping bill for packaging.
- Trees are made into paper bags, cardboard boxes and labels.
- Oil is used to make plastic bags, bottles and films. Some plastics, such as PVC, can be harmful to make and dispose of.
- Bauxite is mined to make aluminium cans, foil and the linings of drinks cartons. This uses huge amounts of energy. Rainforest areas are destroyed during mining and processing.

Source: Women's Environmental Network leaflet

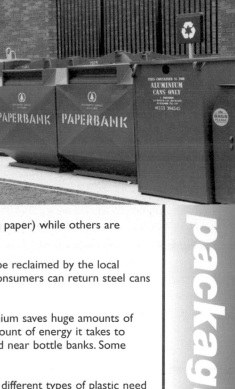

Table 3 Recycling materials

GLASS - Glass bottles and jars can easily be recycled at bottle banks all over the country. It is important that the three colours of glass (clear, green and brown) are kept separate. Glass can be recycled over and over again.

PAPER - There are different grades of paper. Some recycling facilities accept only 'high grade' paper (e.g. office paper) while others are specifically for 'low grade' paper, like newspapers.

STEEL CANS (most food cans) - Steel is magnetic, so it can be reclaimed by the local authority from mixed waste and returned for recycling. Consumers can return steel cans through 'Save-a-Can' banks.

ALUMINIUM CANS (most drinks cans) - Recycling aluminium saves huge amounts of energy - 20 recycled cans can be made using the same amount of energy it takes to make 1 new one. Aluminium can banks are usually situated near bottle banks. Some schools operate a can recycling scheme.

PLASTICS - Many types of plastic can be recycled, but the different types of plastic need to be separated. The triangular symbols and letters (e.g. PET) that appear on plastic packaging help to identify the type of plastic used. There are fewer collection facilities for plastics than there are for glass, cans and paper.

---

of its wrapper. If the key features of a package are changed sales are likely to drop because recognition is not instantaneous.

A package can be thought of as part of the sales team. It communicates with words and pictures. It must sell itself first off the supermarket shelf and then out of the storage cupboard and finally it must secure a repeat sale when the customer next goes shopping.

Packaging not only identifies the brand but informs consumers about the product, and gives an indication of quality.

Consumer demands for economically priced products have led to the development of minimal packaging such as Tesco's blue and white striped 'Value Brand' packs or Safeway's 'Savers'.

Designing packaging

The package designer must consider the following points.

Shape

Packages should be designed to stack neatly and economically on the supermarket shelf, although sometimes it can be an advantage to have an unusual shape package, e.g. Jif lemon juice is instantly recognisable due to the lemon-shaped container.

Size

The packaging should be appropriate for the volume of the product to avoid wastage of materials.

Colour

Colour is important as it gives our messages to the consumer, e.g. red tends to suggest richness and strength; blue is associated with coolness; green used to be an unlucky colour but is now associated with environmental issues; gold is associated with luxury products.

Graphics

The style of graphics reflects the corporate image of the company and is often the major factor in identifying the product, e.g. Coca-Cola's characteristic swirling letter forms and Polo's bold graphics.

Key Terms

Use by - the date by which a food must be eaten.
Best before - the date after which the quality of a product may deteriorate.
Primary packaging - the packaging in which food products are sold.
Secondary packaging - the packaging required for distribution.
Tamper proof - seals which guarantee that the product has not been opened.
Modified atmosphere packaging - packaging containing a mixture of gases which help to preserve food.

activities

Make a study of the advertisement of food products on television.

1. Design a pro forma (see Unit 24) to help you record the data.

2. Choose a selected time to record the data, e.g. a weekday evening between the hours of 5pm and 9pm.

3. Collate your results in whatever form you consider appropriate, e.g. bar charts, tables, pie charts, written text.

4. What conclusions do you draw from your results?

Kellogg's corn flakes is the brand of cereal that dominates the British breakfast table. The food is good, easy to prepare, and has additional nutrients added to make it an important part of the diet. Most supermarkets now produce their own brand of corn flakes but Kellogg's claim that their own is 'the original and best'. Unlike some other famous brand manufacturers, Kellogg's do not make corn flakes for anyone else. One of their advertising slogans was: 'If you don't see Kellogg's name on the box, it isn't Kellogg's in the box.'

In August 1996, Kellogg's threatened legal action against Tesco, accusing the store of copying Kellogg's packaging on three of its own label cereals (see Unit 25 for a picture of Tesco corn flakes). A spokesman for Kellogg's said: 'It is flattering that Tesco is trying to mimic our products, because Kellogg's is the gold standard'. Tesco denied that the packaging was similar.

The Times carried out a test to find out if people really could tell the difference between breakfast cereals. Two samples of Tesco corn flakes were set up alongside a single bowl of Kellogg's. The samples were labelled A, B and C. Tasters were allowed milk but no added sugar. Tasters were asked the question: 'Which is Kellogg's?' Out of 47 testers, only 5 chose the correct sample. *The Times* also tested other brands of corn flakes. The results are shown in Table 1.

Source: adapted from The Times, 16 August 1996

Activities

1. Why do Kellogg's advertise the fact that they do not make corn flakes for anyone else?

2. a) Why might competitors wish to mimic Kellogg's packaging?

   b) Why are Kellogg's threatening legal action against Tesco?

3. *The Times* used three samples of corn flakes in its test. What is the name of this type of test?

4. Why were the bowls of corn flakes labelled A, B and C?

5. Why were tasters not allowed to add sugar to the corn flakes?

6. Choose a famous brand (e.g. Walkers crisps, McVities digestives, Tetley tea). Your aim is to compare the brand with own label versions of the same product.

   a) Choose a sample of people to test the product.

   b) Decide which sensory test you will use.

   c) Decide which questions you want to answer and design a pro forma.

   d) Carry out the test, recording the results on the pro forma.

   e) Evaluate your results.

   f) What conclusions do you draw from your research?

Table 1 Corn flakes test

Brand	Appearance	Texture	In milk	Flavour	Mark/20
Kwik Save	large, pale	good crunch	floppy	nutty	5
Safeway Savers	light yellow	bubbly	absorbent	crisp	6
Sainsbury Economy	sandy	dull	soggy	missing	3
Iceland	mixed colour	average	collapsed	neutral	4
Asda	orange, pale blots	like Tesco	soon drowned	pleasant	8
Safeway	orange, blistered	light	short lived	cooked	10
Sainsbury	vivid orange	crinkly	crunchy	toasty	13
Tesco	orange, dotted	soggy	second best	moreish	15
Kellogg's	neat, bouncy	extra crunchy	best	attractive	19

Source: adapted from The Times, 16 August 1996

DESIGN AND PACKAGING AT CADBURY

Design is a way of communicating a company's corporate identity. The three key elements of the Cadbury design are

• the script logo based on William Cadbury's signature
• the glass and a half of milk symbol
• the purple and gold house colours.

These elements appear on signs, stationery and brands creating a memorable and distinctive logo which assures customers of the traditional Cadbury quality.

Design and packaging are closely interrelated. Packaging fulfils both a functional and a marketing role. In choosing packaging materials, Cadbury packaging technologists look for the most suitable materials available at competitive prices. Materials must be attractive, protect against odour and moisture transfer, run through the machinery well and be themselves free from odour. Wherever possible, the materials should be recyclable. The main packaging materials used at Cadbury are paper, board, cellulose film, plastic films, plastic sheet, aluminium foil and tinned steel, plus glass and rigid plastic which are used in the seasonal gift ranges. Table 1 shows how each material is used.

Packaging represents a significant investment for the manufacturer. At the Cadbury Assortments factory (just one part of the company's production, producing chocolate assortments, filled eggs and Christmas lines) packaging materials cost £23 million a year.

Legislation dictates how products are described, ingredients listed and weight displayed. Commercial requirements mean that a bar code is necessary. These elements must be considered by the pack designer along with other information, such as nutritional labelling.

Source: adapted from Cadbury information leaflet

Cadbury products

Table 1 Packaging materials

MATERIAL	USE
Paper	labels, wrappers, liners, box lid covers, component in laminates
Board	boxes (can be coated, laminated, treated and printed)
Cellulose and plastic films	overwrapping, bagging and sweet wrapping
Plastic sheet	chocolate trays, small boxes
Aluminium foil	chocolate wrapping, part of laminates
Tinned steel	export items, gift ranges

A one pound pack of of Cadbury's Roses chocolates has 71 packaging elements. Cadbury says that all of these are essential to maintain the highest standards in quality and appearance.

Activities

1. Why is a memorable and distinctive company logo important for Cadbury?
2. What are the functions of a confectionery pack?
3. Examine a confectionery pack which uses two or more types of packaging material, e.g. a bar of chocolate, a chocolate assortment, an Easter egg.
   a) What types of material are used?
   b) What function is performed by each packaging element?
   c) What is the weight of packaging compared to the weight of confectionery?
   d) Which parts of the packaging can be recycled?
4. Christmas and Easter are peak selling times for chocolates.
   a) How might packaging vary at Christmas and Easter from other times of year?
   b) Design a package for a seasonal confectionery line.

26 Planning work

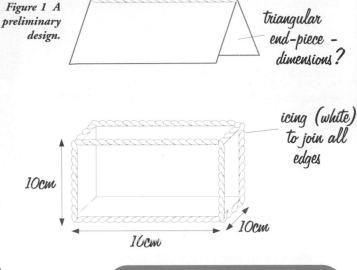

Figure 1 A preliminary design.

triangular end-piece - dimensions?

icing (white) to join all edges

10cm

16cm

10cm

Brainstorming

A cake manufacturer has decided to introduce a gingerbread house as a new line for Christmas. This will involve purchasing new machinery and retraining staff.

The research team is informed and asked to present ideas to the directors in three weeks. The team meet for their first planning session. Their first task is to pool ideas through a BRAINSTORM. A brainstorming session is a meeting where everyone contributes their thoughts on the subject. Preliminary design ideas might be discussed (see Figure 1), but nothing is decided at this stage. At the end of the session, the team has a clearer idea of what if needs to do next. Figure 2 shows some of the directions a brainstorming session might take.

Work schedules

After brainstorming, the team produces a timetable which sets out what needs to be done and within what time. This could be called a WORK SCHEDULE. The timetable takes into account the results of the brainstorming session and could include some of the following tasks.

● Do any other firms produce a ginger bread house? If so, get one and disassemble (see Unit 24).
● Find recipes which produce a suitable dough which, when baked, can be assembled into a house.
● Research the best icing for sticking the house together.
● Research sweets to be used for decorating the outside of the house.
● Decide on colours likely to encourage good sales.
● Design packaging for the finished cake.
● Write packaging information needed to comply with the law.

A work schedule helps the team to focus on the tasks to be tackled within the time available. Table 1 shows how such a schedule could be laid out.

Working as a team

It is worth spending time at the beginning deciding what tasks need to be done and allocating tasks to specific people. The group should work as a team using the strengths of each person. Allowing time for reviewing and evaluating work as it progresses helps to keep the team working well and also allows for any changes which might need to be made to the ongoing plan. It also helps to ensure a quality product.

Flow charts

A FLOW CHART can be used to simplify the work schedule and give the team a reference point from which to work. A flow chart is a 'short hand' diagram setting out tasks in a logical order. Different shapes are used for different stages of the process (see Figure 3). A flow chart should show:
● the order of activities
● what happens where
● crucial elements such as timing or temperature control.

It is sometimes difficult to include all these elements in one flow chart so often more than one is used. In a team there might be several

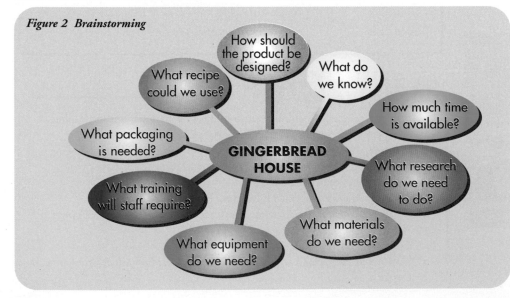

Figure 2 Brainstorming

GINGERBREAD HOUSE

How should the product be designed?

What do we know?

What recipe could we use?

How much time is available?

What packaging is needed?

What research do we need to do?

What training will staff require?

What equipment do we need?

What materials do we need?

flow charts in operation. Figure 3 shows a flow chart created by the Gingerbread team to use alongside the work schedule. Individuals might also produce their own work schedules and flow charts to help them organise their own work.

Time plans

A TIME PLAN sets out the tasks that have to be done and the order in which they should be tackled. A time plan differs from a work schedule because it tends to be concerned with one activity rather than a whole project. It may give a lot of detail about exactly what needs to be done and could include exact timings. Table 2 is an example of a time plan for preparing a lunch dish in one hour.

Table 1 Work schedule

Week 1	Task 1	Task 2	Task 3
	Brainstorm. Draw up time plan. Allocate tasks to team.	Research recipes. Research equipment required for making gingerbread house. Find out what staff training is needed. Discuss finished size and weight of product.	Design questionnaire for tasting panel. Review week's work. Evaluate. Plan for next week and adjust as necessary after week 1.
Week 2	**Task 1**	**Task 2**	**Task 3**
	Compare recipes found. Select which are the best for trialling. Make out shopping order.	Trial recipes. Test for shaping house. Employ the tasting panel. Conduct sensory tests.	Evaluate tasting panel results. Trial assembly of houses. Evaluate and adjust as necessary. Design packaging.
Week 3	**Task 1**	**Task 2**	**Task 3**
	Assemble house and leave to dry. Decide price. Complete designs for packaging.	Decorate house. Assemble packaging. Complete portfolio of designs, recipes, costings and report for directors.	Evaluate completed product. Present completed package to directors for approval.

Table 2 Time Plan

TIME	ORDER OF WORK
12.00	BOIL WATER. WASH SALAD.
12.10	ADD PASTA TO PAN. COMPLETE SALAD AND PUT IN FRIDGE.
12.20	WASH UP.
12.25	DRAIN PASTA AND RETURN TO PAN. PRE-HEAT GRILL.
12.30	DRAIN TUNA. CRUSH CRISPS. OPEN TIN OF CONDENSED MUSHROOM SOUP.
12.40	COMBINE SOUP AND TUNA WITH PASTA AND REHEAT GENTLY.
12.50	POUR INTO OVENPROOF DISH. TOP WITH CRISPS.
12.55	GRILL UNTIL GOLDEN.
1.00	SERVE.

MENU
Crunchy Tuna and Pasta Bake Mixed Salad
Serving time: 1.00pm
Cooking and preparation time: 1hr

Key Terms

Brainstorm - a discussion where everyone pools their ideas.
Work schedule - a timetable showing the tasks that need to be done.
Flow chart - a diagram which shows a sequence of events.
Time plan - a plan to help complete a set of tasks within an allotted time.

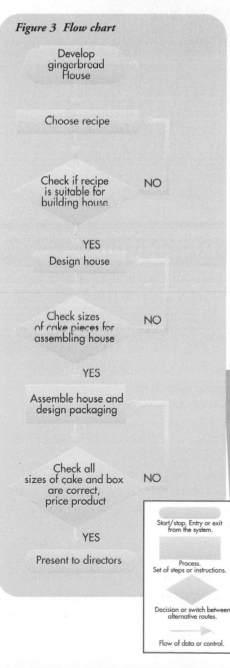

Figure 3 Flow chart

Develop gingerbread House

Choose recipe

Check if recipe is suitable for building house — NO

YES

Design house

Check sizes of cake pieces for assembling house — NO

YES

Assemble house and design packaging

Check all sizes of cake and box are correct, price product — NO

YES

Present to directors

Start/stop. Entry or exit from the system.

Process. Set of steps or instructions.

Decision or switch between alternative routes.

Flow of data or control.

activities

Despite several campaigns to make milk more fashionable, figures show that the amount of milk drunk by young people declines rapidly between the ages of 10 and 15. Develop a new product, using milk, to appeal to older children and teenagers. You have 4 weeks to prepare a presentation of your idea, together with a prototype.

1. In groups, brainstorm some ideas about what needs to be done to develop this product.

2. Draw up a work schedule, allocating tasks to specific people.

3. Produce a master flow chart, showing the key stages in the development process.

4. Draw a flow chart which outlines the tasks that you will have to do as your part of the team's work.

5. Prepare a time plan to help you with one of the activities in the project.

Working economically

Coughlans Patisserie
and COFFEE LOUNGE

In business

A food manufacturer, like any other company, wants to be successful. In order to stay in business, the firm must be COMMERCIALLY VIABLE. This means that the income received from sales must be more than the costs of production. In other words, over a period of time, the company must make a profit.

Costs of production

The costs involved in production at Coughlans Patisserie include:
- food materials
- wages and salaries
- rent
- equipment
- energy use
- insurance.

Some costs remain the same irrespective of the quantity produced. For instance, it costs Hugh and Jean the same amount in rent regardless of the number of loaves and cakes baked in a year. These are called FIXED COSTS. Other costs vary directly with the amount produced. For example, the total cost of flour will go up as more loaves are baked. These are called VARIABLE COSTS.

Revenue v costs

Income from sales, known as REVENUE, must cover the fixed and variable costs of the bakery. If revenue is the same as costs, the business breaks even. If revenue is greater than costs, the business makes a profit. If revenue is less than costs, the business makes a loss.

Hugh and Jean Weeks run a small bakery and shop in Wallington - Coughlans Patisserie. Hugh makes the bread, and employs two workers to help him with finishing the bread and making the pastries, cakes and gâteaux. Toward the end of the bread baking shift a further worker arrives who has sole responsibility for cleaning baking tins, equipment and preparation areas. In the shop there is a manageress and assistant who work full time, and a part timer who comes in from 11am - 2pm to deal with the sandwich trade. On Saturday two students come in for the day to give extra help. Jean keeps the books and orders the ingredients.

Working efficiently

Hugh and Jean know that a successful business depends on using materials and the people employed by the bakery efficiently.

There must be a balance between keeping costs as low as possible and still producing products of the quality that customers expect. There are several ways that the bakery can ensure that revenue is higher than costs - in other words, that it makes a profit:
- accurate budgets
- well managed stock control
- avoiding waste (of food materials, energy, staff time, etc.)
- appropriate pricing
- good portion control.

Budgeting

A BUDGET is a financial plan for a future time period, which could be a week, month or year. Hugh and Jean use a budget to control the family housekeeping. They also use a budget to manage their bakery business. In both cases there needs to be a balance between these factors.
- What do we want?
- What can we afford now?
- What will have to wait until more funds are available?

When preparing the budget for the bakery, Jean looks ahead to the next year and prepares a list of expenditure and income during that period. She is able to do this because the business runs a well managed stock control system and monitors its costs and revenue carefully. Jean uses the figures from the current year to make predictions about the next year. The budget is a plan of what the business hopes to achieve in the coming year. There are several things that could alter a financial plan:

- failing to provide popular types of bread and cakes
- fewer customers coming into the shop
- poor portion control
- wastage of food and fuel.

A good budget should take these things into account. Table 1 shows a simplified version of Jean's budget for the bakery.

Stock control

The baker must monitor carefully the buying and use of food materials. This is called STOCK CONTROL.

Levels of stocks

Hugh needs to keep enough goods in stock so that the bakery does not run out of materials, as this could delay production and disappoint customers. On the other hand, he does not want to hold too many stocks as this can be costly for several reasons, including:

- keeping capital tied up
- storage costs
- spoilage costs.

Some companies have found that just-in-time purchasing can avoid these problems (see Case Study on p. 121).

Rotation of stocks

It is an essential part of stock control that all foods are used in strict rotation. When deliveries arrive, the order is checked. New items are put at the back of shelves or store cupboards and older items are brought forward and used first.

Stock taking

Hugh records the cost of the materials bought every week for the bakery. He adds this to the value of stocks held. At any point, he knows how much the stocks in the bakery are worth. As goods are taken from the dry stores, refrigerators and freezers, Hugh records the value of goods used. At the end of the week, he performs a STOCK TAKE to count the goods remaining in stock. In this way, he can see

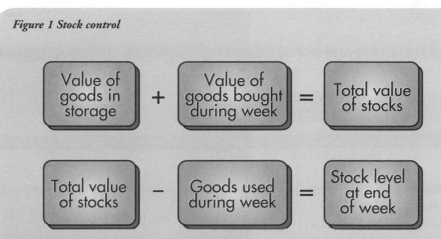

Figure 1 Stock control

The baker keeps a record of all goods bought and used. The stock level at the end of the week should equal the total value of stocks less goods used during the week. If it does not, the baker knows that materials are being wasted or stolen.

if materials are being lost through wastage or theft (see Figure 1).

Avoiding waste

Food

Coughlans Patisserie tries to avoid waste of food materials. This is important at all stages of the production process. For example, in the production of doughnuts, the following factors need to be considered.

The recipe - Hugh uses a standardised recipe for yeast dough. Using standard recipes means that the same amount of ingredients is used each time. This allows Jean to predict how many ingredients will be needed in the coming months. It also means that a check can be made to see if ingredients are being wasted, e.g. if 15kg flour is needed for one recipe but the stock take reveals that 17kg has been used.

The size of the finished product - The shape varies according to type of doughnut, but compared to other shops the cakes are large which is popular with the customers. Each piece of dough is weighed to ensure uniformity of size. If the doughnuts are too large profits will be reduced.

The production process - The fermented yeast dough is shaped into doughnuts, deep fried and drained.

The finish - All doughnuts are rolled in caster sugar after frying. The apple doughnut is filled before frying. The jam, cream and fudge doughnuts are finished after frying. The amount of jam, cream and fudge flavoured icing is controlled, balancing economy of use with customer satisfaction.

Energy

Energy bills for the bakery form a large

activities

Table 1 shows the budget for Coughlans Patisserie for the next financial year.

1. Does the budget show that the business will make a profit or a loss?

2. What sales would the bakery have to make in order to break even?

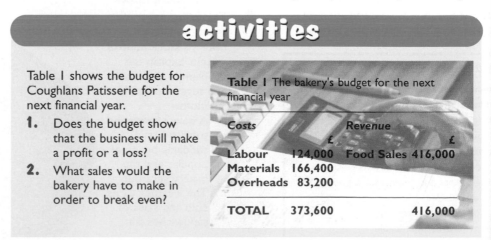

Table 1 The bakery's budget for the next financial year

Costs	£	Revenue	£
Labour	124,000	Food Sales	416,000
Materials	166,400		
Overheads	83,200		
TOTAL	**373,600**		**416,000**

part of Hugh and Jean's budget. In order to keep these costs as low as possible, they try to avoid waste. Table 2 shows some of the energy saving measures used at Coughlans Patisserie.

Pricing

There are several methods that a business can use in order to set a price for its goods.

Competition based pricing

The business could look at the price of similar products sold by its competitors. The business will then choose whether to charge the same price or a slightly lower price in order to attract customers. This kind of pricing system is usually used by large companies who face strong competition. Medium sized businesses and sole traders may not be able to compete with the prices charged by large companies like supermarkets. They rely on regular customers who are willing to pay a higher price for their products.

Market orientated pricing

The business could set its price after analysing the market for which its products are intended. For example, a company might decide to charge a very low price for one of its products. The price charged is so low that it does not cover the costs of production. The company makes a loss on every item they sell. However, the low price would encourage people into the shop and they may buy other items. The low priced item would be known as a LOSS LEADER.

People are often prepared to pay more for goods which they see as luxury or novelty items. Hugh and Jean could decide to charge a higher than usual price for their cream and

Doughnuts

fudge doughnuts because they are seen to be luxury items. Estimating the price people will be prepared to pay is known as CUSTOMER VALUE PRICING.

Cost plus pricing

The business works out the cost of producing a product and then adds a 'mark up' to give a certain profit. In order to do this, the business must calculate or estimate the unit or AVERAGE COST of producing each

item. It then adds the desired mark up to give a selling price.

Portion control

There are some items which have to be portioned after baking and finishing, e.g. gâteaux and pizzas (see Figure 3). The cakes are circular and the pizza rectangular. The number of slices created

---

Table 2 Reducing energy use

- Ovens are programmed to turn on when needed and are turned off as soon as the baking is completed for the night.
- Equipment, ovens and ventilation extractors are regularly cleaned and serviced to ensure maximum efficiency.
- Refrigerators and freezers are opened as little as possible.
- Economy (fluorescent) lights are used wherever practicable.

---

activities

1. Explain why it might be a problem for the bakery to hold:
   a) too much stock
   b) not enough stock.

2. The following situations affect the bakery's stock control system. Explain the problem in each case and suggest possible solutions.
   a) A new 'cheese and tomato bread' suddenly becomes popular and the bakery sells out.
   b) The weather turns cold and sales of sandwiches fall

rapidly.
   c) A fruit cake requires a large number of ingredients, which always seem to be running out.

Cheese and tomato bread

from each of these items must ensure that:
- all costs are covered
- the customer is getting value for money
- there is a minimum of waste.

Coughlans Patisserie find that a circular cake has the problem of the centre point breaking off. This can be overcome by cutting a small circle in the centre of the cake which can be sold later at a cheaper price. Pizzas are either made as individual portions (not as economical to bake as large rectangles), or as large slabs which are cut after cooking. Large slabs of pizza must be cut so that the customer receives the same value for money each time a portion of pizza is purchased.

Key Terms

Commercially viable - when revenue from sales is greater than costs so that, over a period of time, a profit is made.

Fixed costs - costs that remain the same whatever the level of output of the business.

Variable costs - costs that vary depending on the level of output of the business.

Revenue - income from sales of products.

Budget - a financial plan for a future time period.

Stock control - the monitoring of all food materials purchased for the business.

Stock take - a regular procedure to check the level of stocks held.

Competition based pricing - setting a price based on prices charged by competitors for similar products.

Market orientated pricing - pricing method based on an analysis of the market.

Loss leader - selling a product at a loss-making price, in order to bring customers into the store.

Customer value pricing - pricing method based on estimating what customers will be prepared to pay.

Cost plus pricing - setting a price by adding a percentage mark up onto the costs of producing an item.

Average cost - total production costs divided by number of products made.

Figure 2 Pricing doughnuts

Coughlans Patisserie sell four types of doughnut: jam, apple, fudge and cream. Doughnuts are a popular cake and usually sell out quickly. Setting the correct price is important because the owners know it will affect sales. Hugh and Jean decide that they can set a price per doughnut of 40p. This is the price they believe customers will bear. They estimate that the costs of production for each doughnut are:

10p	labour
12p	overheads
10p	materials
32p	total costs

This allows a mark up (or profit) of 8p per doughnut. Charging 40p means that they are covering their costs and also making a profit. They call this 'backward pricing'.

activities

1. A supermarket bakery uses cost plus pricing. It costs the bakery 45p to produce a small loaf.

   a) The bakery decides to set the price of a small white loaf at 40p for one week only. What do they hope to achieve by this?

   b) The bakery sets the price of a small granary loaf at 60p. Why does it do this?

2. Look at the gâteau in Figure 3. It is decorated to help the assistant cut the cake into even slices.

   a) How many portions will the gâteau provide?

   b) It costs £9.00 to produce a gâteau. How much should each slice sell for?

3. Look at the pizza slab in Figure 3. It can be divided into 8 slices. It costs £6.00 to produce a pizza slab.. How much should be charged per slice in order to compete with the takeaway nearby which charges 99p a slice for its pizza?

Figure 3 - Portion control

Markers which show where the cake must be cut can be incorporated into the design of the gâteau.

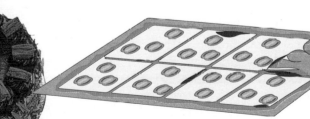

A pizza could be decorated in squares to help the shop assistant to cut it fairly.

FILM CUISINE

On location in Liverpool

Film Cuisine caters for film and television productions all over Britain, e.g. Brookside, Coronation Street, Emmerdale and The Woodlanders. Catering for a crew of 50 or 60 people from a small mobile kitchen, often in remote locations, is a challenging job. Good planning is essential.

There are two Film Cuisine catering units (each consisting of kitchen, dining bus and support van). This allows the company to work on films (often 6-8 weeks work) without disappointing clients who book them for smaller but more regular jobs. The £50,000 kitchen van is equipped with a 6 burner range with oven, grill, deep fryer, water boiler, hot cupboards and fridge. There are 3 separate sinks, for washing dishes, vegetables and hands.

Film Cuisine buys meat from the butcher near its home base, portioned, sealed in Cryovac bags and frozen. Fish is also bought frozen and stored in the same way. Dry goods are bought from the cash and carry. Fruit, vegetables, bread and milk are bought on a daily basis from supermarkets near the location. On longer shoots, fresh and frozen meat and fish are also bought on location.

Menus are planned on a daily basis, depending on what foods are available. As film crews consist of many groups of people, it is important to offer meals to suit different needs. There are always one or two meat dishes, a fish dish and a vegetarian dish. Special needs, such as vegan meals, are also catered for. As many crew members will be eating only Film Cuisine food for up to six days a week, the chef must ensure that nutritional needs are met. Over a 6 or 8 week shoot, the chef rotates 40 or 50 main dishes. However, each type of dish can be served in several different ways, e.g. a curry can be chicken tikka, vegetable balti, mushroom korma, etc.

On a large job, there are usually three workers: a chef, who prepares the main course and sweets and also drives the bus; an assistant who prepares the cold table, starter and cheeseboard; and a dining bus driver, who keeps the bus clean, prepares vegetables and keeps the tea and coffee urns full all day. As space is limited in the kitchen, staff must be organised, tidy and keep to their own space.

Working on location causes particular problems for the caterer. Power is essential. The kitchen and support van cannot be without power for more than 12 hours. Mains power is sometimes available on location. Otherwise diesel-run generators are used. The cooker and grill are powered by gas, carried in bottles.

The kitchen van is equipped with water tanks which will carry 65 gallons of fresh water - enough for a crew of 30 for breakfast, lunch and tea. On a longer shoot, or if crew numbers are higher, local water supplies are essential. Hygiene regulations say that waste water must be held in the vehicle's waste tanks and disposed of in a mains sewer. This has to be done daily.

Waste paper and food must also be collected and disposed of carefully.

On a shoot, filming takes priority over food. Caterers must fit in with the needs of the production. Every evening a call sheet tells the caterers where and when the next day's meals should be served but schedules often have to change. A meal can be brought forward by up to an hour. It can also be delayed for up to three hours. The food is kept warm (above 63°C) in hot cabinets. This keeps it safe to eat, but quality deteriorates the longer it is kept waiting.

Time	Task
5.30am	Travel to location
6.30am	Prepare breakfast
7.30am	Serve breakfast
8.00am	Crew starts work
	Film Cuisine staff eats breakfast
8.30am	Clear up breakfast - wash up all dishes, trays, pans and bain maries
	Clear dining bus
9.30am	Prepare lunch
12.30pm	Serve lunch
1.30pm	Crew starts work
	Film Cuisine staff eats lunch
2.00pm	Clear up lunch - as breakfast
3.00pm	Prepare afternoon tea
4.30pm	Serve afternoon tea where crew is working and close up kitchen for day
5.00pm	Travel home, perhaps shopping on the way

Figure 2 - Typicals day's schedule

BREAKFAST
juice, cereals (and porridge in winter),
full cooked breakfast, toast, rolls

• • • • • • • • • •

LUNCH
Starter: melon or soup
Main courses: Choice of mixed grill,
smoked haddock, vegetable chilli tacos.
Choice of 2 vegetables and
2 or 3 types of potatoes
Cold table: cold meats, salads
Sweets: Choice of 4 or 5, e.g. home made
apple pie, cheesecake, mandarin gâteau
Cheeseboard and fruit basket

• • • • • • • • • •

AFTERNOON TEA
sandwiches (ham, tuna, cheese, beef,
pork, egg mayonnaise), cakes (home made
scones, fresh cream cakes or individual
packet cakes)

HOT TEAS AND COFFEE AVAILABLE
ALL DAY

Figure 1 - Typical day's menu

Activities

1. How does having two catering units help Film Cuisine to schedule their workload?
2. What are the advantages of buying meat ready portioned and frozen?
3. Name TEN items that Film Cuisine might need to buy from the cash and carry.
4. a) List the tasks that would have to be done by the staff of a Film Cuisine unit in order to prepare and serve the menu in Figure 1.
   b) Who would be likely to do each task?
5. State THREE hygiene rules that Film Cuisine staff would need to follow to ensure the safety of their food.
6. What problems do film caterers face that might not affect other types of catering businesses?

AUTOMATIC REPLENISHMENT AT UNITED BISCUITS

At the United Biscuits factory in Harlesden, London (where McVitie's Digestives, Rich Tea, Homewheat and Hobnobs are made), a new computer system has reduced costs dramatically.

The plant has direct computer links to suppliers allowing them to monitor the use of materials and replenish stocks as needed. The Automatic Replenishment Package (ARP) has been designed by Stonefield Systems and is a first in British food manufacturing.

The ARP system has been fully operational in the Harlesden plant since January 1996. Supplies of flour, sugar, chocolate, milk and oils are controlled in this way. Figure 1 shows how the system works.

Each silo is linked to a central computer in the plant. The level of the silo is automatically measured every 5 minutes and the data is updated on the system.

The technical controller monitors all stocks in the plant via a central computer. This terminal is linked by modems to suppliers' terminals.

Suppliers dial in at regular intervals to check the levels of the silos containing their products. This allows them to estimate the plant's needs for the next 24 hours. If there is an alarm condition for the tank (e.g. if the level falls to re-order level) the central computer will automatically dial the supplier to relay the alarm message.

With up-to-date information about the plant's needs, suppliers are able to plan production and delivery schedules more efficiently. United Biscuits saves time by not having to make repeated phone calls to suppliers and benefits from easier stock control, reduced administration costs and an improved quality of supply.

The ARP system reduces United Biscuits' costs in several ways:

- saves time because there is no need to check the level of the silos manually
- saves administration costs because there is no need for United Biscuits' staff to liaise with suppliers to re-order stock
- capital is retained for longer because stocks are only paid for as they are needed.

Source: adapted from United Biscuits Annual Report and Accounts and Stonefield Systems information

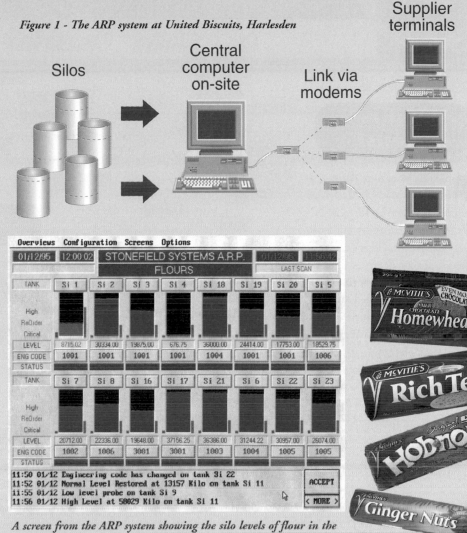

Figure 1 - The ARP system at United Biscuits, Harlesden

Silos → Central computer on-site → Link via modems → Supplier terminals

A screen from the ARP system showing the silo levels of flour in the plant. The technical controller can see at a glance which silos have adequate stocks (blue), which need re-ordering (red) and which are running critically low (pink).

Activities

1. Most food manufacturers monitor levels of ingredients and, when they are running low, order new stocks from suppliers. How does the system at United Biscuits' Harlesden factory differ from this?
2. What happens if the level of an ingredient reaches re-order levels?
3. How does the Automatic Replenishment Package reduce United Biscuits' costs?
4. a) What are the advantages of this system for suppliers?
   b) Can you think of any disadvantages for suppliers?

What is a system?

A SYSTEM can be defined as a set of objects or activities which together perform a structured task. A system can be mechanical, electrical or electronic, or it can be an activity to produce a product. An example of a mechanical system is a hand whisk which is used to mix food. A digital scale is an electronic system used to weigh food accurately. A production line in a pie factory is a system used to manufacture products.

A successful system may be a combination of several small or sub-systems which all rely on each other. If one of the sub-systems breaks down the whole process may be affected. For example, the production of cherry pies relies on the regular delivery of component parts. If the cherries are not delivered on time the pies cannot be made, production ceases and profits are lost. Figure 1 shows how a company relies on many systems in order to operate effectively. These systems all interact with each other.

Why do we use systems?

Systems are used to manage a particular process or situation. They may improve or maintain standards of quality, efficiency and cost effectiveness. A system may do one or more of the following.

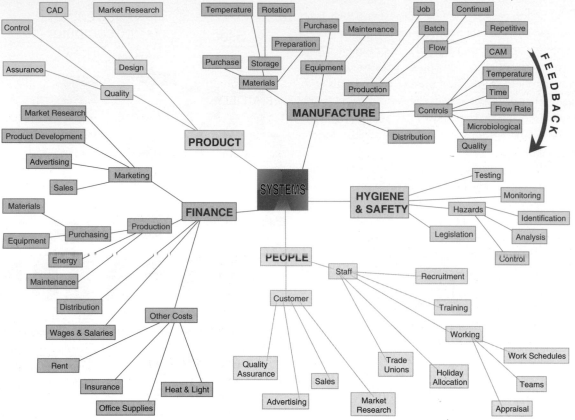

Figure 1 systems in a business This diagram shows some of the systems operating in a large company. The five main 'branches' show systems involving: product; people; finance; hygiene and safety; manufacture. Each branch divides into smaller branches showing some of the sub-systems that make up the larger systems. For example in the manufacture of a product, the production system could be flow production, which in turn could be continual.

● make a task easier
● make a process more efficient
● slow down or speed up a process
● help to analyse an activity.

Input/process/output

A system is made up of three parts: INPUT, PROCESS and OUTPUT (see Figure 2).

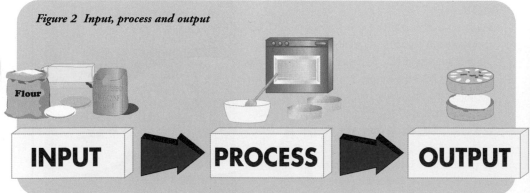

Figure 2 Input, process and output

INPUT → PROCESS → OUTPUT

Input - Information, materials or energy which is put into the system. In the food industry this is likely to be the raw materials or component parts.

Process - What happens to the information, materials or energy. In the food industry this may be the making of the food product.

Output - This is an outcome of the system, for example the finished food product and and its distribution for sale to the consumer.

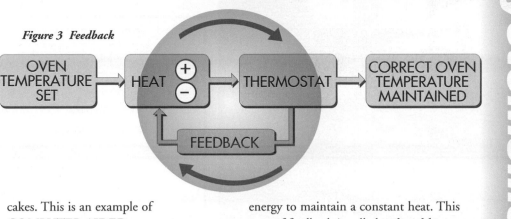

Figure 3 Feedback

OVEN TEMPERATURE SET → HEAT (+ −) → THERMOSTAT → CORRECT OVEN TEMPERATURE MAINTAINED

FEEDBACK

With computer aided manufacture, one person can supervise many operations.

Controlling systems

It is necessary to CONTROL the information, materials or energy as they move through a system. Various methods can be used to vary the speed and quality of production, for example:

● switches
● sensors
● dials
● gauges
● tests.

Many food manufacturers use computers to help them control the production system. Computer aided design (CAD) is used during the design stages (see Unit 22). In large companies, the manufacturing process is also often controlled by computers. For example, the thermostats in a series of ovens in a cake factory are linked to a computer. Specially designed software controls the temperature of all the ovens, adjusting it to the specifications of each batch of

cakes. This is an example of COMPUTER AIDED MANUFACTURE (CAM). Computers can also be used to control the monitoring of stock levels, and in some cases, the re-ordering of ingredients (see Case Study on p. 121).

Feedback

FEEDBACK is information that is passed from a later stage of a system to an earlier stage. Feedback is important because it alerts the system to any changes that may need to be made in order for the system to run more efficiently.

A thermostat in an oven is an example of how feedback works (see Figure 3). A thermostat is a sensor used to control temperature. In a conventional domestic oven the required temperature is pre-selected. The oven then heats up until this temperature is reached. At that point the thermostat cuts in and interrupts the flow of energy. When the temperature falls the thermostat cuts out automatically increasing the flow of energy heating the oven again to the pre-selected temperature.

This becomes a continuous process, the thermostatic sensor regulating the flow of

energy to maintain a constant heat. This type of feedback is called a **closed loop system** and results in a circular pattern on the flow chart (see Figure 3).

Feedback can be positive or negative. Positive feedback acts to increase the signal (e.g. to turn the heat up). Negative feedback acts to reduce the signal (e.g. to turn heat down).

Manufacturing systems

Production systems fall into three main categories according to the products made. Companies often employ a mixture of these systems. These categories are:

● JOB PRODUCTION
● BATCH PRODUCTION
● FLOW PRODUCTION.

The production method chosen depends on the:

● number of products to be made
● the type of product
● the selling price of the product.

Job production

One product is made. The product is designed and made to specific

activities

1. Draw a diagram showing the different systems that could be involved in the making of a lemon meringue pie.
2. Name THREE possible inputs into this system.
3. What controls might be used when making this product?

Loaves made by the batch production system.

Table 1 Types of production system

	Job	Batch	Flow
Product	unique item individual orders e.g. celebration cakes	relatively small number of a variety of standard items e.g. bread, cheese	usually mass production of standard product e.g. pasta, frozen vegetables
Labour	highly skilled craftsperson	semi-skilled or unskilled	limited range of tasks low level of individual skill
Market	individual orders repeat orders unlikely	selling to wider market steady demand for variable quantities	large market regular, long term demand

requirements. The finished product is unique. Job production can be used in the following situations:

- making a prototype in response to a brief (see Unit 22)
- custom producing a specialised product.

Products made in this way are often of high quality and take a long time to make. This leads to a high cost per unit.

Batch production

Relatively small numbers of identical or similar products are made. Equipment and labour are then switched to another product. For example, a bakery may make different kinds of bread and cakes using the same equipment. They may produce a batch of wholemeal loaves, followed by a batch of Victoria sandwich sponges. Batch production is cheaper than job production because:

- materials can be purchased in bulk
- labour can be less skilled
- fixed production costs are spread over a larger number of products.

Problems could occur if the batch size is too large, leading to goods remaining unsold.

There may also be time lost between batches as machinery is reset to the requirements of the new batch.

Flow production

CONTINUAL FLOW PRODUCTION is where products pass through a number of stages with each stage adding to the product, e.g. a frozen pizza (see Case Study on p. 128). At each stage, machines or workers carry out a specialised task. REPETITIVE FLOW PRODUCTION is where large numbers of identical products

activities

Clare Bradburn makes and decorates wedding cakes. Each cake is made to order for a customer. When customers wish to buy a cake, Clare meets them, shows them photographs and discusses their requirements (e.g. number of guests, colours, type of icing, shape of cake, flowers). Clare starts making the cake about 3 months before the wedding. The most time-consuming aspect of the job is the making of the sugar flowers. Each petal and leaf is hand crafted and added to the flower in stages. The flower must be left to dry for 24 hours between each stage. When all the flowers are made they are bound together with ribbon and wire. About 10 days before the wedding, Clare completes the final stages of the cake: almond paste, icing, assembling and decoration. Each cake takes up to 200 hours to make.

1. What production system is used to manufacture the wedding cakes?
2. What are the advantages to the customer of this type of system?
3. Comment on the costs involved in this type of production system.

are produced as cheaply as possible. Flow production is usually, but not always, used to make thousands or millions of products. This is called MASS PRODUCTION. Although there is a high investment associated with buying the machinery to set up a production line, this system leads to lower unit costs. This is because:

● materials can be purchased in bulk
● semi-skilled or unskilled labour can be used
● production costs are spread over a large output.

If some parts of the production line are automated, for example if computer aided manufacture is used, unit costs will fall even further. This system relies on large and regular sales of the products made. Work may be boring and monotonous for workers which could lead to labour problems. If there is a breakdown on one part of the production line, the whole system will be affected.

An example of flow production

activities

Handmade Foods is a company which makes specialist food products for the gift market. Its products are available in gift shops, tea rooms and by mail order. Handmade Foods wants to introduce a selection of flavoured oils and vinegar to its range. After testing the market, Handmade Foods decides to go ahead with a range of 4 flavoured oils and 4 flavoured vinegars. It also decides to add 3 mixed salad dressings to the range. Initially it plans to make 1000 bottles of each variety.

1. a) Name the production system that Handmade Foods would have used to make a single sample of flavoured vinegar for the test market.

   b) What stages would take place when making the sample?

2. a) Suggest a suitable production system for the manufacture of the complete product range.

   b) What are the advantages and disadvantages of this system?

What is quality?

Manufacturers try to produce QUALITY products. A product may be said to have quality if it achieves a high grade or level of excellence. Quality can also be seen in standards of customer service.

By aiming for quality a company can hope to achieve a good reputation, good sales and customer loyalty. Quality can also save the company money by reducing waste and improving efficiency during the production of goods. When judging the quality of a food product you might consider:

● sensory qualities
● nutritional content
● fitness for purpose
● size and weight
● value for money
● consistency
● hygiene and safety
● energy efficiency
● packaging.

Table 1 suggests some questions to ask when judging the quality of a ready meal.

It is possible to distinguish between quality of design and quality of manufacture. Quality of design refers to the ideas and planning that went into the design of a product. Quality of manufacture refers to the production process used to make products. Methods used to evaluate quality include quality control and quality assurance.

Quality control

QUALITY CONTROL is a way of checking the quality of a product during or at the end of the production system, e.g. quality of ingredients; texture, colour and flavour of product; portion size; uniformity. Table 2 suggests some quality control points to consider when making Cornish pasties.

Table 1 Judging quality

This Broccoli Mornay ready meal is described as 'broccoli spears with a tomato sauce covered in a creamy cheese sauce'. The label states that the product 'provides approximately 1 serving' and can be cooked in 4½ minutes in a 750W microwave. Is it a quality product? You could ask the following questions.

• How far does it meets the specified need?
  e.g. Does it supply an adequate portion? Is it 'creamy' and/or cheesy?
• Is it fit for its purpose?
  e.g. Is the dish capable of being cooked in a microwave safely and effectively in the time stated?
• Does it meet the dietary needs of the market/s for which it is intended?
  e.g. Is it suitable for vegetarians?
• Is it an appropriate use of resources?
  e.g. Does it save time, money or effort?
• What is its environmental impact?
  e.g. How much energy is used to make and distribute the product? What packaging waste is created? Can packaging be reduced/reused/recycled?

In an industrial context, quality control procedures might include:

● visual inspections
● check weighings
● random sampling
● metal detector tests.

Figure 1 shows some of the methods Birds Eye use to ensure the quality of their frozen peas.

Sometimes, quality control takes place at the end of production. If a product does not conform to requirements, it is rejected. This method identifies poor quality products before they reach the consumer but it may not necessarily discover the cause of the problem.

TOTAL QUALITY MANAGEMENT is a way of involving everyone who works in a company. Each person is responsible for the quality of his or her work. Inspection and testing take place at all stages of the process (design, development and production). This reduces the chance of poor quality goods reaching the final stages of production.

activities

1. a) How do you judge the quality of a product? Brainstorm a list of at least SIX questions you might ask.

   b) Choose a food product you like and check it against the quality criteria you have drawn up. How does it perform?

2. Quality control is as important in your kitchen as it is in a large factory. Look at Table 2 and then draw up a quality control checklist for the following products:
   - cheese and tomato sandwich
   - ham and mushroom omelette
   - roast chicken, new potatoes, carrots and broccoli
   - apple pie.

Table 2 Quality control when cooking

These are some quality points you could consider when making Cornish pasties:
- all ingredients fresh - visual check and check date marks
- correct proportion of ingredients - use reliable recipe and accurate scales
- safe preparation of foods - use different boards for meat and vegetable preparation
- ensure even cooking - cut vegetables into equal size pieces, using a food processor
- pastry rolled evenly - do not stretch or it will shrink in the oven
- cut same size pastry circles - use plate or saucer as template
- even distribution of filling - visual check
- bake at correct temperature - set dial correctly and check with oven thermometer or built in thermostat
- bake for correct time - use timer
- cool quickly and store in fridge or freezer - within 1 1/2 hours.

Visual checks on the production line are a part of quality control.

Quality assurance

When goods are sent out to customers the company gives its assurance that certain standards have been met in the following areas:

- **the product** meets nutritional and advertising claims; is the correct weight; is safe to eat
- **quality control** has been maintained throughout manufacturing process
- **legal requirements** have been met (see Unit 30).

In addition to legislation and the guarantees offered by manufacturers, a number of CODES OF PRACTICE have been established. These tell a customer that work has been carried out to a set standard.

Many countries use their own codes of practice and there are European and international standards as well. In 1979, the BS 5750 standard was set up by the British Standards Institute. In 1987, the International Quality System standard was set up. This is known as the ISO 9000 series. These two standards are measures against which a company's quality system can be compared.

There are a number of steps to achieving ISO 9000 registration:
- company prepares quality system to meet requirements of standard
- company applies for registration
- independent auditor visits company and suggests any modifications that need to be made
- continual monitoring takes place to ensure standards are maintained

Once registered the ISO 9000 logo may be used on company stationery (see Figure 2). This assures customers that the company is operating to a high quality standard.

Key Terms

Quality - a high grade or level of excellence.

Quality control - a way of checking the quality of a product during or at the end of the production system.

Total quality management - making quality the responsibility of everyone in the business.

Quality assurance - guarantees to the customer about the quality standards of a company.

Codes of practice - standards which indicate that the quality of production meets a certain level.

activities

Figure 1 shows the quality control measures carried out during the production of Birds Eye frozen peas.

1. List the quality control checks used.

2. What is the purpose of each of these checks?

3. Using your knowledge of the manufacture of a specific food product:
   a) draw a diagram showing the stages in the production process
   b) indicate what quality control measures might be needed and where they should be carried out.

frozen peas arrive from the cold store

visual inspection of frozen peas

peas are automatically weighed into portions

peas pass along production line on moving belts

bags pass through a metal detector

bags pass over a weight checker

bags are packed into cardboard boxes

boxes are sealed

boxes are loaded onto pallets for dispatch

Figure 1 Quality control at Birds Eye

weighed portions of peas drop down into bags, which are then sealed

The pizza production line (see Figure 1) at McCain Foods is an example of a continual flow system. The pizza passes through several stages, and at each stage something is added to it.

Once a variety of pizza has been developed, it is then manufactured to set specifications so that the product is always the same.

All procedures from the raw ingredients to the finished pizza are monitored to ensure a quality finished product. There are several control systems in operation (see Table 1).

Table 1 - Controlling the system

INGREDIENTS
Frozen ingredients arrive individually quality frozen (IQF) and are stored at between -20°C and -25°C. Chilled ingredients, such as cheese, yeast and pepperoni are stored at 4°C. Flour is delivered by the tanker load and goes straight into a silo. All other ingredients (e.g. spices, canned tomatoes and olives) go into a large dry store. All incoming products are checked to strict specifications for quality and are analysed microbiologically, before being allowed to be used in production.

TEMPERATURE AND TIME
Throughout the pizza base production process (from dough mixing to base cooling), controls for time and temperature are all computer controlled. Thermostats within the equipment are linked to computers and are set to the correct temperature for each stage as set out in the specification.

The first stage is the dough mixing stage. The water temperature is critical: water that is too hot could make the dough too sticky to run down the line.

The next stage is the prover. Humidity and temperature are set according to the type of pizza base being made. The longer the bases are in the prover the deeper the bases will be.

Next, the bases are baked. Temperatures are set for the top and bottom of the oven. The time the pizza bases are in the oven is also critical.

The pizza bases are then chilled, before being topped.

Once topped, the pizzas are quick frozen to -18°C before being flow wrapped, packed into cartons, outer cases and pallets.

The pizzas move straight into the cold store at between -20°C and -25°C. They are dispatched by frozen trunkers to their various destinations.

LINE RATE
This refers to the speed that the pizzas move along the production line. The aim is to produce the best quality goods in as short a time as possible. The line rate is determined by the rate the bases can be cut out, the time they need in the prover and the time they need to be baked.

The topping line rate is different to the rate that the bases are produced. The number of pizzas that can go down the topping line at any one time depends on the complexity of the topping (more ingredients take more time) and whether any hand finishing is required as this will slow the line rate down.

QUALITY CONTROL
The bases are inspected manually to check that they are the correct size, weight and that they are organoleptically (see p.105) acceptable.

As the pizza passes down the line, the sauce is checked for viscosity and taste. Topping weights for each pizza are checked. The weight of the final pizza is checked. In addition, all products pass through a metal detector to check for any pieces of metal.

Every hour, sample products are cooked and sampled. Before the pizzas are allowed to be released from the factory, they are analysed microbiologically.

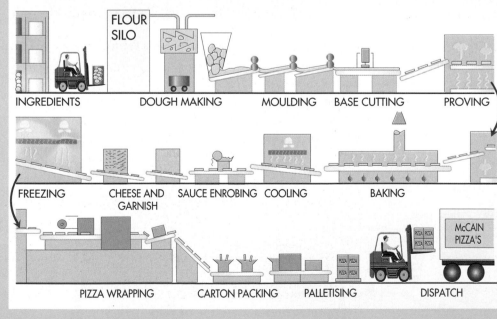

Figure 1 - Pizza production line

Labels: INGREDIENTS · FLOUR SILO · DOUGH MAKING · MOULDING · BASE CUTTING · PROVING · FREEZING · CHEESE AND GARNISH · SAUCE ENROBING · COOLING · BAKING · PIZZA WRAPPING · CARTON PACKING · PALLETISING · DISPATCH · McCAIN PIZZA'S

Activities

1. Name some inputs into the pizza production system.
2. a) At what points in the pizza production line is temperature important?
   b) How do McCain foods use computers to help control temperature?
3. a) What manual checks are made during the process?
   b) Why are these checks important?
4. What other food products might be made using a continual flow system?
5. In groups, simulate an assembly line. Use the checklist below to help you.
- Choose a product to make.
- Find a recipe and divide the work into separate tasks.
- Allocate each task to a member of the group.
- Plan your working area.
- Draw up a time plan (see Unit 26).
- When you have planned the activity thoroughly, start the assembly line..
- Make a note of any problems you encounter. How could you have avoided these problems?

Heygates is a small family owned flour mill. It receives grain from local farmers and mills it into flour which it distributes to the food industry. Here are some of the problems it faces.

- Farmers bring wheat of varying qualities, some wheat is only suitable for animal feed.
- Quantities of wheat delivered may vary depending on climatic conditions.
- Wheat may need to be imported from Canada.
- Manufacturers using the flour may experience problems, for example, bread doughs may not rise sufficiently.

Checking the quality of wheat as it arrives.

Heygates has a laboratory which tests the wheat on arrival at the mill. Six tests are carried out within 25 minutes of arrival to ensure standardisation of quality. Only then is the wheat accepted by the mill. The wheat then goes through a fully automated and computerised milling procedure before being packaged and distributed with a *certificate of quality* guarantee. The mill has an experimental kitchen where the technical advisor is able to check each week that the newly ground flour produces consistently good bread. A selection of breads are baked and the results checked for colour, size, texture and flavour. Recipes are developed for a variety of breads which will give consistently reliable results.

An important part of the technical advisor's job is to help customers who are getting poor results from their baking. The experimental kitchen is fitted with several different dough mixers so that the customer's preparation methods can be replicated exactly using the same equipment. This helps the technical advisor to pinpoint the problem. Once the problem has been identified, the technical advisor informs the baker and suggests a change in preparation methods or type of flour.

Activities

1. How does Heygates assure its customers that they are receiving a quality product?
2. Suggest some food manufacturers who may be interested in buying flour from Heygates.
3. Why does Heygates to have an experimental kitchen?

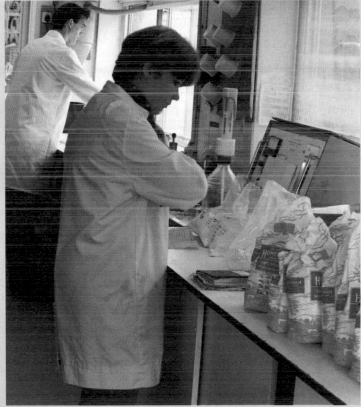

Quality control checks in the laboratory.

Legislation

This unit looks at the main laws which concern the food industry (see Table 1). Laws exist to safeguard both employees and the consumer. The law can be complex and food handlers must understand how the laws regarding food safety and hygiene affect them. There is a saying: 'ignorance is no defence', which means that you can be prosecuted for breaking the law even though you may not have realised that you were doing anything

Table 1 Legislation

These are the main pieces of legislation which concern the food industry:

• Food Safety Act 1990
• Food Safety (General Food Hygiene) Regulations 1995
• Health and Safety at Work Act 1974
• Control of Substances Hazardous to Health (COSHH) Regulations 1994
• Reporting of Injuries, Diseases and Dangerous Occurrences Regulations (RIDDOR) 1995
• Trade Descriptions Act 1968
• Food Labelling Regulations 1996
• Weights and Measures Act 1985
• Consumer Protection Act 1987
• Sale of Goods Act 1979
• Sale and Supply of Goods Act 1994

There are many more regulations on the composition and labelling of particular foods, e.g. flour, milk and meat.

wrong. Offences are seen as criminal cases rather than civil cases and the punishments range from a fine to imprisonment.

At the time of writing, the information in this unit was correct. However, it must be remembered that the law changes as legislation is updated and new laws are passed. When using data for coursework, source material must always be checked to ensure that the information is still valid.

The Food Safety Act 1990

Aims

The aims of this act are to ensure that food is safe and does not mislead the consumer in the way it is presented.

Who is affected?

Anyone involved in the production, processing, storage, distribution and sale of food must comply with the Food Safety Act. This includes self employed people and charity fund-raising events as well as larger organisations.

What is covered?

The word 'food' can cover dietary supplements, food ingredients, drink, and even water used in the production process. The act also covers equipment and wrappings which come into contact with food.

Food safety requirements

The act demands that food must not:
● injure the health of consumers, e.g. botulism in a manufactured food product
● be unfit, e.g. rotten fruit, meat which is not designated for human consumption
● be contaminated - e.g. food containing metal, glass, pest droppings or harmful chemicals.

Offences

The Food Safety Act lists four main offences.
1. Selling food which does not comply with the food safety requirements (see above).
2. Rendering food injurious to health (doing something to food which may make it harmful).
3. Selling food which is not of the nature,

activities

1. What are the 'food safety requirements' mentioned in the article?

2. Invent TWO other cases which involve offences under the Food Safety Act 1990. Write a description of the case, explaining the offence and suggesting an appropriate punishment.

A confectionery firm was fined £7,000 for selling a nut brittle sweet containing a knife blade. A man bought a bag of chocolate covered nut crunch sweets from a sweetshop in Nottingham. His wife put one of the sweets into her mouth and discovered it not to be a sweet but the blade of a Stanley knife enrobed in chocolate. It cut her tongue and drew blood, causing soreness which lasted for two days. The firm were found guilty of selling 'food for human consumption that failed to comply with food safety requirements' - an offence under the Food Safety Act 1990. 'Manufacturers of food or confectionery must take all precautions to prevent incidents such as a knife blade becoming covered with chocolate and being sold as confectionery', said the judge.

Source: adapted from The Times, 8 March 1995

substance or quality demanded, e.g. using a butter substitute when butter has been specified or selling 'lean' minced beef which has a large amount of fat in it.

4. Describing food in such a way as to mislead the consumer, e.g. putting a picture of strawberries on the front of a yogurt which contains no real strawberries but only flavourings.

Enforcing the act

The Food Safety Act 1990 requires that all food premises register with the local authority so that they can be inspected on a regular basis by Trading Standards Officers and Environmental Health Officers, who have the power to enforce the act.

The Food Safety (General Food Hygiene) Regulations 1995

Aims

The regulations aim to ensure common food hygiene rules acrosss the European Union.

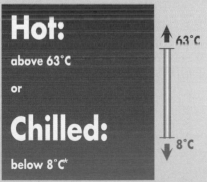

Figure 1 - Temperature control of food

The Food Safety (General Food Hygiene) Regulations state that foods which need temperature control for safety may be stored either:

Hot: above 63°C

or

Chilled: below 8°C*

Environmental Health guidelines recommend that fridge temperatures are kept between 1°C and 4°C so that the temperature remains well within the legal limit even if the door is opened and the temperature rises temporarily.

Table 2 Food Safety (General Food Hygiene) Regulations 1995

These are some of the key points covered by the regulations.
- Food premises should be clean and in good repair.
- Design and layout should permit adequate cleaning and disinfection.
- There should be adequate toilets and wash hand basins.
- Any food area must be well ventilated and have adequate lighting.
- Floors and walls must be non-absorbent and easy to clean. Ceilings must be designed to minimise condensation and prevent the growth of moulds.
- Windows, if opening, should be designed to prevent insects getting in, or be covered with a screen.
- All preparation surfaces must be smooth, washable and easy to clean and disinfect.
- Food must be stored in hygienic conditions and protected from contamination.
- A pest control policy must be in place.
- Vehicles which transport food must be clean and in good condition and must be designed to allow for cleaning and disinfection.
- Bulk food may only be moved in vehicles which are solely used for the carriage of food and they must carry signs showing "for foodstuffs only".
- Temperature controlled vehicles must be designed so that the temperature can easily be monitored and controlled.
- Equipment and packaging that comes into contact with food must be clean and be made of a material that is easily disinfected.
- Food waste must be regularly removed from food areas.
- Bins must be kept in good condition, fitted with lids and be made of a material which will allow for easy cleaning and disinfection.
- Areas where rubbish is held must be kept as clean as possible, and away from drinking water, food stores and equipment.
- A supply of drinking water must be available when preparing and cooking foods.
- All food handlers must maintain a good standard of personal hygiene.
- Food handlers must wear appropriate clean protective clothing.
- Food handlers suffering from illness must not work in food areas.
- It is the responsibility of the proprietors of food businesses to ensure that food handlers are properly trained in food hygiene.

Who is affected?

Anyone who owns, manages or works in a food business, except people working in primary food production (e.g. growing crops, slaughtering or milking). Like the Food Safety Act, this includes people selling privately or for charity, as well as profit-making organisations. Food cooked at home for private consumption is not covered.

What is covered?

The regulations cover three main areas:
- temperature control of food likely to support the growth of harmful bacteria or toxins (see Figure 1)
- general food hygiene (see Table 2)
- hazard analysis and risk assessment (see Unit 31).

Employee protection

There are three important pieces of legislation which aim to protect employees at work. These are:
- Health and Safety at Work Act
- COSHH (Control of Substances Hazardous to Health) Regulations
- RIDDOR (Reporting of Injuries, Diseases and Dangerous Occurrences Regulations).

Health and Safety at Work Act

This act makes employers responsible for the health and safety of their employees. If employers fail to meet regulations, they can be charged with a criminal offence. The Health and Safety Executive is responsible for checking that the act is being followed. Its inspectors visit workplaces to check that health and safety regulations are being met.

COSHH

These regulations protect people from hazardous substances in the workplace. Examples of substances that could be hazardous to people working in the food industry include: cleaning fluids; pesticides; food colourings, flavourings and preservatives. The risks involved include: skin irritations; asthma; inhalation of toxic fumes; poisoning from swallowing a substance; cancer from long term use of a

Figure 2 Hazardous substances labels

Figure 3 - Flow of work in Café Vert

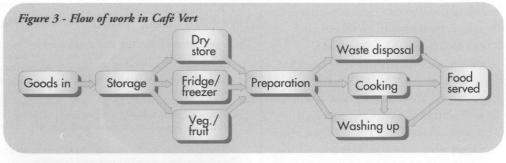

Consumer protection

There are several pieces of legislation designed to protect customers.

The Trade Descriptions Act makes it illegal to make false or misleading claims about products. It covers statements, advertisements and labels that make false claims.

The Food Labelling Regulations specify what information should be included on food labels (see Unit 25).

The Weights and Measures Act makes it illegal to sell goods which are underweight or short measured.

The Consumer Protection Act makes it illegal to give misleading information about the price of goods.

The Sale of Goods Act and the **Sale and Supply of Goods Act** state that goods when sold must be of satisfactory quality, fit for their purpose and as described.

A safe working area

All working environments should be designed with safety and hygiene as the first priority. In the food industry, these factors must be taken into consideration:

● work flow

substance; infections from micro-organisms.

COSHH requires businesses to inform, instruct and train employees about:

● the type of substances with which they are working
● any precautions they need to take.

Substances hazardous to health are identified by their warning label (see Figure 2).

RIDDOR

These regulations require work related accidents, diseases and dangerous occurrences to be reported. If there is an accident at work resulting in death or major injury it must be reported immediately to the Environmental Health Department or the local authority (depending on the type of business). Within ten days an accident report form must follow. Dangerous occurrences must also be reported. These include: major failures of load-bearing equipment; electrical overload resulting in fire or explosion; accidental release of substances harmful to health. There is also a list of diseases which must be reported.

activities

The Café Vert is a small restaurant serving 60-80 covers daily. The owner is planning a major refit of the kitchen and storage areas. Figure 3 shows the work flow in the café and Figure 4 shows the current layout of the kitchen and storage area. Food is prepared and cooked and then loaded into the dumb waiter, a lift which transports the meals to the restaurant downstairs.

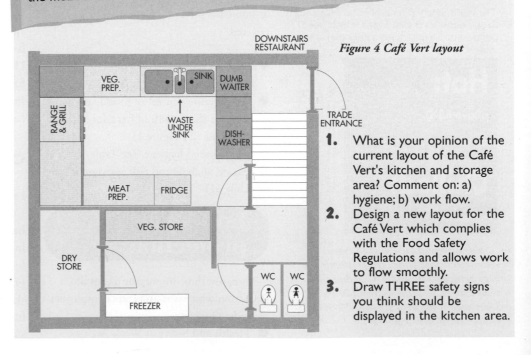

Figure 4 Café Vert layout

1. What is your opinion of the current layout of the Café Vert's kitchen and storage area? Comment on: a) hygiene; b) work flow.

2. Design a new layout for the Café Vert which complies with the Food Safety Regulations and allows work to flow smoothly.

3. Draw THREE safety signs you think should be displayed in the kitchen area.

- ease of cleaning
- temperature control of food
- prevention of contamination from surfaces and equipment
- facilities for staff and customers.

There are many legal requirements that must be fulfilled (see Table 2 on page 131). Many areas of the food industry have their own guides to help people to interpret the law and ensure that their establishment meets health, safety and hygiene requirements. For example, the *Industry Guide to Good Hygiene Practice - Catering Guide* is produced by the catering industry in liaison with Environmental Health Officers and other government organisations. This guide gives detailed advice to owners and proprietors of catering establishments about how to comply with the Food Safety (General Food Hygiene) Regulations.

Kitchen design

Kitchens must be designed to meet the Food Safety (General Food Hygiene) Regulations (see Table 2 on page 131). In addition, kitchens should be laid out so that work can progress in a logical, convenient way. Ideally, each part of the process should take place in a different area and it should be possible for work to flow from one stage to the next without crossovers. For example, Figure 3 shows the flow of work in the Café Vert. In order for work to progress smoothly, it would make sense for the storage areas to be located near to the entrance or loading

All workplaces should have at least one person qualified in first aid and possess a clearly marked and well stocked first aid kit.

bay. It would not be hygienic or efficient if goods had to be carried through the cooking area in order to reach the storage area.

There should be adequate working space. If there is not enough space, staff will get in each other's way, cleaning will be difficult and accidents will be more likely. With limited space, areas of the kitchen are more likely to be used for more than one task, running the risk of cross-contamination.

Safety procedures

All working environments should have written safety procedures. These cover the following situations:

- fire drill
- guidelines for conduct in the work area
- instructions in case of accidents.

Procedures must be clearly displayed so that all employees are familiar with them.

Safety signs

There is a large number of signs used in the field of health and safety. Signs are divided into five categories:

- **prohibition** (red circle) - you must not do this
- **warning** (yellow triangle) - take care with this
- **mandatory** (blue circle) - you must do this
- **safe condition** (green square) - information about safety issues
- **fire equipment** (red square) - information about dealing with fires.

Employers must use approved signs to inform workers about health and safety issues. They must also ensure that their workforce is trained in the meaning of

Figure 5 Safety signs

PROHIBITION

WARNING

MANDATORY

SAFE CONDITION

FIRE EQUIPMENT

No smoking

Warning
It is dangerous and illegal to operate this machine without the proper guards in position

First aid

Fire extinguisher

these signs. Figure 5 shows some examples of safety signs.

Trading Standards

The Trading Standards Department is part of the local authority. It used to be called the Department of Weights and Measures. The aim of Trading Standards is to protect consumers from unfair trading. Trading Standards Officers work in the following areas:

- **quantity** - inspect and check measuring equipment in factories, shops and markets
- **quality** - test samples of food and drink

RATS & MICE (RODENTS)
- Examples - brown rats, black rats and house mice.
- Carry disease. Droppings may spoil food. May damage woodwork, pipes, cables and food packaging
- Control - baits, contact dusts or rodenticides. Prevent entry by filling holes in bricks, doors and pipes.

Figure 6 Pest control

The Environmental Health Department can give advice about PESTS and how to control them. Pest control officers may visit premises to apply a pesticide. Pests can be a particular nuisance in food premises because of the risk that they might carry disease.

Brown Rat

House mouse

ANTS
- Examples - garden ants and Pharaohs ants.
- Garden ants are a nuisance but not a health risk. Pharaohs ants carry harmful germs.
- Control - insecticidal sprays or powders. Baits containing boric acid used against Pharaohs ants.

Pharaohs ant

WASPS
- A nuisance but do not spread disease. Damage ripened fruit. Can inflict a painful sting.
- Control - spraying nests or using baits.

Wasp

FLEAS
- Examples - cats, dogs and humans.
- Can carry disease and inflict unpleasant bites.

Flea

FLIES
- Examples - houseflies, bluebottles and fruit flies.
- Carry and spread gastro-enteric illnesses and food poisoning organisms. Can feed and lay eggs on food or feed on rubbish and then land on food.
- Control - attract to ultra-violet light and electrocute with charged grids; sticky fly papers; use insecticides only as a back-up. Seal windows and doors to prevent entry.

Housefly

COCKROACHES
- Examples - German, American and Oriental.
- Found in premises where food is stored and handled. Carry food poisoning germs. Responsible for spread of gastroenteritis and dysentery.
- Control - insecticides applied frequently, baits and traps.

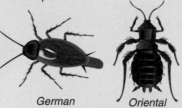

German

Oriental

BEETLES, WEEVILS, MITES AND MOTHS
- Examples - carpet and larder beetles, grain weevils and flour mites.
- Larder beetles scavenge in meat products. Beetles, mites and moths damage stored products such as grain, nuts, chocolate, spices and dried fruit.
- Control - mothproofers, insecticides sprays, fumigation.

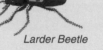

Larder Beetle

Moth

BIRDS
- Examples - feral pigeons, house sparrows and starlings.
- Dropping contaminate food. Pigeons carry diseases.
- Control - netting to prevent entry, cage traps and repellents.

Feral pigeon

for safety and quality
- **safety** - check for dangerous goods and overloaded distribution vehicles
- **fair trading** - check trade descriptions, pricing, confiscate counterfeit goods
- **licensing** - monitor licensed premises, such as late night takeaways
- **consumer advice** - handle complaints about illegal trading, faulty goods, etc.

Environmental Health

The Environmental Health Department is also part of the local authority. It is responsible for enforcing the law in relation to the labelling, composition and safety of food. An Environmental Health Officer (EHO) has the following functions:

- to ensure food is safe and fit for consumption
- to reduce possible sources of contamination
- to monitor working conditions and hygiene systems
- to enforce the law
- to build good relations with management and offer advice and support.

It is part of an Environmental Health

Officer's job to inspect food manufacturers, retailers and catering outlets to make sure that their hygiene practices meet with food safety legislation.

EHOs have the right to enter food premises without notice and carry out inspections. They may also visit as a result of a complaint. EHOs look at the way food businesses are run and ensure that the law is being upheld. They also identify potential hazards. On every visit to a business the EHO carries out a RISK ASSESSMENT. The rating received determines the number of visits a company will receive in the future. Most companies are visited every 9 months to 1 year. A risk assessment is based on:

    type of premises
- whether any high risk processes (e.g. canning) are involved
    number of consumers potentially at risk
- whether vulnerable groups are served (e.g.
- elderly, children under 5, sick people) management
- general hygiene practices.
- EHO inspections usually concentrate on five main areas:

1. **temperature control** - at all points in the food production cycle, from storage of raw material through to preparation and service
2. **cleaning and disinfection** - the effectiveness of systems in operation
3. **hygiene** - including personal hygiene, staff training, food hygiene awareness
4. **control systems** - stock rotation, pest control (see Figure 6), quality control, avoidance of cross-contamination, waste disposal
5. **design of premises** - including structure, equipment, lighting, ventilation, washing facilities and sanitation.

Enforcing the law

During an inspection an EHO may examine records, take photographs and remove samples for analysis. If the officer finds anything wrong, there are several things the Environmental Health Department can do:

- Write a letter stating what the fault is and suggesting a remedy. The letter must make it clear if it is a legal requirement or just a recommendation.
- Serve an improvement notice which specifies the fault and remedy and gives a time limit within which the improvement must take place. If all recommendations are carried out a certificate of compliance is issued.
- If the company does not make the change within this time, it can be taken to court. If the court decides that the business is serving food 'not fit to eat', it may decide to close the business down. The Environmental Health Department will serve a destruction or prohibition order, giving 14 days notice.
- An emergency prohibition order is served if there is serious risk to public health (e.g. major infestation or contamination with *Salmonella* or *Clostridium botulinum*). In these instances only 24 hours notice is required.
- The department can also prohibit one particular process (e.g. canning) if it is suspected of being dangerous.

Food complaints

If you make a complaint about food to the Environmental Health Department, this is what might happen.

1. An EHO or food technician will discuss the nature of your complaint with you.
2. If appropriate a sample of the food will be taken and labelled, sealed and stored.
3. The premises which sold the food may be inspected to ensure that no similar items are on sale and to assess the storage and handling procedures.
4. The EHO will review the severity of the complaint and determine if the law has been broken.
5. You will be kept informed of the progress of the investigation which may take several months.
6. Reasons for lengthy investigations may include: time taken for detailed scientific analysis; contacts with manufacturers, retailers and suppliers; liaison with Environmental Health Departments in other parts of the country. Reports are gathered from these agencies.
7. A decision is taken to proceed with informal or formal action.
8. Informal action involves a written warning to companies of previous good reputation.
9. Formal action involves prosecution. You may need to give evidence, giving details of the incident.
10. Your name will be given to the food company. Many companies, eager to maintain good customer relations, will offer some compensation. However, this is not part of the work of the Environmental Health Department.

Key Terms

Risk assessment - identifying possible hazards in a process and finding out how they can be reduced or eliminated.
Pests - Animals which may contaminate food and food premises.

activities

1. Brainstorm a list of questions that Debbie might ask the catering manager of a nursing home.
2. Give FOUR examples of good hygiene practice in a nursing home kitchen.
3. What might happen if a relative of one of the residents

Debbie Kane is an Environmental Health Officer, specialising in food hygiene. Part of her job involves visiting nursing homes for the elderly to inspect their catering units.

complained to the Environmental Health Department that food served in the home often tasted 'off'?

31 Risk assessment

What is risk assessment?

When food is prepared and processed for public consumption, safety and hygiene are the most important considerations. To meet the Food Safety (General Food Hygiene) Regulations all food businesses must carry out a RISK ASSESSMENT.

These regulations require operators of food businesses to:

● assess what hazards there may be in the business
● identify where they could occur
● find out how hazards can be reduced or eliminated so that the consumer is not affected.

This process is often called HAZARD ANALYSIS. All types of food business must carry out this risk assessment, from an ice cream van to a top restaurant. The regulations apply to non-profit organisations like charities as well as commercial food businesses.

Identifying hazards

A HAZARD is anything which may cause harm to the consumer. It may be:

● biological, e.g. *Salmonella* in chicken
● physical, e.g. glass in food
● chemical e.g. cleaning chemicals in food.

Sometimes hazards are only recognised after an incident such as food poisoning has occurred. By carrying out a risk assessment, businesses can pinpoint problems before any harm is caused.

To identify hazards, the business must look at all aspects of its operation. It can help to draw a flow chart of the whole process. Eamonn Bond owns an ice cream van business. Figure 1 shows the stages in the

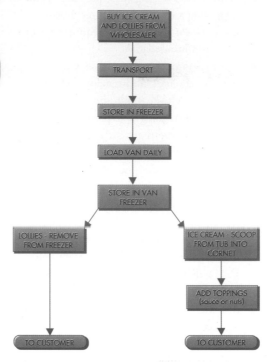

```
BUY ICE CREAM
AND LOLLIES FROM
WHOLESALER
        ↓
    TRANSPORT
        ↓
 STORE IN FREEZER
        ↓
  LOAD VAN DAILY
        ↓
  STORE IN VAN
    FREEZER
    ↙        ↘
LOLLIES - REMOVE    ICE CREAM - SCOOP
FROM FREEZER        FROM TUB INTO
                    CORNET
                         ↓
                    ADD TOPPINGS
                    (sauce or nuts)
    ↓                    ↓
TO CUSTOMER         TO CUSTOMER
```

Figure 1 Flow chart of ice cream business

purchase and sale of ice creams. The main hazard that could occur in this type of business is that correct temperature control is not maintained. This could lead to bacterial contamination and food poisoning. There are several points where this could occur:

● in wholesaler's freezer
● during transportation
● in company freezer
● during loading
● in van freezer.

These points are called CRITICAL CONTROL POINTS (CCPs). A CCP is a point in the production system where control must be applied to ensure that a hazard is eliminated or reduced to an ACCEPTABLE LEVEL. Another CCP is the service of ice creams. The ice cream must be scooped from the tub into a cornet and toppings may be applied. This offers a further opportunity for bacterial contamination.

Control and monitoring

Once a business has established possible hazards and where they might occur, it can work to reduce or eliminate the risk. In order to do this, CONTROL and MONITORING must be introduced. For example, Eamonn can reduce the risk of the temperature in the ice cream van freezer rising to unsafe levels by:

activities

A school wants to sell home made cakes at its Summer Fête.

1. How would you explain risk assessment to the organisers of the fête?

2. Draw a flow chart of the likely stages in the production and sale of the cakes.

3. Identify the critical control points in this process.

control - ensuring the freezer is fitted with a thermometer and adjusting the control dial to the correct temperature.
- monitoring - checking the freezer thermometer regularly.

The business should decide how to control each CCP to ensure that hazards are either eliminated or reduced to a safe, acceptable level. Controls may include:
- buying from suppliers with a good reputation
- rotating stock
- storing food at the correct temperature
- storing raw and cooked foods separately
- cooking food at the correct temperature
- cooking food for the right length of time
- holding hot food at the correct temperature
- training staff in food and personal hygiene
- cleaning and disinfection of equipment
- establishing cleaning routines
- pest control.

Once controls have been established, the food business must make sure that they are working properly by monitoring the process. Monitoring means observing or measuring parts of the production process to check whether a CCP is under control. This might include the following checks:
- visual checks for cleanliness
- checking date marks on food labels
- checking the condition of food on arrival
- checking cooking temperatures
- checking cooking times.

If the monitoring shows any problems, the business must take steps to remedy the situation.

Keeping records

The law does not **demand** that food businesses keep written records of hazard analysis, controls or monitoring. However, a brief written explanation of the system can be helpful to the Environmental Health Officer (see Unit 30) to show that the business has complied with the Food Safety (General Food Hygiene) Regulations. Keeping records can also help a business to monitor the controls it has put in place. Documentation might include:
- temperature logs of fridges, freezers and

This catering business monitors and keeps records of all foods stored in the freezer. The stock control sheet shows the date the food went in; its temperature; the date food was taken out and the quantity removed.

cold stores
- pest control records
- cleaning schedules
- staff training records
- delivery checks
- equipment maintenance records
- management audits.

Risk assessment systems

In order to help businesses carry out risk assessment, several formal systems have been designed. The main system is **Hazard Analysis and Critical Control Points** (HACCP). **Assured Safe Catering** is a risk assessment system for caterers based on HACCP principles.

What is HACCP?

HACCP stands for Hazard Analysis and Critical Control Points. It is a food safety system based on prevention of hazards. The original HACCP system was designed by the Pillsbury company in the 1960s. Pillsbury was asked to design and manufacture the first space foods. The company wanted to provide safe food for astronauts on space flights. The results of astronauts having food poisoning in space could be catastrophic and every attempt had to be made to reduce this risk. Pillsbury decided that the only way to ensure safe food would be to have control over the raw materials, the process, the environment and the people, beginning as early in the system as possible. Previous control systems relied on fault identification at the end of the production

activities

A takeaway sells whole roasted chickens. Figure 2 shows the production process.
1. Suggest a possible hazard of this process.
2. Where does this hazard occur?
3. What can be done to control and monitor this point in order to reduce or eliminate the hazard?

Figure 2 Roast chicken production process

Figure 3 Risk assessment of pork pie production

This page shows a risk assessment of the batch production of pork pies, highlighting critical control points in the production process, controls which should be used and suggestions for monitoring.

1. PURCHASE AND DELIVERY

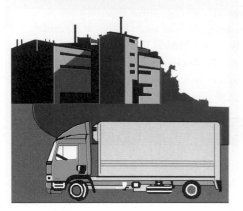

Raw materials are delivered to the factory.

Hazard
Harmful bacteria mould or foreign bodies may be present.

Control
Use reputable suppliers.
Check goods on delivery: temperature; condition of food; date marks.
Carry out quality control analysis on suppliers.

Monitoring
Check delivery vehicles, date marks, temperature and condition of food.
Regular checking and record keeping is required to ensure consistency of product quality.

2. STORAGE

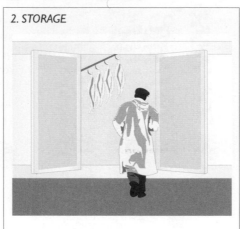

Raw materials are stored until required.

Hazard
Bacterial growth or contamination by micro-organisms, chemicals and pests.
Cross-contamination of components.

Control
Store at safe temperatures.
Cover, wrap and label foods.
Separate raw and cooked foods.
Ensure efficiency of low temperature storage equipment.
Use foods within date marks.
Effective pest control.
Employ a 'first in, first out' stock system.

Monitoring
Check temperatures and date marks.
Check storage conditions.
Install computer controlled equipment, sensors or integral thermometers.

3. PREPARATION

Three processes are involved in the preparation of the pork pies:
• preparation of the meat
• preparation of the filling
• assembling the pie.

Hazard
Bacterial growth or further contamination.
Contamination from humans, pests, incorrect temperatures, foreign bodies, incorrect cleaning of machinery.

Control
Limit handling times.
Effective cleaning routines.
Good personal hygiene.
Hygienic premises.
Staff training.

Monitoring
Visual checks.
Regular sampling for quality control.
Documentation of cleaning schedules.

4. COOKING AND FINISHING

Hazard
Survival of harmful bacteria.

Control
Adequate cooking to a safe centre temperature.
Automated and computerised ovens and timing controls.
Ensure pies are cooled to AMBIENT temperature before adding the jelly.

Monitoring
Cooking times and routine temperature checks.
Use of temperature probes to ensure meat in the pie is cooked in the centre.

5. PACKING AND STORAGE

Pork pies are packaged and stored ready for distribution.

Hazard
Growth of bacteria and further contamination.
Contamination from foreign bodies.
Pies are stored past use by date.

Control
Store at safe temperature.
Wrap pork pie in parchment and mark with appropriate use by date.
Ensure pies are boxed, stored, checked and dispatched at 1-5°C.

Monitoring
Check temperature.
Visual checks.
Record keeping of low temperature equipment in holding areas and distribution vehicles.

HACCP was originally developed to ensure the safety of food on space flights.

process. This resulted in a lot of waste as products which did not meet the required standards were discarded. HACCP helps companies to identify, monitor and control risks throughout the whole process of food production.

Using HACCP

Any food business can use HACCP. It can be applied to the entire production process or to one part of the business, such as storage or distribution. HACCP is a quality assurance system, like ISO 9000 (see Unit 29). Knowing that a company uses HACCP gives consumers the confidence that the food product they are eating is safe.

There are 7 basic principles in the HACCP system:

1. Hazard analysis
Prepare a list of steps or a flow chart of the production process.
Identify the hazards.
Describe the controls.

2. Critical control points
Identify the CCPs using a decision tree (see Figure 4).

3. Critical limits
CRITICAL LIMITS establish target levels

which must be met to control each CCP (e.g. correct operating temperature for fridge, maximum cooling time for cooked food before refrigeration).

4. Monitoring
Establish a monitoring system for each CCP (e.g. checking temperature of fridge every hour; visual checks).

5. Corrective action
If monitoring indicates a problem, decide on action which will correct it (e.g. adjust or repair fridge; staff training in hygiene).

6. Record keeping
Keep records of all procedures (e.g. keep log of recorded fridge temperatures).

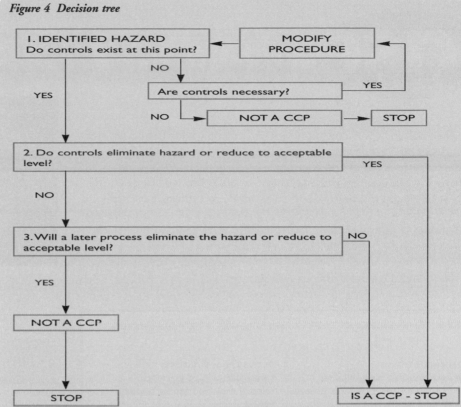

Figure 4 Decision tree

```
1. IDENTIFIED HAZARD              MODIFY
Do controls exist at this point?  PROCEDURE

              NO
                    Are controls necessary?    YES
YES
              NO        NOT A CCP         STOP

2. Do controls eliminate hazard or reduce to acceptable
level?                                                YES

              NO

3. Will a later process eliminate the hazard or reduce to    NO
acceptable level?

YES

NOT A CCP

STOP                                          IS A CCP - STOP
```

When conducting a hazard analysis for the first time, businesses may be tempted to identify too many points in the production process as critical control points. While many points may be considered control points, only a few are actually critical control points. This decision tree can help determine which stages in production should be identified as CCPs.

7. Verification
Establish procedures which check that HACCP system is working.

Key Terms

activities

Design a risk assessment based on the production of a food product with which you are familiar.

1. Identify the steps in the production process.

2. What hazards could occur at each stage?

3. Which of these steps are critical control points?

4. How could hazards be controlled?

5. Suggest ways of monitoring the controls in place.

Present the risk assessment as a table.

case study DESIGNING HYGIENIC KITCHENS

When designing a kitchen, caterers must comply with The Food Safety (General Food Hygiene Regulations) 1995 (see Unit 30). These regulations set out certain practices that will help deal with hygiene problems, e.g. the cleaning and disinfection of walls. The *Industry Guide to Good Hygiene Practice: Catering Guide* gives advice to catering businesses on how to comply with the regulations. The guide covers all the food hygiene requirements of the regulations. The guide also gives additional guidance on 'good practice' - action which, though not demanded by law, would help a business to meet higher standards of hygiene and safety. Table 1 shows the section in the guide relating to wall surfaces.

Table 1 - Requirements for rooms where foodstuffs are prepared, treated or processed

Legal requirement
Wall surfaces must be maintained in a sound condition and they must be easy to clean and, where necessary, disinfect. This will require the use of impervious, non-absorbent, washable and non-toxic materials and require a smooth surface up to a height appropriate for the operations.

Guide to complying with the law
Walls must be properly maintained so that they can be kept clean. Wall surfaces immediately behind food preparation surfaces or equipment must be able to be disinfected.

Acceptable wall surfaces include:
• washable painted plaster
• epoxy resin and similar coatings
• ceramic tiles
• stainless steel sheeting
• PVC sheeting
• GRP (glass fibre-reinforced polyester) sheeting.

Good practice
Junctions between floors and walls and vertical wall angles should be coved. Walls should be able to be disinfected to a height of at least 1.80m. Walls above this height should be cleanable but do not need to be so durable.

Source: adapted from the Industry Guide to Good Hygiene Practice: Catering Guide, 1995

These pictures show a range of food businesses using PVC and GRP wall gladding, fitted by Advanced Hygienic Walls, Ceilings and Floors

Table 2 - Advantages and disadvantages of wall cladding materials

Ceramic wall tiles
Neat seal between floor and wall tiles.
Individual tiles can be repaired.
Easily knocked or chipped.
Must use correct grout.
Approximately £26/sq m.

PVC/GRP sheeting
Synthetic sheet material glued to walls.
Avoids need for grout.
Very hygienic.
Easily washed and disinfected.
PVC tends to be more brittle than GRP and can split or shatter under very cold conditions.
GRP = approximately £34/sq m.

Stainless steel sheeting
Hard-wearing, easy to clean, smooth finish.
Good appearance.
Resistant to high temperatures.
Holes for fixing to walls must not be allowed to deteriorate and let water in.
Approximately £40/sq m.

Acrylic polymer
Paint-on wall cladding.
Can be applied to tiling, metal and plaster.
Good for those on low budget.
Approximately £64 to cover up to 50 sq m.

Source: adapted from Caterer & Hotelkeeper, 29 August 1996

Activities

Sheila Dutton and her son Ben are opening a new sandwich shop, 'The Lite Bite', in the business district of Manchester. Food will be prepared and served in the same room. They are confused by the variety of wall coverings available. They want the shop to look bright and modern and they must comply with the law. However, their budget is limited. Using the information in Tables 1 and 2, what wall coverings would you advise them to use in the shop? Remember, they do not have to use the same surface throughout the room. They could use different types of wall covering for:

• the wall immediately behind food preparation areas
• the wall behind the oven, grill and hob
• the wall in the customer service area
• higher parts of the wall.

case study: HACCP IN BURNABY HOSPITAL

Burnaby Hospital uses Hazard Analysis Critical Control Points (HACCP - see Unit 31) to help it to manage its cook-chill food production system (see Unit 10 for more information on cook-chill). It uses HACCP because it is a prevention based system which aims to identify and eliminate food safety hazards before the food is eaten, rather than to react to an outbreak of food poisoning.

Because of the numerous steps involved in cook-chill food production, it is particularly important to identify the stages critical for food safety. The catering department decided to concentrate on 4 critical control points (CCPs):

- ingredient control - to reduce the risk of contaminated food entering the system
- equipment and sanitation - because hygiene during food preparation is vital
- staff hygiene and training - in order for the HACCP system to be effective, all staff need to be involved
- time/temperature relationships - because it is essential that food is cooked at a high enough temperature for a long enough time, and that it is cooled rapidly below 3°C.

Table 1 is a summary of the controls established to eliminate or reduce hazards at these CCPs.

Source: adapted from Burnaby Hospital Dietetics Department

It is important that all staff understand the importance of the HACCP system. It only takes a mistake by one person to cause a food safety hazard.

Table 1 - Critical control points

Ingredient control
- Good quality ingredients bought from reputable suppliers. This is particularly important for products that do not require cooking before serving to the consumer.
- Ingredients and packaging inspected on arrival.
- Correct storage: chilled and frozen goods promptly placed in fridge or freezer; groceries that do not require chilling in well ventilated area; separate storage of raw and cooked foods.
- One person works in Ingredient Control Room, issuing recipe ingredients to food preparation staff. This reduces risk of cross-contamination between storage and preparation areas.
- All recipes modified to reflect HACCP principles.

Equipment and sanitation
- Cook-chill production uses specialised equipment. Many of the machines are equipped with monitoring systems, e.g. timers, temperature probes and monitoring graphs.
- Regular maintenance of equipment ensures that all mechanisms are functioning correctly.
- Written procedures for cleaning and equipment sanitation.
- Random microbiological checks on equipment, personnel, work surfaces and utensils.

Staff hygiene and training
- Mandatory food and personal hygiene training.
- Regular in-service training to reinforce knowledge.
- Written procedures for dress code, use of hair nets and general cleanliness.
- Training in HACCP principles and importance of procedures, monitoring and keeping records.
- Staff trained to understand the CCP for which they are responsible.

Time/temperature relationships
- Temperature of food monitored during cooking process using thermometer or probe. Minimum temperature for centre of cooked food = 74°C for at least 2 minutes.
- Once cooked, food cooled rapidly to below 3°C (within 1½ hours).
- All cooked food stored in chilled storage below 3°C. Fridges and freezers equipped with automatic alarms which alert staff if temperature reaches inappropriate levels.

Activities

1. Why is it important, particularly for a hospital, to identify hazards before food is eaten?
2. Burnaby Hospital has modified the recipes it uses to reflect HACCP principles. What information could be included in a recipe which could help prevent a food safety hazard?
3. How does the hospital verify that cleaning and sanitation procedures are being followed and that they are effective?
4. How does the hospital monitor the time/temperature relationship in the cook-chill process?
5. Why is it important that all staff understand the HACCP system?